THE THERMAL THEORY OF CYCLONES

A History of Meteorological Thought in the Nineteenth Century

American Meteorological Society
Historical Monograph Series

The History of Meteorology: to 1800—$15.00

The History of American Weather (All four volumes—$40.00)

Early American Hurricanes (1492-1870), 1963—$12.00

Early American Winters (Two volumes—$22.00)
(1604-1820), 1966—$12.00
(1821-1870), 1967—$12.00

Early American Tornadoes (1586-1870), 1970—$12.00

The Thermal Theory of Cyclones: A History of Meteorological Thought in the Nineteenth Century—$30.00

The picture is a collage composed from parts of the figures in this book. The individual components illustrate important physical concepts and observations emerging over a period of six decades of cyclone research. Pieced together, they helped shape the thermal theory of cyclones. The underlying framework, provided by theoretical achievements, is partially exposed at the lower right.

THE THERMAL THEORY OF CYCLONES

A History of Meteorological Thought in the Nineteenth Century

Gisela Kutzbach

HISTORICAL
MONOGRAPH
SERIES

AMERICAN METEOROLOGICAL SOCIETY

ISBN 0-933876-48-3
Library of Congress Catalogue Card No. 79-51009

American Meteorological Society
45 Beacon St., Boston, Mass. 02108

Printed in the United States of America
by Lancaster Press, Lancaster, Pennsylvania

PREFACE

The discovery of the laws of thermodynamics during the 1840's and 1850's produced profound changes in many fields of Nineteenth Century science. Thermodynamics also played an essential role in the emergence of modern meteorology. This becomes apparent when analyzing the historical roots of the idea that midlatitude storms are thermally driven circulation systems. During the Nineteenth Century this idea took shape in the form of the thermal theory of cyclones. Considering the development of this theory also provides an insight in the particular problems and methods of problem solving in Nineteenth Century meteorology. The account that follows aims to display the significance of thermal and energetic studies of cyclone development for Nineteenth Century cyclone theory and to show the impact and dependence of these studies on the general development of the field.

In the writing of this book, I have tried to keep at least two audiences in mind. I have written for the historian of science and the professional meteorologist who is interested in tracing the origin and development of a basic concept in meteorology. Further, I have tried to illustrate for the student of meteorology that the science is a human activity and that its development is an open-ended process involving the constant testing of hypotheses.

Having to write almost exclusively from the primary sources, I am aware that the results presented in this study are only a beginning; there is still much to be learned. I have strived to retain some of the flavor and the richness of the original works by providing a large number of quotations. I have translated all the foreign language quotations, except those few for which translations were available. I have also prepared an appendix with short biographical sketches of 33 scientists whose works are discussed in this book.

The idea for this study germinated about ten years ago, when Professor Erwin N. Hiebert's enthusiastic lectures and seminars on the history of the laws of thermodynamics sparked my interest in the influence of these laws on the development of meteorology. He provided generous stimulation, encouragement and guidance throughout my graduate studies and the preparation of my dissertation. The present study is an outgrowth of this dissertation. Most of the essential initial research was done during an extended stay in England, and I am indebted to the librarians of the British Meteorological Office, Bracknell, for their assistance. A Travel Grant of the University of Wisconsin made possible visits to several European libraries and a Vilas Fellowship helped support a year of my graduate studies. Professor Werner Schwerdtfeger made many helpful suggestions in the early stages of the book and his kind assistance is appreciated.

I am happy to thank Dr. Eugene Bierly, editor of the *Meteorological Monographs*, who persistently encouraged me through the past five years to continue my historical studies despite the many delays in revising and redrafting of the manuscript. The reviewers of the manuscript will recognize the effects of their many valuable suggestions for improvements of the text, and special thanks goes to them. I am indebted to Mr. John Gerhardt for his sympathetic guidance and skillful technical editing. Finally I wish to thank my family without whose enthusiastic support this book could not have been written. Angela and Katrina cheered every page. John, my husband, has been an active participant throughout the book's development and he provided much productive criticism and unflagging encouragement.

Madison, Wisconsin Gisela Kutzbach

PREFACE

The discovery of the laws of thermodynamics during the 1840's and 1850's produced profound changes in many fields of Nineteenth Century science. Thermodynamics also played an essential role in the emergence of modern meteorology. This becomes apparent when analyzing the historical roots of the idea that midlatitude storms are thermally driven circulation systems. During the Nineteenth Century this idea took shape in the form of the thermal theory of cyclones. Considering the development of this theory also provides an insight in the particular problems and methods of problem solving in Nineteenth Century meteorology. The account that follows aims to display the significance of thermal and energetic studies of cyclone development for Nineteenth Century cyclone theory and to show the impact and dependence of these studies on the general development of the field.

In the writing of this book, I have tried to keep at least two audiences in mind. I have written for the historian of science and the professional meteorologist who is interested in tracing the origin and development of a basic concept in meteorology. Further, I have tried to illustrate for the student of meteorology that the science is a human activity and that its development is an open-ended process involving the constant testing of hypotheses.

Having to write almost exclusively from the primary sources, I am aware that the results presented in this study are only a beginning; there is still much to be learned. I have strived to retain some of the flavor and the richness of the original works by providing a large number of quotations. I have translated all the foreign language quotations, except those few for which translations were available. I have also prepared an appendix with short biographical sketches of 33 scientists whose works are discussed in this book.

The idea for this study germinated about ten years ago, when Professor Erwin N. Hiebert's enthusiastic lectures and seminars on the history of the laws of thermodynamics sparked my interest in the influence of these laws on the development of meteorology. He provided generous stimulation, encouragement and guidance throughout my graduate studies and the preparation of my dissertation. The present study is an outgrowth of this dissertation. Most of the essential initial research was done during an extended stay in England, and I am indebted to the librarians of the British Meteorological Office, Bracknell, for their assistance. A Travel Grant of the University of Wisconsin made possible visits to several European libraries and a Vilas Fellowship helped support a year of my graduate studies. Professor Werner Schwerdtfeger made many helpful suggestions in the early stages of the book and his kind assistance is appreciated.

I am happy to thank Dr. Eugene Bierly, editor of the *Meteorological Monographs*, who persistently encouraged me through the past five years to continue my historical studies despite the many delays in revising and redrafting of the manuscript. The reviewers of the manuscript will recognize the effects of their many valuable suggestions for improvements of the text, and special thanks goes to them. I am indebted to Mr. John Gerhardt for his sympathetic guidance and skillful technical editing. Finally I wish to thank my family without whose enthusiastic support this book could not have been written. Angela and Katrina cheered every page. John, my husband, has been an active participant throughout the book's development and he provided much productive criticism and unflagging encouragement.

Madison, Wisconsin Gisela Kutzbach

CONTENTS

LIST OF FIGURES

TABLES

JOURNAL ABBREVIATIONS

Am. Journ. Sci.	Silliman's American Journal of Science and Arts (New Haven)
Ann. Chim. Phys.	Annales de Chimie et de Physique (Paris)
Ann. Hydr.	Annalen der Hydrographie und maritimen Meteorologie (Berlin)
Ann. Phys. Chem.	J. C. Poggendorff's Annalen der Physik und Chemie (Leipzig)
Beitr. Phys. f. Atm.	Beiträge zur Physik der freien Atmosphäre (Leipzig)
Biogr. Mem., Nat. Ac. Sci.	Biographical Memoirs, National Academy of Sciences (Washington)
Bull. Am. Met. Soc.	Bulletin of the American Meteorological Society (Boston)
Bull. Hebd. l'Ass. Sci. France	Bulletin hebdomadaire de l'Association Scientifique de France
Comp. Ren.	Comptes Rendus de l'Académie des Sciences (Paris)
Denks. Ak. Wien	Denkschriften der Wiener Akademie der Wissenschaften, math.–naturw. Klasse
Kongl. Svenska Vet.-Akad. Handl.	Kongl. Svenska Vetenskaps-Akademiens Handlingar (Stockholm); also Bihang till . . . and Oversigt af . . .
Met. Zeits.	Meteorologische Zeitschrift (Braunschweig)
Mon. Wea. Rev.	Monthly Weather Review (Washington)
Quart. Journ. Roy. Met. Soc.	Quarterly Journal of the Royal Meteorological Society (London)
Scott. Met. Soc. Journ.	Journal of the Scottish Meteorological Society (Edinburgh)
Sitzber. Ak. Berlin	Sitzungsberichte der Preussischen Akademie der Wissenschaften zu Berlin, phys.-math. Klasse
Sitzber. Ak. Wien	Sitzungsberichte der Wiener Akademie der Wissenschaften, math.-naturw. Klasse
Smith. Inst., Ann. Rep.	Annual Report of the Smithsonian Institution (Washington)

Smith. Misc. Coll.	Smithsonian Miscellaneous Collections (Washington)
Trans. Am. Phil. Soc.	Transactions of the American Philosophical Society (Philadelphia)
Trans. Roy. Soc.	Philosophical Transactions of the Royal Society, London
Trans. Roy. Soc., Edinb.	Transactions of the Royal Society, Edinburgh
Wetter	Das Wetter (since 1928: Zeitschrift für angewandte Meteorologie)
Wien, Met. Zeits.	Zeitschrift der Österreichischen Gesellschaft für Meteorologie (Wien)

Chapter

1 Introduction

One of the most important events in the history of early Twentieth Century meteorology was the emergence of the polar front theory of cyclones. According to this theory, cyclones of middle latitudes develop along a polar front that is viewed as a boundary between polar and subtropical or tropical air masses. The initial wave-shaped perturbation is transformed into a thermally asymmetric migrating cyclonic vortex.

In a modified form, this theory is still accepted today, and interest in its origin and early development has yielded a number of historical studies. By comparison, little has been written about the theory of cyclones that dominated meteorological thought during the decades before 1900. During this period, the thermal or convective theory of cyclones stood in the foreground of scientific discussion. This theory explained the formation and maintenance of cyclonic circulation systems on the basis of the thermodynamic processes associated with the ascent of warm air and condensation of water vapor. My historical analysis will focus on the origin and development of the thermal theory of cyclones during the Nineteenth Century.

Viewing the development of the thermal theory of cyclones within the context of Nineteenth Century meteorological thought opens the door to a wide range of questions. What exactly was the thermal theory? How and why did the idea of the thermal origin of storm circulation evolve, and what significance did the theory have for the general development of meteorology? Did the thermal theory attain some degree of theoretical maturity or was it never more than an informed guess? Was it an obstacle in the long-term development of cyclone theory, or was it a fruitful approach, stimulating scientific debate and uncovering important theoretical issues? Why, among great Nineteenth Century meteorologists such as Espy, Ferrel, Mohn and Helmholtz, did the thermal theory have so many followers, and how did they cope with evidence unfavorable to it? Why, during the Nineteenth Century, were there so few attempts to formulate dynamic theories of cyclones, and why were they so ineffective? Finally, what precisely were the links between the thermal theory and the polar front theory of cyclones?

In the search for answers to these and other questions it is important to realize that the emergence of the thermal theory was closely related to the rise of modern meteorology in the Nineteenth Century. Before 1800, authors could draw upon only very limited common theoretical and empirical knowledge in meteorology; rather, the concepts which they employed in the explanation of meteorological phenomena were largely conditioned by their particular and often unique philosophical and scientific outlooks. This situation changed during the Nineteenth Century, when a common body of theory, observational techniques and terminology began to emerge. From about 1820 onward the cyclone problem enjoyed increasing popularity as a subject of scientific inquiry. During the 1830's and 1840's a small number of views on the nature of storms received limited attention and support. The thermal or convective theory of cyclones, formulated during the 1860's, became the first theory that gained wide acceptance among practitioners of meteorology in Europe and in the United States. The striving toward a unified cyclone theory reflects the establishment in meteorology, during the second half of the Nineteenth Century, of a generally agreed upon conceptual framework within which questions were asked; the same framework provided criteria for judging the acceptibility of answers proposed.

Key elements in the emergence of modern meteorology were decisive advances in the areas of theory, observation and organization. Advance in theory derived primarily from the systematic reordering and reformulation of principles of physics so as to suit the special needs of meteorology. The foundations for the development of an "atmospheric physics" were based upon the application of the fundamental equations of hydrodynamics and thermodynamics. The equation of motion for a body moving on a rotating earth was formulated in 1860. The first law of thermodynamics and with it the principles of energy conversion and conservation were introduced into meteorology at about the same time, during the 1860's. In this historical analysis I will trace the influence of the first law of thermodynamics on Nineteenth Century meteorology within the context of the thermal theory of cyclones. It will be shown that the thermal theory of cyclones, which was conceived independently of hydrodynamic assumptions, played an important role in attempts of Nineteenth Century meteorologists to link atmospheric thermodynamics and hydrodynamics for the comprehensive treatment of atmospheric circulation systems.

In a parallel development, the improvement and expansion of observations and their systematic collection and dissemination greatly accelerated with the advent of telegraphy and the establishment of national weather services after 1850. Unlike the physicist who could collect his data under simplified conditions in the laboratory, the meteorologist was faced with a highly complex system of constantly interacting parts whose behavior was beyond his control. Consequently, the establishment of a permanent meteorological network of ultimately global extent became a major goal and challenge for Nineteenth Century meteorology. Observations available from this network were particularly important for the construction of synoptic charts which evolved as a basic research tool during the 1860's and acquired wide-ranging practical applicability. The evaluation of synoptic charts, which were seen as a prerequisite for the systematic investigation of large-scale atmospheric motions, played a major role in the development of the thermal theory of cyclones. Equally important was the extension of the meteorological network into the upper layers of the atmosphere, beginning during the 1870's, which made it possible to study the three-dimensional structure of cyclones.

The rapid growth of Nineteenth Century meteorology cannot be fully understood without considering aspects of the professionalization of the field and the recognition of meteorology as a separate academic discipline. The often close association between universities and meteorological institutes not only helped direct scientists from related fields to meteorology, but facilitated the training of meteorologists both in the physical foundations and the practical aspects of meteorology. Finally, professional societies and journals, beginning during the 1860's, initiated efficient dissemination of meteorological theory and provided channels of communication among meteorologists.

1.1 A SYNOPSIS

One of the cornerstones of modern meteorological theory is the principle of conservation of energy, i.e., the first law of thermodynamics as related to interconversions of thermal and mechanical energy. Just as in physics, where partial manifestations of the principle of energy conservation were perceived in germinal form long before explicit formulation, so the recognition of the main forms of energy operating in the atmosphere preceded the insight that energy was conserved and that conversion processes occurred. The path toward proper recognition of these thermodynamic and dynamic processes was neither a straight nor easy one. The following synopsis will introduce the various pathways to be traced in subsequent chapters.

Storm theories of the early Nineteenth Century, summarized in Section 1.2, dealt primarily with kinematics and were largely devoid of physical concepts. During the 1830's, James Pollard Espy took an initial step toward the recognition of the main forms of energy and physical processes in storms. As will be seen in Chapter 2, Espy identified processes in the atmosphere which are now known as adiabatic processes, using results from laboratory experiments on the expansion and compression of dry and moist air. Linking the two concepts of adiabatic change and thermal convection, Espy arrived at a correct explanation of the large-scale formation of clouds and, in many cases, of precipitation, by considering the expansion and cooling of ascending currents of air. On the basis of the well-known observation that storms are often associated with precipitation, Espy made the far-reaching conclusion that the latent heat released during the condensation of water vapor in convective currents of moist air cooling adiabatically was the "motive power" of storms.[1] Espy's theory of storm development became widely known as the convective theory of storms.

In the 1830's adiabatic processes were interpreted according to the caloric and not the mechanical theory of heat. Significantly, the caloric theory did not allow for conversion processes between heat and work nor for their equivalence. Espy's hypothesis, therefore, could not lead to a quantitative calculation of the motive power of storms from the amount of heat available. Such a calculation depends upon the application of the first law of thermodynamics, including a knowledge of the mechanical equivalent of heat, and became possible only after the radical revision of the theoretical concepts underlying the interpretation of the nature of heat that occurred in the 1850's and 1860's. Espy's conception of the release of latent heat as the motive power of storms should be viewed as foreshadowing the inference of a process of conversion of heat into mechanical energy in cyclones.

From about 1860 onward, as will be discussed in Chapter 3, adiabatic processes in the atmosphere were reinterpreted on the basis of the first law of thermodynamics, and the corresponding superstructure of thermodynamic formulas applicable to atmospheric conditions was developed. Criteria for determining the stability of the atmosphere with regard to vertical displacements of parcels of air were formulated. These criteria allowed prediction of the conditions under which convection would occur. Whereas Espy had been forced to rely almost exclusively on laboratory experiments, the greatly improved meteorological observations of the 1860's and 1870's clearly demonstrated adiabatic temperature changes taking place in the atmosphere.

Concurrently with these studies on adiabatic processes, scientists began to reexamine the problem of cyclone theory, shifting emphasis from the explanation of the center of low pressure and the wind field, essentially questions of mechanics prevelant during the first half of the Nineteenth Century, to the physical problem of the source of energy in cyclones. Having available the constant conversion factor between heat and work it now appeared possible—at least in principle—to quantify Espy's bold conclusions of the 1830's. As will be seen in Chapter 4, formulas as well as graphical methods were devised for the evaluation of the quantity of the thermal energy associated with the release of latent heat, and there were first attempts to formulate an energy balance equation for the cyclone. When the results of these theoretical investigations were viewed in conjunction with empirical studies on the distribution of surface temperatures and cloud and precipitation patterns associated with cyclones the hypothesis became almost inevitable that thermal energy derived from the release of latent heat during

---

[1] In physics, the phenomenon of adiabatic compression was also of particular importance in connection with the general formulation of the principle of conservation of energy. It provided an ideal demonstration of the conversion of work to heat and furnished the only means of computing a conversion coefficient with the data then extant. Acquisition of these important data was stimulated by efforts to improve the design of engines producing work through heat, in particular the steam engine. See T. S. Kuhn, "Energy conservation as an example of simultaneous discovery," in *Critical Problems in the History of Science*, M. Clagett, Ed. (Madison, University of Wisconsin Press, 1959), p. 335.

condensation of water vapor was a primary source of the kinetic energy exhibited in cyclones. During the 1870's, empirical studies based on evaluations of synoptic charts and quantitative studies of storm energetics and dynamics all lent support to the thermal theory of cyclones.

According to this thermal hypothesis of cyclone formation, the initial diminution of pressure in the central part of the storm was attributed to heating caused by the release of latent heat during condensation of water vapor in ascending currents of warm moist air. It was thought that localized heating and vertical expansion, resulting in a raising of the isobaric surfaces in the central part of the storm, caused outflow of air at high levels, and, therefore, a lowering of surface pressure. Consequently, air flowed in from all sides and cyclonic motion was induced on account of the deflecting force of the earth's rotation. The maintenance of low pressure was assured by the assumption that horizontal divergence in upper levels compensated the low level convergence of air. It was supposed that the cyclone progressed in the direction of greatest moisture. Several versions of this so-called thermal or convective theory of cyclones were developed during the 1860's and 1870's, their main difference being found in the degree to which they incorporated dynamic principles. These various versions will be referred to collectively as the thermal or convective theory of cyclones. Certain features of the thermal theory described above are illustrated in Figure 1, in a horizontal and vertical cross section through a warm core cyclone.

In an age when energy considerations stood in the foreground of scientific discussions, it was an important asset of the thermal theory that it appeared to be perfectly plausible from an energetic point of view. It seems almost paradoxical, therefore, as will be seen in Chapter 5, that the first serious challenge to the theory rested on arguments pertaining to the energy budget of cyclones. Around 1890, when meteorological observations were systematically extended from the earth's surface into the free atmosphere, upper level temperature observations of American and European cyclones furnished contradictory evidence. American observations seemingly conformed to the concept of a direct thermal circulation between cyclones and anticyclones, namely, warm air rising in the cyclonic branch of the circulation and cold air descending in the anticyclone. European data appeared to be incompatible with this assumption because they frequently indicated lower temperatures above surface cyclones than above surface anticyclones.

This discrepancy called for systematic studies of the thermal structure of cyclones. On account of these studies, a number of meteorologists focussed their attention on the role of horizontal thermal asymmetry resulting from the confluence of air currents of different geographical origin and thermal properties and the associated field of vertical motion within cyclones. As discussed in Chapter 6, around the turn of the century several investigators concluded that it was the potential energy associated with horizontal temperature contrasts that accounted for the kinetic energy exhibited in cyclones. Thus, thermal energy continued to be regarded as the primary source of kinetic energy in cyclones, but emphasis shifted from the latent heat release to the advection of warm and cold air as the major

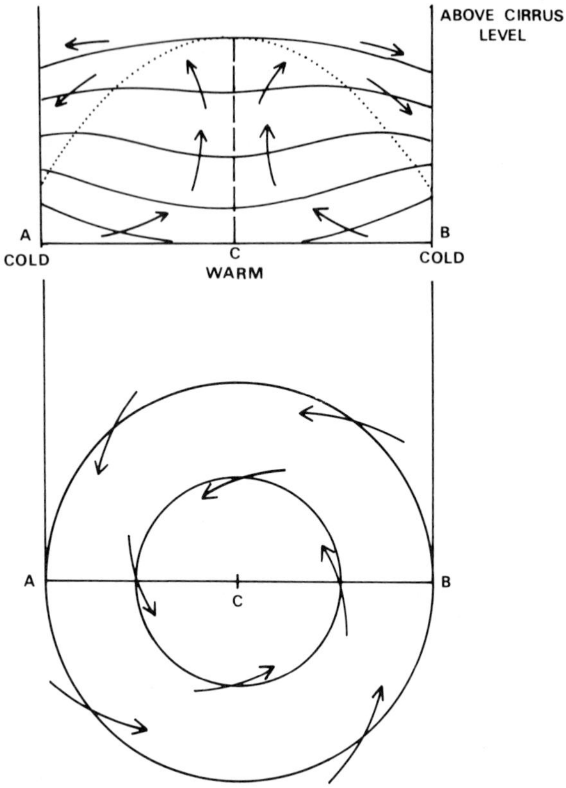

FIGURE 1. Schematic illustration of the thermal theory of cyclones (1860's and 1870's). Horizontal and vertical cross section, taken along line A–B through the center C of the cyclone. Solid lines are isobars, arrows indicate direction of flow. The dashed line represents the vertical axis of the cyclone, along which the air is warmest and the vertical spacing of the isobars is greatest. The circulation is cyclonic under the dotted line and anticyclonic above. Thermodynamic processes associated with the ascent of warm moist air and the condensation of water vapor initiate and maintain the cyclonic circulation.

source of localized heating. Max Margules in 1903 confirmed this view by quantitative calculations based on simple models of initially unstable mass distributions of warm and cold air. He showed that isentropic redistribution of the air masses, associated with rising of warm air and sinking of cold air to a state of thermal stability, would lead to the lowering of the center of gravity of the whole system and conversion of potential into kinetic energy.

Investigations of the temperature structure of cyclones led some scientists to trace the life history of cyclones from an energetic point of view. These studies, carried out in the early 1900's, at least partially resolved the conflict that had resulted from the differing European and American upper level temperature observations. American cyclones began to be regarded as young, developing and fast-traveling cyclones representing a thermodynamic engine that transformed thermal energy into kinetic energy. European storms frequently appeared to be slow-traveling or stationary systems which had reached a mature stage of development or were in the process of decay, and whose store of available potential energy was no longer replenished by horizontal advection. The discovery of the tropopause around the turn of the century provided additional information: observations indicated that the tropopause was low and warm over decaying cyclone systems with a warm stratospheric layer above. This vertical temperature distribution helped account for the low pressure at the base of the air column in mature or decaying surface cyclones.

The study of the thermal asymmetry of cyclones also made apparent the need for detailed investigations of dynamic processes operating in storms. Such investigations showed, for example, that ascending currents of air might also be produced dynamically by the horizontal divergence observed in upper levels of the atmosphere above the leading portion of traveling surface cyclones. The recognition that neither thermodynamic nor dynamic forces can be neglected without grossly simplifying and distorting the actual processes inspired investigators to seek ways of linking the previously separate fields of atmospheric thermodynamics and dynamics. William Ferrel made a significant step in this direction when he derived the important thermal wind equation which relates the vertical shear of the wind to the horizontal temperature gradient. Around the turn of the century V. Bjerknes applied to meteorology the theorem of velocity circulation which had been developed earlier for homogeneous and incompressible fluids. Whereas Nineteenth Century investigators generally treated density as a function of barometric pressure in studies of atmospheric dynamics, following classical hydrodynamics, Bjerknes' circulation theorem was applicable to situations where density is not constant along pressure surfaces and it allowed quantitative evaluation, from observational data, of the thermal energy available for the circulation in cyclones.

Investigations of the asymmetric horizontal temperature distribution and vertical circulation in cyclones were fruitful in still another respect. In earlier theoretical and synoptic studies it had often been assumed that a cyclone was an isolated vortex. This assumption was made partly for mathematical convenience and partly because, on the synoptic chart, the barometric pressure field associated with the cyclone consisted normally of a system of closed isobars. In the 1880's and 1890's, the three-dimensional analysis of the temperature distribution and flow patterns in cyclones made it clear that cyclones must be regarded as open circulation systems (thermodynamically as well as dynamically) and indicated a wave-like character of cyclone propagation. After the conditions for dynamic stability along boundaries of different masses of moving air had been specified in the early years of the Twentieth Century, and after it had been shown empirically that cyclones are normally associated with such surfaces of discontinuity, it became feasible to view cyclogenesis as a problem of wave formation. As will be discussed in Chapter 7, the development of the frontal cyclone model and the polar front or wave theory of cyclones by the Bergen School of meteorologists during the early 1920's represented the first successful attempt in this direction. According to this theory, the initial frontal wave was first transformed into a thermally asymmetric cyclonic vortex. The rising of warm air and the descent of cold air resulted in a lowering of the center of gravity of the whole system and were associated with the conversion of potential into kinetic energy. During this process the cyclonic vortex was further transformed into a large cold vortex with more or less thermal symmetry.

It was a great asset of the polar front cyclone model that it clearly defined the borders between warm and cold air within the storm and during its life history and thus clarified the description and graphical representation of midlatitude cyclones. Developed in relative isolation, the polar front theory of cyclones initially was often viewed as an abrupt break with the past. No doubt this was due in part to the Norwegian method of analyzing synoptic charts, which was strikingly different from the traditional method of routine weather analysis. Nevertheless, a number of scientists noted that the new theory was a logical extension of current and earlier research, pointing out that essential aspects of the theory had been partially anticipated in earlier works. My historical research has led me to the conclusion that there was indeed a continuity in the development of theories of cyclones from the time of introduction of the first law of thermodynamics into meteorology in the 1860's to the achievements of the early Twentieth Century, and that this continuity is reflected in the work of many prominent meteorologists. In this study, I will trace and specify the historical elements in this continuity with regard to the thermal and energetic aspects of cyclones. My historical analysis ends with the discussion of the work of Margules. The polar front theory, and the research of the short period that elapsed between Margules' investigations and the emergence of the polar front theory, have been treated only briefly. I feel that defining the historical problem within these limits is justified because the polar front theory is well known to modern meteorologists, although in modified form. Besides, no major new developments were made in atmospheric energetics between the publication of Margules' papers and the emergence of the polar front theory, which was based energetically on Margules' work.

The preceding synopsis of the development of the thermal theory of cyclones has been restricted to the discussion of salient empirical results and significant theoretical contributions. The scientists, however, who carried out these investigations have been mentioned in but a few cases. Developed over a period of several decades, the thermal theory is not the story of the single-minded effort of one particular investigator or a small group of scientists, nor can a nationality label be attached to it; rather, it is the product of the combined effort of a surprisingly large number of workers of widely different backgrounds and interests, and from many different countries. This circumstance helps to explain the emergence of several versions of the thermal theory during the 1860's and 1870's, and the continual modifications undertaken during the 1880's and 1890's. In a broader sense, since cyclone research was at the core of meteorological activity during this period, the emergence of the thermal theory of cyclones portrays the spirit and the scope of Nineteenth Century meteorological thought at large.

In order to gain some perspective now and for subsequent reference, I have constructed Figure 2, which summarizes the names, life spans and years of major

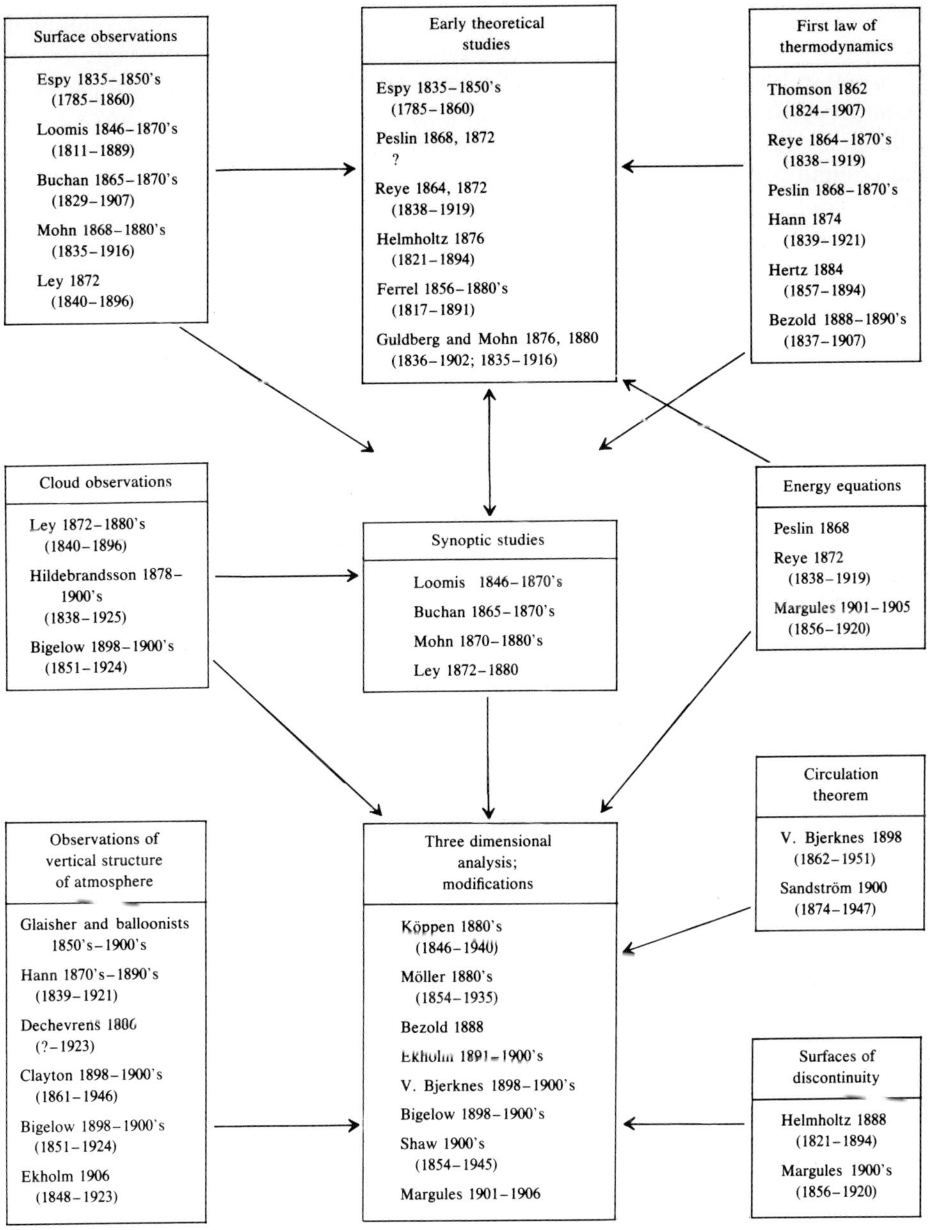

FIGURE 2. Summary of the historical development of the thermal theory of cyclones (1830's to 1900's). Names, life spans and years of major contributions of scientists are given. Contributions of scientists relating to the same subject have been grouped under explanatory headings in separate boxes and in more or less chronological order from top to bottom. Boxes in the left column comprise relevant empirical studies and observations; boxes in right column indicate pertinent theoretical studies. Arrows indicate interactions with and influences on the emergence, development and modifications of the thermal theory, featured in the central column.

contributions of the scientists whose work significantly influenced the development of the thermal theory.[2] The entries are arranged in more or less chronological order from top to bottom. Contributions of scientists relating to the same subject have been grouped under explanatory headings in separate boxes. The boxes in the column on the left comprise relevant empirical studies and observations; boxes in the column on the right indicate pertinent theoretical studies. Arrows indicate interactions with and influences on the emergence, development and modifications of the thermal theory of cyclones, featured in the central column. The detailed analysis of the contributions by scientists listed in Figure 2 will be the primary content of the following chapters.

Finally, an overview of the organization and professionalization of meteorology during the Nineteenth Century may be obtained from Table 1. This table, arranged in chronological order, shows the heightening of meteorological activity after 1850: The establishment of national weather services in rapid succession between 1850 and 1870 was closely related to the emergence of a meteorological network with almost instantaneous communication. Perfection and expansion of this network accelerated when international cooperation was organized on a permanent basis, as is indicated by the onset of international meteorological conferences and enterprises after 1870. Meteorological societies and journals, providing effective channels of cummunication, emerged in parallel development. In the following chapters, details on organizational and professional aspects of Nineteenth Century meteorology will be noted in so far as they related to the evolution of the thermal theory of cyclones.

1.2 SETTING THE STAGE

In setting the stage for the analysis of early studies of adiabatic change and the subsequent emergence of the convective or thermal theory of cyclones, I shall briefly outline the state of cyclone theory in the early part of the Nineteenth Century. This will help, by way of contrast, to illuminate the novelty of the concepts employed in the thermal theory. Among the most prominent problems in meteorology during the 1830's was the question of the nature of the wind field associated with storms. Contemporary theories showed striking differences in the storm's wind field as well as in the stated causes for storm formation. The great diversity found in these theories reflects the lack of a generally accepted conceptual framework in meteorology; it also indicates that the data base for testing of theories was still inadequate.

In the ensuing debate on the nature of the wind field associated with midlatitude storms, three storm models became particularly well known and enjoyed substantial yet limited support: in Europe, Heinrich Wilhelm Dove's "linear two

[2] In this book, I have dealt primarily with publications of scientists in the United States and European countries, i.e., England, Germany, France, Austria and the Scandinavian countries. Russian scientists have received virtually no consideration. Some indication of their contributions to Nineteenth Century meteorology may be obtained from A. Kh. Khrgian, *Meteorology—A Historical Survey*, Vol. 1, Translated from Russian, 2nd ed., rev. by Kh. P. Pogosyan (Jerusalem, Keter Press, 1970), 387 pp.

current" theory, and in the United States, W. C. Redfield's "centrifugal" theory and the "centripetal" theory of James Pollard Espy. The theories of Dove and Redfield were based exclusively on mechanical principles, reflecting the mechanistic outlook of early Nineteenth Century science in general. Deviating from this approach, Espy took account of thermal factors in his attempt to identify the major physical processes involved in storm formation. Before Espy's work, consideration of thermal processes had been restricted largely to discussions of atmospheric motion on a global scale. The astronomer and natural philosopher Edmond Halley, for example, applied the principle of thermal convection as early as 1686, when he proposed that the ascent of warm air in equatorial regions was the cause of the trade wind circulation.[3] It was therefore indicative of a new direction in meteorology during the 1830's, when Espy contended that thermal convection plays a decisive role in atmospheric motions on the scale of storms. The lively scientific dispute that developed in the United States over the theories of Redfield and Espy will be treated in detail in Chapter 2. However, a brief review of the mechanical theories of storms put forward by Dove and Redfield will serve to underline the novelty of Espy's ideas and will help us appreciate the difficulty and the resistance Espy's views encountered.

In the first part of the Nineteenth Century most European scientists sought the cause of weather changes in features of the global wind system, i.e., the general circulation, rather than in subordinate disturbances within it.[4] In this viewpoint, they were following Dove, the leading European expert in meteorology.[5] Dove was director of the Preussische Meteorologische Institut in Berlin for three decades, from 1849 to 1879. Beginning in 1827 and continuing throughout his professional career, he developed a meteorological system of linear opposing wind currents that related weather changes to changes in the direction of the prevailing winds. Within Dove's scheme of the global wind system, air currents of midlatitudes were either of equatorial or polar origin. He regarded the warm and humid southwesterly currents of midlatitudes, i.e., the equatorial currents, as the continuation along the surface of the southwesterly winds above the trades (then called anti-trades). The polar currents that were experienced as cold and dry northeasterly surface winds in midlatitudes gradually changed into the trade winds on their path southwestward toward the equator.

This concept of two basic currents underlying Dove's scheme of the global wind system was also fundamental to his explanation of locally observed storms and weather changes in midlatitudes. Developing an easily applicable and convincing model of midlatitude storm formation, he proposed that storms resulted from "the conflict between two currents which alternately displaced each other at

---

[3] E. Halley, "An historical account of the trade winds and monsoons," *Trans. Roy. Soc.*, **16** (1686), 153–168.

[4] The term general circulation came into use during the second half of the Nineteenth Century. For example, Ferrel wrote on the "general motions of the atmosphere" in 1859/60; J. Thomson in 1857 discussed the "grand currents of the atmosphere." By 1885, the term general circulation was well established and was used by Teisserenc de Bort, A. Sprung, W. Köppen and many others.

[5] For short biographies on Dove, Redfield and other scientists discussed throughout this book, see the Appendix.

TABLE 1. Development of weather services, meteorological societies and journals, and meteorological conferences during the Nineteenth Century

WEATHER SERVICES AND DIRECTORS	SOCIETIES	JOURNALS	CONFERENCES
1826 *Belgium:* Observatoire Royal: A. Quetelet (1826–74); E. Quetelet (1874–76); J. C. Houzeau (1876–85).			
1847 *Germany:* Meteorologische Institut Berlin: H. W. Dove (1848–78); G. Hellmann (1878–85); W. v. Bezold (1885–1907). Deutsche Seewarte, G. v. Neumeyer (1876–1903).			
1849 *Russia:* Central Physical Observatory, Leningrad: A. T. Kupffer (1849–1865); L. F. Kämtz (1866–68); H. Wild (1868–95); M. Rykatcheff (1896–1913).			
	1850 Royal Met. Soc.		
1851 *Austria:* Zentralanstalt für Meteorologie und Geodynamik, Wien: K. Kreil (1851–63); K. Jelinek (1863–76); J. Hann (1877–97); J. M. Perntner (1897–1908).			
	1853 Soc. Météorologique de France	1853 Ann. de la Soc. Mét de France	1853 Congress of seafaring nations, Brussels
1854 *Holland:* Koninklijk Nederlandsch Meteorologisch Instituut, Utrecht: C.H.D. Buys Ballot (1854–89); M. Snellen (1889–1902).			
1854 *Great Britain:* Met. Dept. of the Board of Trade, London: R. Fitzroy (1854–65); Babington (1865–67). Met. Office: R. H. Scott (1867–76). Met. Council (1876–1905). Met. Committee, W. N. Shaw (1905–1919).			
1855 *France:* Observatoire: LeVerrier (1855–77). Bureau Central Météorologique: E. Mascart (1878–1907); C. A. Angot (1907–20).			
	1856 Scottish Met. Soc.		
1859 *Sweden:* Statens Meteorologisk-Hydrografiska Anstalt, Stockholm: E. Edlund (1859–75); R. Rubenson (1875–1902); H. E. Hamberg (1902–13); N. Ekholm (1913–1918).			

1863 *Italy:* Ufficia Centrale di Meteorologia, Rome: P. Tacchinni (1863–1900).			
1866 *Norway:* Det Norske Meteorologiske Institut, Oslo: H. Mohn (1866–1913)			
1870 *United States:* Weather Bureau, Washington: Chiefs of the Signal Service: A. J. Myer (1870–80); W. B. Hazen (1880–87); A. W. Greely (1887–91). Chiefs of the Weather Bureau: M. W. Harrington (1891–95); W. L. Moore (1895–1913).	1865 Oesterreichische Meteorologische Ges.	1865 Wien. Met. Zeits. 1866 Quart. Journ. Scott. Met. Soc.	
1872 *Denmark:* Det Danske Meteorologiske Institut, Copenhagen: N. Hoffmeyer (1872–84); A. Paulsen (1884–1907).		1871 Ann. Hydr. 1872 Quart. Journ. Roy. Met. Soc. Met. Magazine	1872 Conference in Leipzig
1875 *India:* Imperial Met. Reporter: H. F. Blanford (1875–89); J. Elliott (1889–1903).		1873 Mon. Wea. Rev.	1873 First Met. Congress, Vienna
1880 *Switzerland:* Schweizerische Meteorologische Zentralanstalt, Zürich: R. Billwiller (1880–1904).		1875 Ann. de Bureau Central Mét.	1874 Utrecht 1876 London } Permanent Committee 1878 Utrecht
	1881 Associazione Meteorologica Italiana	1878 Archiv der Deutschen Seewarte	1879 Second Internat. Congress, Rome 1880 Berne } Internat. Met. Committee 1882 Copenhagen
	1883 Deutsche Meteorologische Gesellschaft		1882–83 Internat. Polar Year
	1884 New England Met. Soc.	1884 Met. Zeits. merged with Wien, Met. Zeits. 1886 1884 Am. Met. Journ. 1884 Das Wetter	1889 Internat. Met. Congress, Paris 1891 Conf. of Directors, Munich 1896 Internat. Met. Congress, Paris

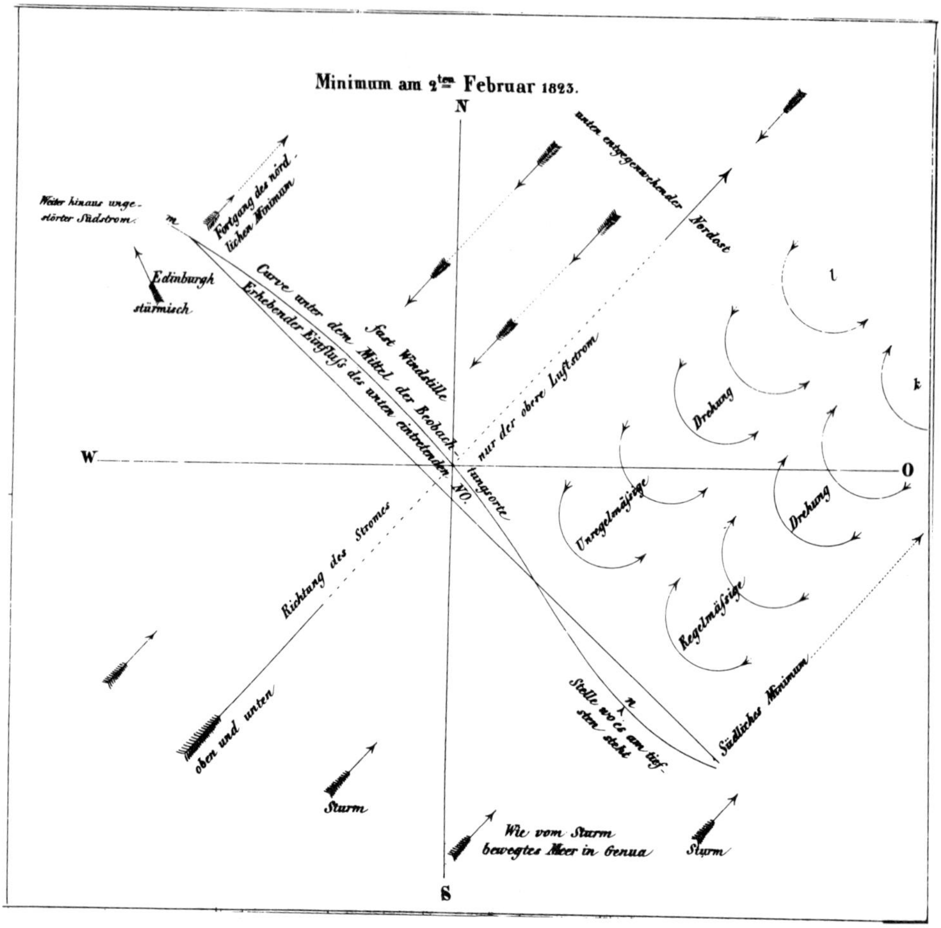

FIGURE 3. Chart illustrating wind and pressure conditions associated with the storm of 2 February 1823 according to Dove, from *Meteorologische Untersuchungen* (Berlin, Sanders, 1837), first published by Dove in "Ueber mittlere Luftströme," *Ann. Phys. Chem.*, **13** (1828). The northeast current has split the barometric minimum associated with the southwest current into two parts, the stronger one at n in southern France, and one at m, along the western coast of England. The curved arrows in the eastern quadrant of the figure indicate changes in the windrose as observed at individual stations. Changes in the wind depend upon the location of the station with regard to the center line of the southwest current or storm, i.e., along the line n–k the direction of the wind changes from south over southwest to west to northwest (with the sun), and along the line p–l from south to southeast to northeast (against the sun; p, omitted on the figure, denotes the intersection of the diagonal line with the sinuous curve in the southeast quadrant).

the place of observation," and that the "absolute extremes" of weather changes "must be due to the sole predominance of one of these currents."[6] Thus, meteorological variables such as barometric pressure, temperature and moisture content could be regarded as functions of the direction of the wind and the associated current. Dove introduced the so-called law of gyration of the wind (Drehungsgesetz, literally "law of turning"), defining the veering or backing of the

[6] W. H. Dove, "Ueber das Gesetz der Stürme," *Ann. Phys. Chem.*, **52** (1841), p. 7.

wind when one current replaced the other. Accordingly, during the replacement of the equatorial current by the polar current, winds recorded at the observation station should always veer from south over southwest to northwest, i.e., with the sun, as was commonly said; vice versa, during the replacement of the polar current by the equatorial current winds should back from east over northeast to north and northwest, i.e., against the sun.

Dove consistently opposed the idea that all storms are of vortical nature. He believed that rotary storms were largely restricted to tropical regions (where they were referred to as cyclones). He made it a point to show "as clearly as possible how unjustifiable it is to confound the effects of the law of gyration with those of rotary storms."[7] The decisive difference between midlatitude storms, arising "from the conflict of opposite currents," and tropical cyclones was "that the fluctuations of the barometer, which are associated with the change of the wind into the opposite direction, are accompanied by great variations of temperature"[8] in the former while the temperature remained unchanged in the latter. Veering of the wind with the sun, he insisted, dominated throughout the entire storm area. (This feature, it might be added, is generally borne out by the storms in central Europe because the center of low pressure and circulation is normally north of the observation station.) Dove's analysis of a storm on the basis of the two current theory is given in Figure 3.

At a time when the baric wind relationship, describing the interdependence of the pressure field and wind field, had not yet been established and when no synoptic charts were available that could have provided a grasp of the spatial distribution of weather phenomena at a given instance in time, Dove's scheme had the definite advantage of providing a temporal framework into which series of local observations could be fitted. For this reason Dove's law of gyration, first expounded in 1827, was commonly used in the interpretation of weather changes in Europe up to the 1860's. Practically all meteorologists in central Europe active during the 1860's and 1870's received their early training in Dove's theories, and the concept of polar and equatorial currents can be traced in the work of most of them.[9]

Both Dove and Redfield sought to determine empirically the important

---

[7] W. H. Dove, *Das Gesetz der Stürme*, 2nd ed. (Berlin, Reimer, 1861), p. 218. Dove was not always as clear about this point as he indicated here. For example, he called midlatitude storms whirling winds, although he *meant* only a half turn of the wind rose, from southwest to northwest, with the polar current taking the place of the equatorial current, which Dove regarded as the true carrier of the barometric minimum [*Meteorologische Untersuchungen* (Berlin, Sanders, 1837), 277ff]. Dove formulated the law of gyration in 1827 on the basis of data by H. W. Brandes in the paper "Einige meteorologische Untersuchungen über den Wind," *Ann. Phys. Chem.*, **87** (1827), 545–590. Dove opposed the idea that storms are centripetal in nature, with air flowing radially toward the center of pressure diminuition, as advocated by Brandes, his teacher in meteorology, and Espy.

[8] *Das Gesetz der Stürme*, p. 170.

[9] The air mass concept, embodied in the concept of polar and equatorial currents, was a fruitful approach to certain meteorological problems. The term current, rather than mass, was prevelant in the meteorological literature until about the turn of the century. The air mass concept continued to play an important role in meteorological research, even though Dove's teaching fell into discredit in his old age. James D. Forbes, in his *Supplementary Report on Meteorology for the British Association for the Advancement of Science for 1840* (London, Taylor, 1841), 155 pp, introduced the British readers to Dove's ideas. For a contemporary summary of Dove's work see E. E. Schmid, *Lehrbuch der Meteorologie* (Leipzig, L. Voss, 1860). Dove's views made essentially no impression on meteorology in France.

relationship between wind and pressure distribution in a storm. They arrived at diametrically opposed results, as we shall see, partly because they investigated different types of storms. No clear distinction had yet been made between storms of various scale size and origin; in fact, throughout the first half of the Nineteenth Century authors often used the same general, non-specific term storm, while referring to quite different phenomena, such as hurricanes, tornadoes or large-scale cyclones.[10] This loose terminology contributed significantly to confusion and misunderstandings among early Nineteenth Century meteorologists. Thus, in his investigations of storms occurring in central Europe, Dove encountered primarily large-scale midlatitude cyclones, whose vortical nature is not easily discernible by an observer relying on the so-called local method, i.e., examination of the temporal succession of weather phenomena at a fixed locality. On the other hand, Redfield investigated comparatively small-scale storms, namely, hurricanes and tornadoes. Both of these storm types readily revealed their revolving character even to the casual observer, and, quite naturally, Redfield soon regarded rotation as the salient feature of storms.

Redfield was by profession a marine engineer working in steam transportation. He had acquired his scientific reputation through paleontological and meteorological investigations. Redfield meticulously studied storm data for ten years before summarizing his results in 1831. These results appeared to demonstrate beyond doubt that the direction of the wind in the storms he had examined was "in all cases, compounded of both the rotative and progressive velocities of the storm, in the mean ratio of these velocities."[11] It appears that Redfield here attempted to describe the winds in a storm as the vector sum of rotary and progressive velocities.[12] The circular motion, he suggested, was produced when the northeast trades press against the "obstruction" formed by the chain of islands along the northern limit of the Caribbean Sea:

> These masses of atmosphere, thus set into active revolution, continue to sweep along the islands. . . . Gradually assuming a different direction as they recoil from these obstructions and receive new impulsive forces, the stormy masses continue to sweep over, or along the American coast, . . . till they finally become lost, or dissipated . . . or perhaps even reach the coasts of Europe or its northern islands.[13]

He contended that it was "the centrifugal tendency, or action, which pertains to all revolving or rotary movements," that produced the low barometric pressure

---

[10] The term cyclone was first used by Piddington in 1842 (*The Sailor's Horn-Book for the Law of Storms*, London, 1842), with reference to all strong or weak winds revolving around a common center. In order to avoid ambiguities, Piddington himself used the older terms such as gale, storm or orcan only to denote the strength of the wind. In the second half of the Nineteenth Century, a midlatitude cyclone was also referred to as barometric depression, barometric minimum or minimum, simply as low or disturbance, vortex, cyclone, etc., the exact terms used varying from author to author, much as today.

[11] Redfield, "Remarks on the prevailing storms of the Atlantic coast of the North American States," *Am. Journ. Sci.*, **20** (1831), p. 29.

[12] Vectorial representation was not introduced into meteorology until the end of the Nineteenth Century.

[13] Redfield (1831), p. 32.

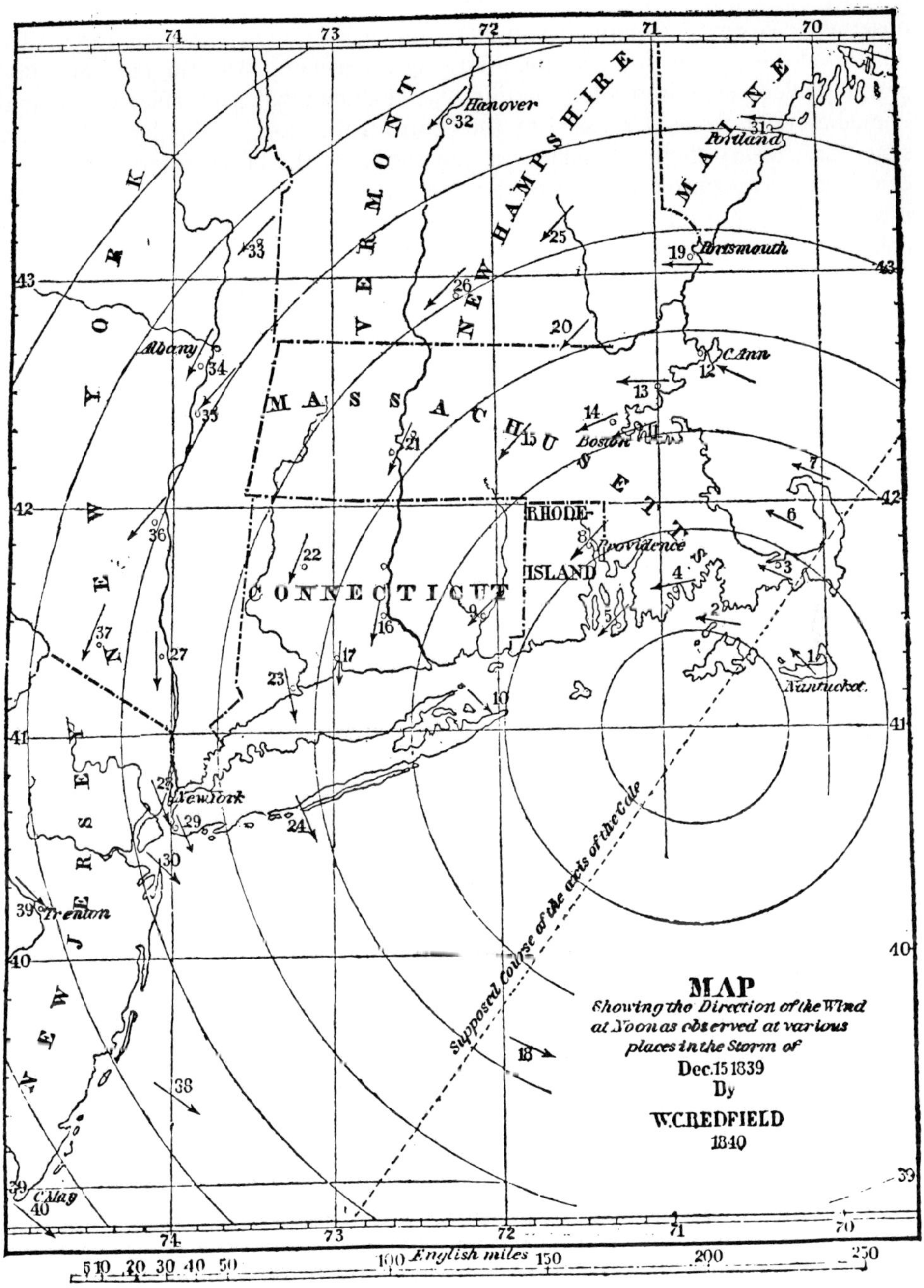

FIGURE 4 The vortical nature of storms (Redfield, 1843), from Redfield, "Observations on the storm of December 15, 1839," *Trans. Am. Phil. Soc.*, **8** (1843). Arrows indicate wind direction, corresponding to eight and in some cases to sixteen points of the compass. Numbers next to arrows refer to observation stations. Superimposed concentric circles indicate an average inward inclination of about 6° for the direction of the wind. Note that the southeast portion of the storm contains no wind data, a fact that Loomis later emphasized in his critique of Redfield's view of storms.

observed in storms and maintained it by balancing the pressure gradient forces. He illustrated this proposition with the following experiment: Bringing the water in a partially filled vessel into rotary motion "we shall find that the surface of the fluid immediately becomes depressed by the centrifugal action."[14] Similarly, Redfield suggested, rotary motion produces a depression of the atmosphere toward the center of the storm on account of the "centrifugal action," causing barometric pressure fall. Thus the pressure distribution was explained as a result of the wind field. In an attempt to explain the commonly observed counterclockwise rotation in storms, Redfield suggested vaguely that the causes initiating rotation also "uniformly tend to produce the rotative movement in the direction . . . from *right* to *left*, or *against* the sun."[15] In his analysis of a storm of 1843 (Figure 4) Redfield noted a "slight vortical movement" of revolving storms, i.e., an inward directed component of the wind. Explaining that "the concentric lines, drawn at invervals of thirty miles, were added, not as precisely indicating the course of the wind, but to afford better means of comparison for the several observations;"[16] he found that the direction of the winds in the storm area indicated "an average convergence, or inward inclination, of about six degrees."[17] Despite these findings, Redfield's contemporaries continued to associate him with the view of "pure circular rotation" in storms.[18]

By the 1840's the question of the nature of the wind field associated with cyclones had developed into one of the most urgent meteorological problems. An exact solution was needed for the practical purpose of navigation. The existing theories of Dove and Redfield were questioned on the basis of improved observations and physical reasoning. Their cyclone models soon were seen as typifying a group of storm theories which Nineteenth Century meteorologists labeled mechanical theories since they were concerned primarily with the kinematic description of the wind field. It is against this general backdrop of mechanical theories that the emergence and evolution of the thermal theory of cyclones will now be traced.

---

[14] *Ibid.*, p. 46.

[15] *Ibid.*, p. 32.

[16] Redfield, "Observations on the storm of December 15, 1839," *Trans. Am. Phil. Soc.*, **8** (1843), p. 77.

[17] As early as 1837, Redfield confided in a letter to Loomis "that the wind does not blow towards the center of the tornado but in a whirl or circuit, winding no doubt spirally inward and upward at the same time, in the manner of all ascending vortices." See letter to Loomis of 2 December 1837, in Reingold, *Science in Nineteenth Century America* (New York, Hill and Wang, 1964), p. 97. When, thirty years later, Th. Reye (see Chapter 3) reanalyzed this and other storms investigated by Redfield, he observed that Redfield had underestimated the angle of "inclination inward" (angle between wind direction and isobars); see Reye, *Wirbelstürme, Tornadoes und Wettersäulen* (Hannover, Rümpler, 1872), p. 80. Later estimates, based on synoptic charts of the 1860's, yielded much larger values for the angle of inclination than those quoted by Redfield and Reye, namely, between 10° and 30°. In 1880 Mohn calculated as "normal values" for the angle of inclination 22° over the ocean and 42° over land [Guldberg and Mohn, "Studies on the movements in the atmosphere," Part II, translated from the French by Cl. Abbe, *Smiths. Misc. Coll.*, **51** (1910), p. 233].

[18] Redfield to some extent anticipated Buys Ballot's law of 1857, that the wind is in general perpendicular to the direction of maximum barometric slope and that the wind velocity depends on the pressure gradient rather than pressure. The term barometric gradient was introduced by Th. Stevenson in 1868. W. Köppen introduced the term baric wind law in 1878.

Chapter

2 Early Applications of the Principles of Adiabatic Change and Vertical Convection

2.1 INTRODUCTION

A key factor in the formulation of the thermal theory of cyclones was the application to atmospheric conditions of the principle of adiabatic change, and, closely related, the reinterpretation of the principle of vertical convection. Since the principle of adiabatic change, which constitutes the process of compression or expansion of a gas with no transfer of heat between gas and environment, was of such importance for Nineteenth Century cyclone theory, its development within the broader context of physics will be briefly reviewed.

The phenomenon of adiabatic change in gases emerged as a recognized scientific problem in physics during a period of several decades before 1800.[1] Its firm experimental foundations were established during the early 1800's, beginning with the important discovery by John Dalton and Louis Joseph Gay-Lussac (1802 and 1803) that the coefficient of thermal expansion was the same for all gases.[2]

---

[1] Comprehensive historical discussions of adiabatic change may be found in T. S. Kuhn, "The caloric theory of adiabatic compression," *Isis*, **49** (1958), 132–140; and R. Fox, *The Caloric Theory of Gases from Lavoisier to Regnault* (Oxford, Claredon Press, 1971).

[2] Dalton, "Experiments and observations on the heat and cold produced by the mechanical condensation and rarefaction of air," *Memoirs of the Manchester Literary and Philosophical Society*, **5**. part 2 (1802), 515–526; and "On the expansion of elastic fluid by heat," *ibid.*, pp. 595–602. Gay-Lussac, "Recherches sur la dilation des gaz et des vapeurs," *Ann. Chim. Phys.*, **43** (1802), 137–175.

Dalton also dealt with the compression and expansion and subsequent condensation of vapors and clarified the laws of saturation. Subsequently, French scientists applied these phenomena to the problem of heat capacities. In 1807 Gay-Lussac carried out experiments on the expansion of a gas from a full chamber into an empty chamber of equal volume.[3] His result that the cooling taking place in the one chamber was equal to the heating in the other was repeatedly cited in the early papers of thermodynamics during the 1840's as evidence for the assumption that the heat content of a gas does not change if the gas does no external work.

In 1816 Pierre Simon de Laplace made the first quantitative application of the principle of adiabatic change when he accounted for the discrepancy between Newton's theoretical value for the velocity of sound and experimental values by allowing for adiabatic rather than isothermal compression and rarefaction of air.[4] Laplace's work initiated a long series of experiments on the determination of the ratio of the specific heat of air at constant pressure to the specific heat at constant volume.[5] Finally, Laplace's student Siméon Denis Poisson derived in 1823 the adiabatic equation of volume change that had not been given explicitly by Laplace.[6] The term "adiabatic process" was not used until much later, in connection with the development of thermodynamic diagrams. In 1854, when W. J. M. Rankine reconstructed E. Clapeyron's pressure-volume diagram of 1834 on the basis of the mechanical theory of heat, he introduced the term curves of "no transmission of heat" for curves along which the expansion of a substance took place without receiving or emitting heat. Later Rankine proposed the corresponding term adiabat.[7]

---

[3] Gay-Lussac, "Premier essai pour déterminer les variations de température qu'éprouvent les gaz en changeant de densité, et considération sur leur capacité pour le calorique," *Mémoires de Physíque et de Chemie de la Société d'Arcueil*, **1** (1807), 180–203.

[4] Laplace, "Sur la vitesse du son dans l'air et dans l'eau," *Ann. Chim. Phys.*, **3** (1816), 238–241. Laplace distinguished between specific heats of gases at constant pressure and volume, c_p and c_v, thereby confirming and quantifying a belief held by scientists in the three preceding decades. See also: B. S. Finn, "Laplace and the speed of sound," *Isis*, **55**, (1964), 7–19.

[5] N. Clément and C. B. Desormes, "Détermination expérimentale du zéro absolu de la chaleur et du calorique spécifique des gaz," *Journ. Phys.*, **89** (1819), 321–346, 428–455; Gay-Lussac and J. J. Welter, who measured the ratio c_p/c_v for Laplace, never published the details of their experiments; a short note of their computations is found in "Note sur la vitesse du son," *Ann. Chim. Phys.*, **20** (1822), 266–269.

[6] Poisson, "Sur la vitesse du son," *Ann. Chim. Phys.*, **23** (1823), 5–15, and "Sur la chaleur du gaz et des vapeurs," *ibid.*, 337–352. Poisson derived the equation for the adiabatic compression of gases, pV^γ = constant, by using the equation of state (combined laws of Mariotte and Gay-Lussac) and the definitions of the specific heats c_p and c_v; these were related by the ratio $c_p/c_v = \gamma$, as Laplace had shown. The model of heat underlying these equations did not enter in the calculation. (According to the caloric theory of adiabatic compression the "total heat" remained constant, while the temperature increase indicated that some "latent caloric" had become perceptible.)

[7] The first application of a geometrical diagram to represent the expansive action of heat was made by James Watt (about 1782), in the steam engine indicator diagram. See further, Rankine, "On the geometrical representation of the expansive action of heat, and the theory of thermodynamic engines," *Trans. Roy. Soc.*, (1854), reprinted in Rankine, *Miscellaneous Scientific Papers* (London, Griffin and Co., 1881) p. 349. Clapeyron's treatise, "Memoir on the motive power of heat," was translated by E. Mendoza in *Reflections on the Motive Power of Fire* (by S. Carnot, New York, Dover. Publ., 1960). In 1873 W. Gibbs proposed the term isentropes for adiabats, indicating that the entropy remained constant during an adiabatic process ["Graphical methods in the thermodynamics of fluids," *Trans. Connecticut*

Meteorologists and physicists alike failed to appreciate the significance of Poisson's equation for the temperature changes taking place in the atmosphere during vertical motions of a parcel of air, until adiabatic changes in the atmosphere were reinterpreted on the basis of the first law of thermodynamics. In contrast, Dalton's experimental work became widely known and inspired in part the first significant empirical investigations of adiabatic phenomena in the atmosphere. These studies were carried out in the United States during the early 1830's by James Pollard Espy. Espy recognized that vertical atmospheric motions could be associated with adiabatic temperature changes. His most important result was the explanation of large-scale formation of clouds and precipitation by ascent and subsequent adiabatic cooling of moist air. Furthermore, Espy and his supporters Elias Loomis and William Ferrel were led to regard the release of latent heat during condensation of water vapor in ascending currents of moist air as essential for the formation of storms. This hypothesis provided a plausible alternative to the storm theories of Dove and Redfield. It must be seen as anticipatory of the thermal or convective theory of cyclones treated in subsequent chapters, although a theoretical understanding of the physical processes on which the thermal theory was based was not achieved until more than two decades after Espy began to expound his views.

Espy's two principal supporters (Loomis and Ferrel) approached the study of meteorology in ways essentially different from Espy's; they were led to adopt Espy's ideas on the thermal nature of storms on the basis of independent evidence found in their respective areas of research. This undoubtedly added to the credibility of the convective theory among American meteorologists. Espy based his conclusions for the most part on laboratory experiments. Loomis' point of departure was the analysis of large-scale storms using the synoptic charts that he had developed; Ferrel chose to adopt Espy's ideas on the role of latent heat release in storms in his first analytical treatment of the dynamics of midlatitude cyclones.

In his historical account of meteorology, Sir Napier Shaw noted that Espy's "view on the nature of storms" was accepted in modified form "by meteorologists, with or without some mental disquietude, until the close of the nineteenth century."[8] I will reexamine to what extent Espy's view actually influenced the thinking of meteorologists of his time and during the second half of the Nineteenth Century, and I will explore the reasons that made his theory attractive and the reservations that were raised against it.

Academy, **2** (1873), p. 311]. The concept of entropy was introduced by Clausius in 1854, when he gave a new interpretation for the second law of thermodynamics. At that time, he proposed the term "Verwandlungsinhalt" (transformation content) for the ratio of the heat transferred to the temperature at which it is transferred, a ratio which remains constant in a perfect Carnot cycle. In 1865 Clausius used the Greek term entropy [*Ann. Phys. Chem.*, **125** (1865), p. 390]. The term adiabatic process was widely used in meteorology after Heinrich Hertz employed it in an important paper of 1884 ("Graphische Methode zur Bestimmung der adiabatischen Zustandsgleichungen feuchter Luft," *Met. Zeits.*, **1**, 421–431). In the meteorological literature, the adiabatic process has often been taken to be a reversible process. Although this interpretation applies strictly only to isentropic processes, I have adhered to it in this book.

[8] Sir N. Shaw, *Manual of Meteorology*, Vol. 1 (London, Cambridge University Press, 1926), p. 301.

2.2 ESPY'S INVESTIGATIONS OF ADIABATIC CHANGE AND HIS CONVECTIVE THEORY OF STORMS (1840's)

Espy was, next to Redfield, the most prominent American investigator of storms during the 1830's and 1840's.[9] He succeeded in procuring support for himself and his programs, notably the promotion of a national weather service, not only from a highly influential segment of the American scientific community, the circle around Joseph Henry and A. D. Bache, but also from men of the Congress. He became interested in the subject of meteorology in general and storms in particular around 1828 when studying the effect of heat on the expansion of a parcel of air. Preliminary results appeared to be of such significance for understanding certain atmospheric phenomena that he believed he had found the "lever with which the meteorologist was to move the world."[10] He decided to give up his position as teacher of classical languages and mathematics at the Franklin Institute in Philadelphia in order to devote his time and energy to meteorological investigations.[11] The starting point for his studies was John Dalton's work on the laws of vapors. Espy "was much struck by one of his [Dalton's] results," as he later recalled:

> . . . namely that the quantity of vapor in weight, existing at any time in a given space, could be determined with great accuracy in a few minutes, by means of a thermometer and a tumbler of water cold enough to condense on its outside a portion of the vapor in the air.[12]

Espy, who did not give a precise reference, obviously had read Dalton's *Meteorological Observations and Essays* of 1793 in which these experiments were described.[13] For Espy, the meteorological implications of the results reduced to the question of "what connection there is between rain and the quantity of vapor in the atmosphere."[14]

First of all, it was important to determine the amount of water vapor contained in air saturated with moisture. Viewing this problem as a question that could be solved by experiments, the practical and ingenious Espy devised an instrument—the nepheloscope or cloud examiner—that allowed him to measure the degree of cooling of dry and moist air for a given expansion. The expansion occurred so rapidly that the transfer of heat between the air in the chamber and the environment was negligible, thus the process was essentially one of adiabatic cooling. Espy studied the special case where, for a given expansion and corresponding reduction in pressure, the moist air in the nephelоscope cooled to its dew point temperature

---

[9] See biographical note on Espy in the Appendix.

[10] James Pollard Espy, *The Philosophy of Storms* (Boston, Little and Brown, 1841), Preface, p. iii.

[11] He published his first results in 1835 under the title "Theories of rain, hail, snow and the water spout, deduced from the latent caloric of vapour and the specific caloric of atmospheric air," *Trans., Geological Society of Pennsylvania*, **1** (part 2), (1835), 342–346.

[12] Espy (1841), Preface, p. iii.

[13] John Dalton, *Meteorological Observations and Essays* (London, T. Ostell, 1793), 115–139.

[14] Espy (1841), Preface, p. iii. For a detailed review of Espy's work, see J. E. McDonald, "James Espy and the beginnings of cloud thermodynamics," *Bull. Am. Met. Soc.*, **44** (1963), 634–641.

and water vapor condensed. This process, he suggested, was analogous to the formation of clouds in a current of ascending air.

Espy stressed that the latent heat released during the process of cloud formation was large enough to merit close analysis. Combining his own experimental results with the data on specific heats and latent heat then available, he was able to give fairly accurate estimates of the latent heat released during cloud formation and thus to calculate temperature lapse rates in ascending moist air currents. These results formed the basis for his far-reaching conclusions on the role of convection and the formation of clouds and precipitation.[15]

> When the air near the surface of the earth becomes more heated or more highly charged with aqueous vapor, . . . its equilibrium is unstable, and up-moving columns or streams will be formed. As these columns rise, their upper parts will come under less pressure, and the air will therefore expand; as it expands, it will grow colder about one degree and a quarter for every hundred yards of its ascent. . . . The ascending columns will carry up with them the aqueous vapor which they contain, and, if they rise high enough, the cold produced by expansion from diminished pressure will condense some of its vapor into cloud. . . . As soon as cloud begins to form, the caloric of elasticity of the vapor or steam is given out into the air in contact with the little particles of water formed by the condensation of the vapor. This will prevent the air, in its further progress upwards, from cooling so fast as it did up to that point . . . that is, about five-eighths [sic] of a degree for one hundred yards of ascent, when the dew point is about seventy degrees.[16]

Espy then compared the lapse rate which he had determined for moist air forming clouds, now called saturation-adiabatic, with the average vertical temperature decrease as observed by "aeronauts and travellers on mountains."

---

[15] Espy's apparatus for experiments is described in his book (1841), Introduction, p. viii: "By means of the condensing pump *a*, air may be forced into the glass vessel *b*, and its degree of condensation can be measured by the barometer gage *c*.

After the instrument is charged, the stopcock is turned, and the pump removed. When the air within acquires the temperature of the air without, a measure is carefully applied to the barometer gage to ascertain how much higher the mercury stands in the outer leg than in the inner; the cock is then turned, and the air permitted to escape, and at the moment of equilibrium, the cock is closed again. Now as the cock is closed at the moment the greatest cold is produced by expansion, the mercury in the outer leg will begin to ascend, and that in the inner leg to descend, because the air within receives heat from without, and the difference of level being measured as before, will indicate the number of degrees cooled by a given expansion." He used values for specific heat of air and latent heats from J. E. Bérard and Delaroche, N. Clément and C. B. Desormes, J. Apjohn, J. Black and Dalton.

[16] Espy (1841), Introduction, pp. viii–x.

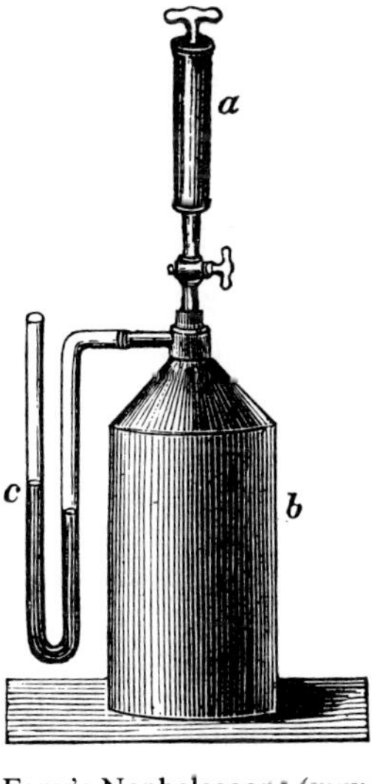

Espy's Nephelescope (now spelled nepheloscope).

FIGURE 5. Formation of cumulus clouds by convection (Espy, 1841), from Espy, *Philosophy of Storms* (1841).

Since this latter lapse rate was about one degree Fahrenheit for every hundred yards, it followed that

> . . . when the cloud is of great perpendicular height above its base, its top must be much warmer than the atmosphere at that height, and consequently much lighter.[17]

Condensation of water vapor thus enhanced the rising of air, i.e., thermal convection and therefore cloud growth (see Figure 5). This explanation of Espy's stood in outright contradiction with traditional teaching. Customarily it had been assumed that "when a portion of atmospheric vapor is condensed into cloud, the air in the cloud becomes specifically heavier than it was before,"[18] because the density of water vapor is less than that of air. Accordingly, condensation of water vapor appeared to inhibit convection of air. Espy's experiments with the nepheloscope, however, showed that the reverse was true, namely that during cloud formation the air becomes less dense than before and convection is enhanced. This, he remarked, "was an instantaneous transition from darkness to light."[19]

---

[17] Espy (1841), Introduction, p. x.

[18] Espy (1841), Preface, p. iii.

[19] Espy (1841), Preface, p. iv. He stated already in his paper of 1835, *op. cit.*, "that all phenomena of rains, hails, snows and water spouts, change of winds and depressions of barometer follow as easy and natural corollaries from the theory . . . that *there is an expansion of the air containing transparent vapour when that vapour is condensed into water* [Espy's emphasis]. It is now more than three years since I formed this theory . . ." (p. 344).

Scientists indeed quickly realized that Espy's explanation of condensation and rain was superior to the prevelant mixing theory of rain by the Scottish geologist James Hutton. Hutton's theory incorporated the fact that the maximum water vapor content of air increases nonlinearly with its temperature and it stated that clouds and rain are produced when cold and warm air masses, both saturated with water vapor, are mixed. Without accurate humidity measurements or the knowledge of the laws of saturation, the theory dating from 1784 had stood acceptable for over half a century.[20] Both Redfield and Dove had relied on it for their explanation of precipitation commonly associated with storms. Espy demonstrated experimentally that only an insignificant percentage of rain could be explained by mixing. In fact, he pointed out that the vertical motions observed during the formation of cumulus type or shower clouds precluded any substantial mixing of warm and cold currents except along the boundaries of the cloud elements. As the major cause of rain, Espy emphasized instead the adiabatic cooling that takes place during vertical convection. Thus, these two processes, adiabatic cooling and thermal convection, concepts understood separately for decades, were linked by Espy into a powerful explanatory device in meteorology.

Espy appears to have known Poisson's equation but did not realize that it provided a theoretical foundation for his experiments. The Frenchman Pierre Hermand Maille seems to have been the first who applied Poisson's equation, which is valid for dry air, for calculating the temperature changes of an ascending parcel of air. Since Maille's work had no noticeable impact on meteorological research, it will not be covered here.[21]

Espy applied his new explanation for the formation of clouds and precipitation to elucidate the nature of storms. He defined a storm as a system of winds flowing radially toward the center of low barometric pressure that resulted from the relatively higher temperatures and lower density of the cloudy air of that region:

> If the cloud is of great size, then the supply of air to keep up the ascending column cannot be afforded without reaching down to the surface of the earth, even when the lower part of the cloud may be at a considerable distance above the surface of the earth. Thus the

[20] James Hutton (1726–1797), "The theory of rain," *Trans. Roy. Soc., Edinb.*, **1** (1788), 41–86. For further comments see Shaw, *Manual, op. cit.*, 125–126.

[21] Maille studied adiabatic changes of rising moist air during the 1830's and 1840's. By profession a merchant, he was motivated to undertake this work when the French Academy of Science offered a prize for a treatise on the theory of hail in 1830. In calculating the temperature changes of an ascending parcel of moist air, Maille applied Poisson's equation until the condensation level was reached. He proceeded numerically above the condensation level using the available data on heat capacities of air, latent heat release and saturation vapor pressures [see Maille's "Mémoire sur les phenomènes météorologiques aqueux et sur la formation de la grêle," Manuscript No. 7 received by the Academy, Paris, 28 February 1834, 90 pp.; I used a Xerox copy of the memoir deposited in the Archives of the Royal Meteorological Society, Bracknell, England]. Maille restricted his discussions to the explanation of the formation of clouds and precipitation. He did not incorporate his findings into a theory of storms as Espy did. In 1846 Maille accidentally became acquainted with Espy's work. Maille's repeated attempts to obtain recognition and publication of his own work by the French Academy remained unsuccessful. He finally published his results at his own expense in a book of 1853, entitled *Nouvelle Théorie des Hydrométèores* (Paris, Bachelier, 1853), 368 pp. The details of Maille's battle for recognition have been recorded by W. E. Middleton, "P. H. Maille, a forgotten pioneer in meteorology," *Isis*, **56** (1965), 320–326.

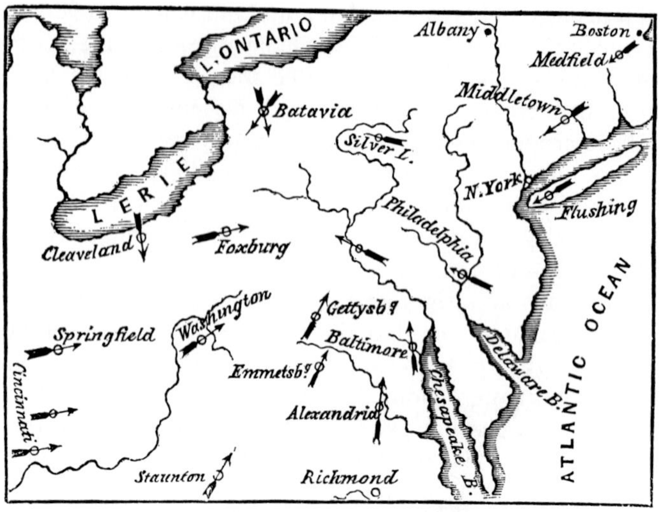

FIGURE 6. Chart of storm of June 20, 1836, by Espy, from *Philosophy of Storms* (1841). Arrows indicate direction of wind; storm center was assumed to be at Silver Lake where precipitation was greatest.

> law will become general, that *in all very great and widely extended rains or snows, the wind will blow towards the centre of the storm*.[22]

In support of his views he presented weather charts which he had constructed. For the chart of 20 June 1836 (Figure 6), Espy assumed that the storm center was at Silver Lake where the winds seemed to converge and precipitation was a maximum (3 inches of rain). He remarked, "it will be seen at a glance that the wind blew from all sides towards the point of greatest rain."[23]

Furthermore, regarding the formation of the low pressure center and the propagation of storms,

> The great expansion of the air in the cloud, will cause a rapid ascent and out-spreading above, which will cause the barometer to fall under the cloud, and if there was no current above, it would spread out on all sides equally in an *annulus*, and cause the barometer to rise all round the storm, as much on one side as another. But as there is known to be an upper current always, or almost always, moving in this latitude towards the north east or N.N.E., this current will cause the out-spreading of the air to be chiefly in that direction. . . .[24]

Espy's theory explained adequately certain important and prominent features associated with cyclones: the relatively high surface temperatures in winter, the

---

[22] Espy (1841), p. 8. His view of radial inflow toward the center of low pressure in storms appears to have been influenced partly by his extensive studies of spouts and tornadoes and in part by the nature of his graphical illustrations. Depicting few observations, often 12 hours apart and using wind arrows which were grossly exaggerated in length, he gives a distorted picture of the true wind field (see pp. 15–17, p. 174, etc., of his book, or Figure 6).

[23] *Ibid.*, p. 105.

[24] Espy (1841), p. 138.

high moisture content of the air, and the cloudiness and precipitation. Espy's theory must have appeared attractive because of the physical reasoning and the experimental evidence employed. It became quickly and widely known, partly because of Espy's own indefatigable efforts to popularize it and collect observations in its favor and partly because of the spirited debate that developed between Espy and Redfield and their respective followers on the relation between the center of low pressure associated with storms and the direction of the wind with respect to the center. In 1840 Espy was invited to present his views at the annual meetings of the British Association for the Advancement of Science and the French Academy of Science. His reviewers, D. F. J. Arago, C. S. M. Pouillet, and J. Babinet, were full of praise for his memoir and urged the American government to support Espy's work.[25] In recognition of his contribution to meteorology he was appointed "American meteorologist" by the U.S. government, a position especially created for him in 1842. This appointment provided him with an opportunity to expand the system of volunteer observers which he had established between 1835 and 1838 while chairman of the Joint Committee of Meteorology of the Franklin Institute and the American Philosophical Society.[26]

Espy's ideas profoundly affected the work of Loomis and Ferrel in the 1840's and 1850's. During the 1860's and 1870's, his work on cloud formation and the role of latent heat in storms was frequently quoted to help pave the way for the acceptance of quantitative thermodynamic theories of convection and cloud formation and a revised version of the convective or thermal theory of cyclones. This will be discussed in Chapters 3 and 4.

2.3 ESPY'S SUPPORTERS

a. Early Synoptic Studies by Loomis (1841–1846)

While Espy had many admirers, we can recognize in retrospect that only a few scientists during his own time had the incentive and competence to pursue his ideas. One of these was Espy's countryman Elias Loomis.[27] Espy, it is recalled, had used empirical evidence to construct his hypothesis. It was highly desirable, therefore, that his hypothesis be confirmed by new evidence, namely by facts that were unknown or ignored when he formulated his hypothesis. Loomis provided such

[25] Both these reports are reprinted in English translation in Espy's *Philosophy of Storms*. They were first published by Arago, Babinet, Pouillet (rapporteurs), "Rapport sur les travaux de M. Espy relatif aux tornados," *Comp. Ren.*, **12** (1841), 454–461, and Espy, "On storms," *British Association Report*, Sec. Math. Phys. (1840), 30–39. Immediately following Espy's paper in the *British Association Report* is an "Extract of a letter from Mr. Redfield to Sir J. F. W. Herschel," (*ibid.*, 40); Redfield had also been invited to the Association meeting but was unable to attend. This juxtaposition of the two rival ideas indicates the extent and the intensity of the controversy between Espy and Redfield and their followers. For further details see, D. M. Ludlum, "The Espy-Redfield dispute," *Weatherwise*, **22** (1969), 224–229, 245.

[26] In addition, Espy organized a service of daily weather reports. Espy's unique position was discontinued after his death in 1860. See also B. Sinclair, "Gustavus A. Hyde, Professor Espy's volunteers, and the development of systematic weather observation," *Bull. Am. Met. Soc.*, **46** (1965), 779–784.

[27] See biographical note on Loomis in the Appendix.

new information in the course of his synoptic and statistical investigations on the nature of midlatitude cyclones. Carried out over a period of several decades (see also Chapter 5), these studies strengthened considerably the thermal or convective theory of cyclones.

Loomis received his education in modern and classical languages, mathematics, physics and astronomy at a time when attitudes towards science were undergoing a significant change in America. During the decade 1815 to 1825 the number of organizations which had declared the promotion of science as one of their aims tripled, and the number of journals dealing with scientific material more than doubled.[28] The teaching of science was significantly upgraded and the curriculum of liberal arts colleges was expanded with special emphasis on geophysics. Meteorology acquired great popularity, attracting both geophysicists and natural historians, as well as the general public.[29]

Loomis became interested in the storm problem while he was a young tutor at Yale from 1833 to 1836. He was particularly attracted to the central problem of the Espy-Redfield dispute: Do the winds blow in circular whirls, or do they blow toward the center of a barometric depression? This problem, of course, could be restated in terms of different explanations for the origin and maintenance of the barometric depression in the central part of the storm: Did the centrifugal forces balancing the pressure gradient forces sufficiently account for the maintenance of low pressure, as Redfield had suggested, or was the tangential component of motion only an accidental feature, the barometric depression being produced and maintained by thermal causes, as Espy insisted?[30]

Loomis began his investigations on this aspect of storms after returning from a year of study in Europe in 1837, loaded with scientific apparatus including meteorological instruments.[31] Rather than attempting to deduce the "truth" by

---

[28] For an analysis of the development of science in America during the first half of the Nineteenth Century see George A. Daniels, *American Science in the Age of Jackson* (New York, Columbia University Press, 1968), in particular pp. 14–15.

[29] Nathan Reingold analyzed the position of meteorology in *Science in Nineteenth Century America* (New York, Hill and Wang, 1964). He points out that amateur scientists like Redfield could make important contributions to the new science. There was a true army of observers, ranging from high public figures to farmers, who kept meticulous meteorological diaries. Reingold lists George Washington and Thomas Jefferson as prominent observers, noting, "it was the proper thing to do if you were an educated person and a friend of science in the late eighteenth and early nineteenth centuries." (p. 92). For a more detailed discussion of early Nineteenth Century meteorology in America see W. E. Gross, "The American Philosophical Society and the growth of meteorology in the United States," *Annals of Science*, **29** (1972), 321–338.

[30] The importance given to the wind field at that time is also seen in the following circumstance: During the 1840's Espy's theory was more often called the *centripetal* theory (according to the corresponding wind field) than the *convective* or *thermal* theory (according to its mechanism). The latter term was applied primarily during the second part of the Nineteenth Century, when meteorologists stressed the thermal aspects of storm formation.

[31] These instruments were to be used in his appointment as professor of mathematics and natural philosophy at Western Reserve University. During the second quarter of the Nineteenth Century "scientific apparatus at the average college increased in value from a few hundred dollars in 1825 to many thousands by mid-century." [Stanley M. Guralnick, "Sources of misconception on the role of science in the nineteenth-century American College," *Isis*, **65** (1974), p. 354].

averaging the results of a great number of storms he proposed to approach the subject by carrying out a case study of a single storm:

> Being well convinced that meteorology is to be promoted, not so much by taking the mean of long continued observations, as by studying the phenomena of particular storms developed over a widely extended country, I resolve to select some single storm of strongly marked characteristics, and trace its progress as extensively and minutely as possible.[32]

This statement must be regarded as an appeal to the application of the Baconian method which favors the accumulation of observations and experiments and their systematization through induction rather than the formation of concepts and deduction. Classification of facts and their comparative analysis was considered particularly important. Naturally, this method appeared highly appropriate for developing sciences, such as meteorology, where the gathering of facts had just begun.[33] Searching for a suitable cyclone event with a relatively large number of observations, Loomis profited from the first international effort toward synchronized and uniform meteorological observations. In 1835, in an attempt to promote the systematic collection of meteorological data, the British Association for the Advancement of Science had recommended the establishment of series of hourly observations at selected stations throughout the world. In addition, the British astronomer Sir John Herschel recommended hourly observations during the equinoxes and solstices at as many stations as possible. The response to his request was particularly enthusiastic in the United States.[34] Consequently, Loomis selected for his study a storm that occurred during the winter solstice of 1836.

The results of Loomis' study were presented before the American Philosophical Society in Philadelphia in 1840. The paper was well received. However, Loomis was unable to confirm either Espy's or Redfield's theory. Rather, his results tended to suggest some features of both, and so a final decision had to be deferred to future study. Although Loomis did not at this time accept Espy's theory of storms, he found compelling evidence to adopt Espy's physical arguments on the formation of rain by uplifting of moist air. He readily agreed with Espy that "air suddenly transported into elevated regions must be allowed to be by far the most efficient of all causes of rain."[35] Going beyond Espy, Loomis inquired in his paper which processes and situations were likely to lead to uplifting of air and which were most important. He concluded that "at least in this latitude, the most common cause of rain" was the following:

> When a hot and cold current, moving in opposite directions, meet, the colder, having the

[32] Loomis, "On the storm which was experienced throughout the United States about the 20th December, 1836," *Trans. Am. Phil. Soc.*, 7 (1841), p. 125. Loomis' minute description of this storm, his "favorite storm" (see Reingold, *op. cit.*, p. 93), provided Espy with an excellent example of what could be achieved by organized observations.

[33] As Daniels, *op. cit.*, has pointed out, Loomis applied the method even in his hobby: the preparation of a family genealogy comprising more than 10,000 entries.

[34] Gross, *op. cit.*, pp. 326–329.

[35] Loomis (1841), 146–157.

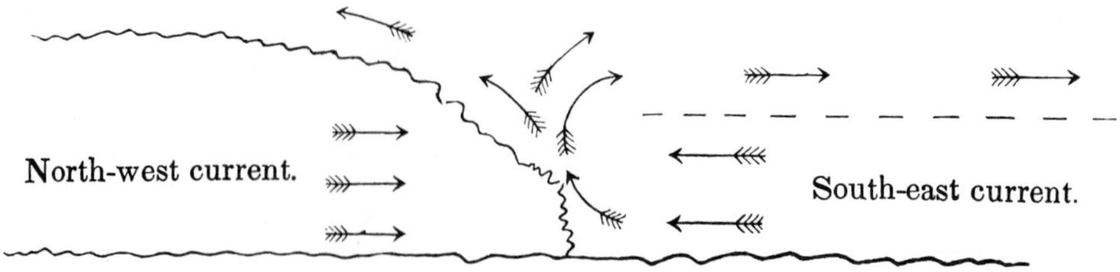

FIGURE 7. Meeting of warm southeast and cold northwest currents of air (Loomis, 1841), from Loomis, "On the storm which was experienced throughout the United States about the 20th of December, 1836," *Trans. Am. Phil. Soc.*, 7 (1841). Loomis' diagram represents the first cross section of what today is called a cold front.

greater specific gravity, will displace the warmer, which is thus suddenly lifted from the surface of the earth, is cooled and a part of its vapor precipitated.[36]

In the case of the storm investigated, he inferred from the examination of precipitation, wind and temperature patterns that a warm moist southeast current was blowing toward the center of the barometric depression north of the United States "by ascending from the surface of the earth."[37] At the same time, a cold current from the northwest, "displacing the south-east one by flowing under it," caused temperature drops up to 38°F during six hours. Such intense cold outbreaks, which are a prominent feature of American climate, were generally referred to as cold waves during the second half of the Nineteenth Century.[38]

Loomis illustrated his idea of the advance of the cold air in a diagram (Figure 7) which, in fact, represents the first cross section of what today is called a cold front. In view of Espy's theory, it was no longer necessary to assume substantial mixing of air for the formation of clouds and precipitation. Instead, Espy's theory provided the rationale for Loomis to distinguish a boundary between the two air currents. Nevertheless, the interpretation of the nature of cold outbreaks or waves and their role in the cyclonic process remained surprisingly narrow for several decades. Loomis himself did not pursue his findings on boundaries between air currents. The view that the confrontation of warm and cold air currents played an important role in the generation of kinetic energy in cyclones began to be discussed in the meteorological literature during the 1880's and did not gain prominence in the United States until the turn of the century, as will be seen in subsequent chapters.[39]

---

[36] *Ibid.*, p. 157. The two currents, originating in southern and northern latitudes, were easily identified with Dove's equatorial and polar currents. No doubt, Loomis knew about Dove's views.

[37] *Ibid.*, p. 155. He then proposed "that the current was mainly turned back upon itself, so that the moisture, as fast as precipitated, fell through the lower current, still blowing from the south-east" (p. 159).

[38] In 1888, the Signal Service added the so-called cold-wave flag to its system of flag symbols. A. W. Greely, forecaster and Chief Signal Officer, noted in his book *American Weather* (New York, Dodd, Mead & Co., 1888), p. 211: "The term 'cold wave' is a technical one devised by the United States Signal Service, not to represent the intensity of the cold, except within certain limits, but . . . to show very decided falls in temperature within a limited time."

[39] Until then, most American investigators did not go beyond general descriptions in their treatment of cold waves. In 1888, Greely (*American Weather, op. cit.*) noted that a "cold wave results from the movement of a strong anti-cyclonic area across the United States (p. 213)." However, he added, "The

Concerning Espy's explanation of the origin of storms, Loomis noted pointedly, "although a fall of the barometer is usually accompanied by an elevation of temperature, the reverse is sometimes the case."[40] In line with the Baconian philosophy of his days, Loomis implied that one exception was sufficient to refute a hypothesis. He concluded that changes of the density of air due to higher temperature and increased water vapor content only produced secondary effects on the "oscillations of the barometer." However, his position on this matter gradually changed over subsequent years.

In 1843, Loomis presented a study of two other great storms to the American Philosophical Society.[41] Again taking to heart Bacon's statement "that errors are imported by words, and that in science names must signify things" Loomis diligently employed classification. He summarized in tables a great number of observations, and then summarized these tables on charts. This procedure was for him and others of his time "the essence of science . . . the limit of legitimate generalizations."[42] His innovative mapping of storm characteristics marked the entry of a new tool into meteorology, the synoptic chart. An example of Loomis' charts is reproduced in Figure 8. The idea of the synoptic chart had been in "the air" for some time and may be regarded as the natural outcome of data accumulation and the growing need for information of weather conditions over an extended area.[43]

---

cold wave occurs not with the centre of the anticyclone, but on its outskirts, far in advance of the centre, and the great and sudden falls of temperature obtain most frequently when the movement of a low area to the eastward has raised in its passage the temperature of the adjacent country to an abnormally high point" (p. 214). Cl. Abbe concluded in 1890 (*Preparatory Studies for the Deductive Methods in Storm and Weather Predictions*. Washington, Government Printing Office, 1890) that cold waves "represent the horizontal flow of immense masses of dry air from northern regions. . . . The advent of the southern limit of such a cold wave is usually preceded in the United States by the appearance of a low barometer to the west of Oregon and Alaska." (p. 125). "The cold air," he noted (p. 77), "that constitutes these waves is simply the dry air . . . cooled by radiation toward the ground below it, and toward the sky above it, until it accumulates in deep layers in the long winter nights of the arctic regions. . ." He remarked, evading any specific statements (p. 77), "Its flow is due to a slight gradient of pressure in the direction of the flow . . . the flow of the cold wave begins while the cyclone is still far off and in its first stages of development." As late as 1912, W. I. Milham noted in his widely read textbook *Meteorology* (New York, MacMillan, p.345), "that a cold wave is made on the spot, so to speak, seems more plausible than that the air is transported long distances."

[40] Loomis (1841), p. 161.

[41] Loomis, "On two storms which were experienced throughout the United States in the month of February, 1842," *Trans. Am. Phil. Soc.*, **9** (1846), 161–184. Read May 1843.

[42] Daniels, *op. cit.*, p. 89.

[43] It is well known that in 1820 H. W. Brandes constructed similar synoptic charts depicting deviations from normal pressure, temperature and the wind field associated with a storm during a period of days in 1783 for which data were available. In a letter of 1816 to Gilbert, then editor of the *Ann. Phys. Chem.*, Brandes remarked: "Even though these charts . . . may appear ridiculous to some, I do believe that one should consider to pursue this thought. So much at least is certain: that 365 charts of Europe, depicting blue sky, and thin and dark clouds or rain, . . . the direction of the wind . . . [and] a few well selected indications of temperature, would give the audience more pleasure and would teach more than meteorological tables" [from *Ann. Phys. Chem.*, **55** (1817), p. 113]. However Brandes' descriptions and farsighted recommendations of the synoptic method were not further pursued at the time. The term synoptic chart was introduced by Fitzroy "being intended to express consecutive simultaneous states of the atmosphere" (*Weather Book*, London, Longman & Green, 1863, p. 103). When the Signal Service began to publish the first American weather charts on a regular basis in 1871, they were constructed after Loomis' model of 1843 (almost 30 years earlier). Most European countries

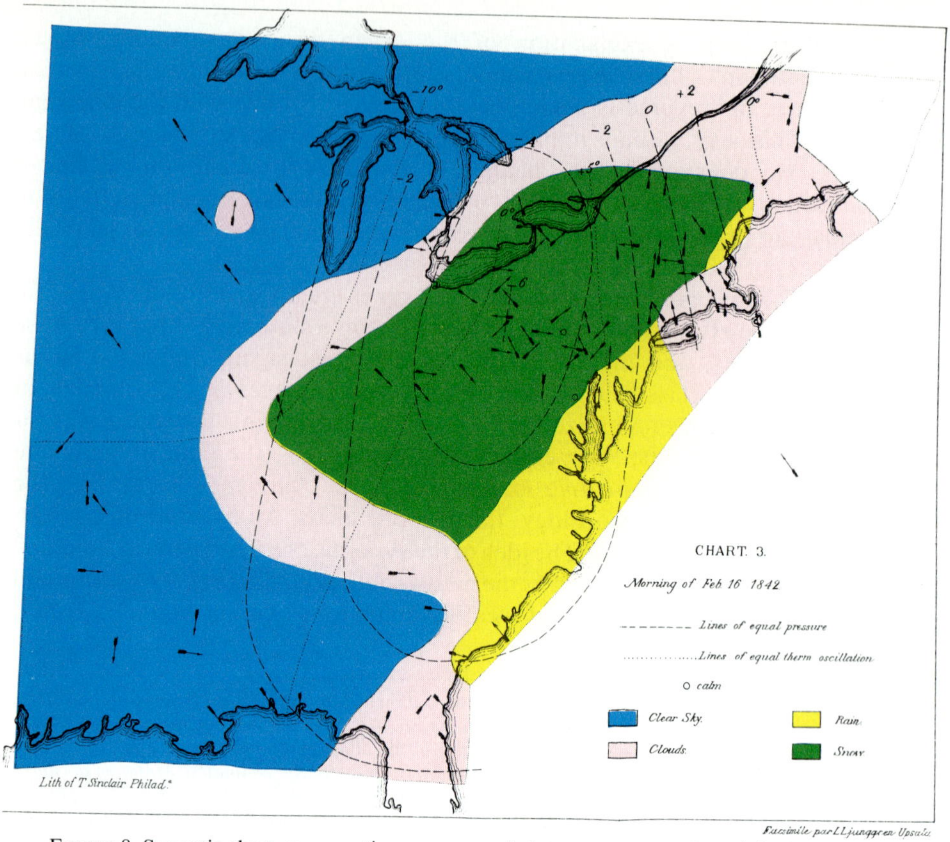

FIGURE 8. Synoptic chart, representing pressure, wind, temperature and precipitation distribution, by Loomis, from "On two storms which were experienced throughout the United States in the month of February 1842," *Trans. Am. Phil. Soc.*, **9** (1846).

Loomis' charts, however, were superior to most earlier attempts. He emphasized the pressure field by analyzing deviations from normal pressure rather than the advance of the line of minimum pressure as Espy had done on his weather charts.[44] In addition, Loomis' synoptic charts contained analyses of lines of equal temperature deviation and observations of cloud cover, precipitation and the wind.

developed their own forms of the synoptic chart during the following decades. On the introduction of the synoptic chart in practice and research, see also Section 4.2. Further information may be found in Hellmann, Ed., *Neudrucke von Schriften und Karten über Meteorologie und Erdmagnetismus*, No. 8, Meteorologische Karten (Berlin, A. Asher & Co., 1897); K. Schneider-Carius, *Wetterkunde/Wetterforschung* (Freiburg, K. Alber, 1955), 156–161, 200–201; A. Kh. Khrgian, *Meteorology*, A Historical Survey, Vol. 1. Translated from Russian, 2nd ed., rev. by Kh. P. Pogosyan (Jerusalem, Keter Press, 1970), 138–158; H. Landsberg, "Storm of Balaklava and the daily weather forecast," *Scientific Monthly*, **7** (1954) 347–352. H. H. Hildebrandsson and T. de Bort, *Les Bases de la Météorologie Dynamique* (Paris, Gauthier-Villars, 1907), Vol. 1, 61–138; M. W. Harrington, "History of the weather map," *Report of the International Meteorological Congress*, Chicago, 1893, O. Fassig, Ed. (Washington, Weather Bureau, 1895), Bulletin No. II, part 2, 327–334; H. R. Scultetus, "Die erste Wetterkarte," *Met. Zeits.*, **60** (1943), p. 356, and "Dove und Loomis als Wegbereiter der Synopsis," *Ibid.*, p. 419.

[44] Most notably, Espy did not draw isobars (see Figure 6). The construction of lines of equal barometric deviations might have appeared as the logical choice for Loomis because of his earlier

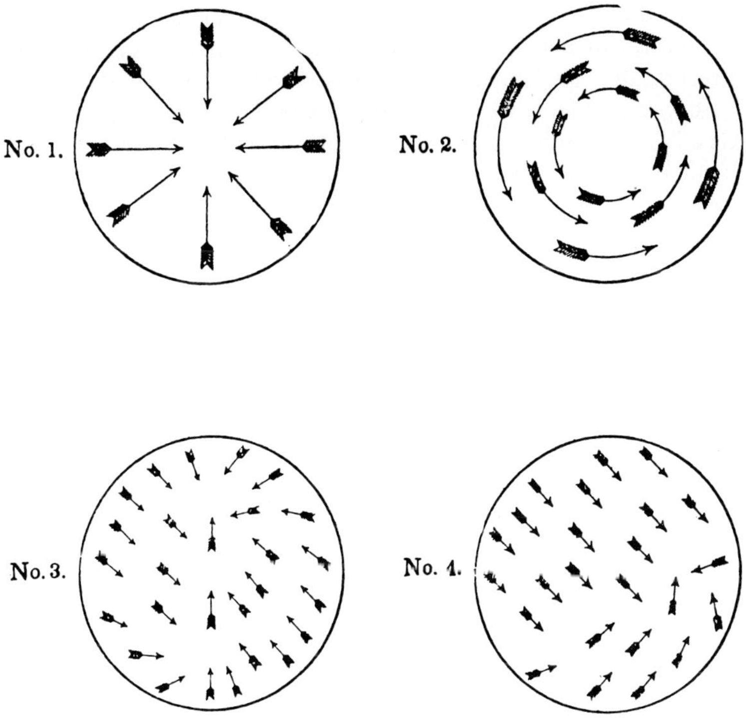

FIGURE 9. Diagrams of surface winds in cyclones: No. 1, according to Espy; No. 2, according to Redfield; Nos. 3 and 4, according to Loomis' own investigations, from Loomis, "On two storms which were experienced throughout the United States in the month of February, 1842," *Trans. Am. Phil. Soc.*, **9** (1846). Loomis' analyses of the wind patterns in two storms clearly indicate the confluence of two different currents and distinct boundaries between these currents.

A series of these synoptic charts provided Loomis with the means to decide conclusively the point of controversy between Espy and Redfield. He showed that the truth lay between the two extreme solutions they had proposed, for "we find certain characteristics, namely, an inward motion, with a tendency to circulate against the sun"[45] (Figure 9). In his explanation of the wind field, Loomis referred to

---

success with the publication of the first map of the United States depicting lines of equal declination of the magnetic needle. Analysis of isobars rather than lines of equal barometric pressure deviation from local mean pressure became customary with the advent of national weather services and daily synoptic charts. On the early use of isolines in meteorology and climatology see H. Landsberg, "Roots of modern climatology," *Journal of the Washington Academy of Science*, **54** (1964), 130–141.

[45] Loomis (1846), p. 181. The terminology used to describe cyclonic motion has been manifold and at times confusing. The expression here used by Loomis—circulation against the sun—was applied earlier by Redfield and was still in use at the end of the century; for example, it can be found in all editions of H. Mohn's widely read textbook on meteorology (first edition 1870, fifth in 1898). Terms such as turning with or against the sun or veering and backing were used mostly when referring to changes in wind direction during passage of a storm. With the introduction of synoptic charts investigators began to describe wind patterns in cyclones with reference to the center of low pressure. At times confusion resulted because it was not always clear which point of reference was used, single observations station or center of storm circulation. Thus Fitzroy noted in 1863 (*Weather Book, op. cit.*, p. 19) that "the wind

the pressure gradient force as well as the effect of the deflecting force of the earth's rotation, whose action neither Espy nor Redfield had considered. It was this force, Loomis argued, that accounted for the spiral inflow toward the center of low pressure. Loomis undoubtedly had learned about this principle of the deviation of the motion of a body on a rotating earth while attending lectures by Arago, Biot, Poisson and others in Paris in 1836–37. However, his understanding of this principle had remained vague. It follows closely the explanation of George Hadley[46] who only accounted for the east-west component of the deflecting force of the earth's rotation.[47]

It was equally significant that in this paper Loomis moved closer to Espy's position on the origin and maintenance of storms. He concluded that the origin or first stage of a storm must be sought in an "abnormal" current in the lower stratum of air interfering with the prevalent westerly current. Such a current, he proposed, may either be the effect of a preceding storm, or, may be the result of an inequality of the surface temperature and moisture within the normally western current, i.e., an area of elevated temperature and moisture content with respect to the surrounding air. Subsequently, southerly and easterly currents of air developing due to the density differences resulted in the formation of clouds and precipitation and local diminuition of pressure; this was the second stage of the process. Arguing in a fashion similar to that of Espy, he wrote:

> The heat liberated in the formation of this cloud raises the thermometer, causing a more decided tendency of the air inward toward the region of condensation. . . . Relative elevation of temperature under the cloud . . . gives increased velocity to the inward current of air. More cloud is thus formed, heat liberated. . . . Thus the storm gains violence by its own action.[48]

Loomis defined the third stage of a storm as the situation in which surrounding colder air rushed into the area of diminished pressure and when "our southerly wind is thus supplanted by a violent north-wester."[49] Eventually, during the fourth

---

usually *appears* to veer, shift or go around *with the sun* (right-handed, or from left to right)," using the single station method. "This, however, is only *apparent*; the wind is actually circulating in the *contrary* direction." He further noted (p. 36), "at present, the gyrations of wind are called direct or retrograde, . . . but the results are unsatisfactory, because whether the wind veers directly, or retrogrades (backs)," depends on the position of the center of the passing circulation system with respect to the observer. In his book of 1867 (*op. cit.*), Buchan uses the rather cumbersome term "in direction contrary to the hands of the watch" in his description of cyclonic circulation. Ley (*Law of Winds*, London, Stanford, 1872) tried to improve terminology by using the terms retrograde, against the watch, and cyclonic or direct, with the watch, and anticyclonic, respectively. By the 1880's, the term cyclonic circulation was widely used alongside the terms quoted above.

[46] Hadley, "Concerning the cause of the general trade winds," *Trans. Roy. Soc.*, **39** (1735), 58–62.

[47] This is seen in the following statement (Loomis, (1846), p. 175): "There is a physical cause for this rotation and for its being uniform in direction, in the case of large storms. The southerly wind has a greater motion eastward than the parallels upon which it successively arrives, arising from the rotation of the earth; and the northerly wind a less motion eastward, or a relative motion westward. Hence in this region the circulation, in great storms, is probably invariable in direction."

[48] Loomis (1846), p. 175. Loomis also believed that radiation from the earth's surface "checked" by clouds contributed significantly to temperature rise. However, he made no quantitative estimates.

[49] *Ibid.*, p. 183.

stage, "currents moving centrally from every point of the compass, interfere with each other, and pursue their routes spirally inward,"[50] thereby forcing up the warmer air which rose in the middle, was consequently cooled by lifting, and gave rise to precipitation. During this process the westerly current was accelerated and the easterly current retarded by the upper current which transported the storm toward the east; thus, "at successive points, farther and farther east, the same storm . . . has a less duration, and thus . . . the [barometric] oscillation becomes nearly extinct." This, Loomis proposed, was the fifth and final phase of the storm.

Although well trained in physics and mathematics, Loomis seldom went beyond minute descriptions and qualitative arguments. His few attempts at explanation had little success. Rather, it was his Baconian methodology that won him the respect and the backing of mid-Nineteenth Century scientists. In the words of his eulogist, his diligent and painstaking work of gathering and classifying meteorological data, carried out over a period of almost five decades was "for a long time to come . . . the basis of facts by which writers in theoretical meteorology must test their formulas."[51] Above all it contributed to the establishment of the convective or thermal theory as the dominant theory of storms in Nineteenth Century American meteorology.

b. Ferrel's Early Theoretical Studies (1860)

If the name of a famous man adds credibility to a theory, then it was fortunate that in addition to Loomis, William Ferrel became a supporter of Espy's convective theory.[52] The most outstanding of Ferrel's many achievements was the formulation of the equations of motion for a body moving on a rotating earth. On them, he built a mathematical model of the general circulation of the atmosphere and ocean, as well as of cyclones, perfecting and revising his scheme during the course of the years. His work was the first great contribution to the field of geophysical hydrodynamics after Laplace. Ferrel's work, begun in the 1850's when he was still a school teacher in Nashville, Tennessee, became generally so well known during the 1870's that he enjoyed a position of high respect among meteorologists and deeply influenced the course of American meteorology. For several decades his position on any meteorological theory set the tone for most of his American colleagues. For this reason his support of the major aspects of Espy's convective theory added greatly to the acceptibility of the thermal theory in the United States and in Europe in the second part of the Nineteenth Century, and, at that, long after Espy's personal influence had ceased.

In order to understand the reasons that persuaded Ferrel to adopt the fundamental concepts underlying Espy's theory it is necessary to appreciate the prevailing view that cyclones formed closed systems and were independent of the

---

[50] *Ibid.*

[51] H. A. Newton, "Biographical Memoir of Elias Loomis," *Biogr. Mem., Nat. Ac. Sci.*, **3** (1895), p. 236.

[52] See biographical note on Ferrel in the Appendix.

general circulation. The growing focus of attention on the cyclone itself can be attributed in part to the expanded station network and improved communication that permitted the study of atmospheric conditions over large areas at a given time. The study of storm features apart from the general circulation can also be explained by the size of the synoptic charts; they were large enough to portray areas of low and high pressure, but could not capture changes in the large-scale general circulation. Many meteorologists, therefore, began to consider it their most obvious task to investigate barometric depressions. Indeed, they believed that an understanding of storm mechanisms, or at least a detailed knowledge of their behavior, would be the key for practical weather forecasting.

While the view of cyclones and anticyclones as being independent of the general circulation can be explained in part with reference to the scale size of synoptic charts of the 1860's, there was still another factor that contributed to the emergence of this view and that appears to have shaped Ferrel's concept of cyclones. During the first part of the Nineteenth Century, models of the general circulation of the atmosphere were idealized, simplified pictures of the actual circulation, mostly symmetrical with respect to longitude. Contradicting observations were ignored by referring to the general circulation as an ideal state representing long-term average conditions. As E. N. Lorenz has pointed out in his historical account of the theories of the general circulation, Dove's model, which related large-scale storms of midlatitudes to the general circulation, was abandoned partly because it was not "idealized" enough, i.e., not symmetrical with respect to longitude.[53] Cyclones presented themselves as rather erratic phenomena. There appeared to be neither a role nor room for them within a symmetrical model of the general circulation. It is perhaps not too surprising, therefore, that cyclones were soon regarded as disturbances rather than as links of the general circulation, thus explaining partially the deviations between observations and the idealized general circulation models.

Largely self-taught, the books that determined Ferrel's scientific outlook and inspired him to write his first scientific papers were Newton's *Principia* and Laplace's *Méchanique Céleste*. Whereas Baconian scientists took Newton's famous statement "I feign no hypothesis" as an endorsement of empiricism and classification of observations, Ferrel, after intimate study of the *Principia*, obviously transcended this simple interpretation in his demand for mathematical demonstration; further study of Laplace's work could only have deepened his appreciation of mathematics as the language of science. He turned to meteorological problems not on his own accord, but when pressed to write a review of Captain Maury's famous book.[54] Ferrel refrained from openly criticizing Maury's explanation of the general circulation of the atmosphere;[55] instead, he

[53] E. N. Lorenz, *The Nature and Theory of the General Circulation of the Atmosphere* (Geneva, World Meteorological Organization, 1967), 57–78.

[54] Matthew Fontaine Maury, *The Physical Geography of the Sea* (London, Sampson Low, 1855). The book enjoyed great popularity, going through eight editions during its first five years.

[55] Maury assumed two distinct vertical circulation cells in each hemisphere: the trade wind circulation between the equator and the belt of calms at about 30° latitude, i.e., the subtropical highs, and

developed his own ideas first in a qualitative discussion ("Winds and currents of the ocean") in 1856 and then in mathematical form in 1859/60 ("Motions of fluids and solids relative to the earth's surface").[56] Apparently inspired by J. B. L. Foucault's pendulum experiment of 1851 (that demonstrated the deflecting force of the earth's rotation),[57] and in the wake of a number of papers on the theory of relative motion, Ferrel sought to elucidate features of the general circulation and also of cyclones and smaller disturbances, "which have always been a puzzle to meteorology," through the correct treatment of the influence of the earth's rotation on atmospheric motions.[58] Since consideration of the deflecting force of the earth's rotation is of such fundamental importance for the analysis of atmospheric motions, I will outline briefly how it emerged as a theoretical concept.

The effect of the earth's rotation on meridional (north–south) currents had been recognized and treated consistently in the meteorological literature since George Hadley's paper of 1735 on the trade winds. The recognition of the influence of the earth's rotation on the zonal (east–west) currents, however, emerged only gradually over a period of several decades. Laplace had developed the general equations for the motion of a particle relative to the rotating earth in 1803. Ferrel, of course, had thoroughly studied that work. C. G. Coriolis (1835) provided the first mathematical treatment of the absolute acceleration of moving solids in a system that was rotating about a vertical axis. Although his name is now associated with the principle of the deflecting force of the earth's rotation, neither his work, nor S. D. Poisson's (1837) more general discussion, with an application of Coriolis' theorem to the relative motions on the earth, had any influence on meteorological thinking of that time.[59] A paper by Charles Tracy also went largely unnoticed.[60] Ferrel's

---

another circulation cell between the poles and the subtropical highs. In this scheme, a parcel of air was oscillating from one pole to the other. The trade wind currents ascended at the equator, crossed (without mixing), and continued as (upper) anti-trades in the opposite hemisphere. Similarly, the upper polar currents and anti-trades, which met at 30° latitude and produced high surface pressure, crossed without becoming mixed as they descended. Thus, the upper polar current fed the trade winds and the descending anti-trades continued as poleward surface winds in middle and high latitudes.

[56] Ferrel, in his first model of the general circulation of 1856, eliminated the crossings of currents proposed by Maury and introduced a third circulation cell centered at the poles, beyond the regions of prevailing westerlies in midlatitudes. As Maury, Ferrel adhered to a symmetrical model with respect to longitude. See Ferrel, "An essay on the winds and the currents of the ocean," *Nashville Journal of Medicine and Surgery*, **11** (1856), Nos. 4 and 5. Reprinted in "Popular essays of the movements of the atmosphere by Professor William Ferrel," *Professional Papers of the Signal Service*, No. 12 (Washington, 1882), 1–19; and "The motions of fluids and solids relative to the earth's surface," *The Mathematical Monthly*, **1** (1859) and **2** (1860); reprinted under separate cover (New York, 1860), 72 pp., and also with notes by F. Waldo in *Professional Papers of the Signal Service*, No. 8 (Washington, 1882), 51 pp.

[57] Harold L. Burstyn, and almost a century earlier Cl. Abbe, pointed out that Ferrel published two papers in the *Nashville Journal* of 1856, one on the movements of the atmosphere and another on Foucault's gyroscope. See Burstyn, "The deflecting force and Coriolis," *Bull. Am. Met. Soc.*, **47** (1966), 890–891, and Abbe, in an extensive footnote on the subject in his translation of L. A. Colding's article "Some remarks concerning the nature of currents of air," in *Smith. Inst., Ann. Rep. 1877*, p. 447.

[58] Ferrel (1856), reprint, p. 1.

[59] Interest in the introduction of the Coriolis force into meteorology has resulted in a number of historical studies. See, for example, J. Hann, "Ueber die Priorität des Buys Ballot'schen Gesetzes," *Wien, Met. Zeits.*, **20** (1885), 94–97; Hann's *Lehrbuch der Meteorologie*, 3rd ed., (Leipzig, Tauchnitz, 1915), 426–434; W. v. Bebber, *Handbuch der ausübenden Witterungskunde* (Stuttgart, Enke, 1885),

investigations, which represent the first mathematical formulation of atmospheric motions on a rotating earth, received widespread recognition only during the 1870's, almost two decades after his first publication on the subject and at a time when his theoretical results on the laws of motion in cyclones had already been partly superseded.[61]

287–290; Ferrel, "Priorität des Buys Ballot'schen Gesetzes," *Wien, Met. Zeits.*, **20** (1885), p. 187; W. Köppen, "Die Stellung von H. W. Brandes und H. W. Dove, 1820 und 1868, zum barischen Windgesetz," *Met. Zeits.*, **2** (1885), 414–416; R. H. Scott, "Note on early notices of the relation between atmospheric pressure and wind," *Quart. Journ. Roy. Met. Soc.*, **11** (1885), 251–252; N. Ekholm, "Ueber die Einwirkung der ablenkenden Kraft der Erdrotation auf die Luftbewegung," *Bihang, Kongl. Svenska Vet.-Akad. Handl.*, **15** (1890), Afd. 1, No. 14; Schneider-Carius, *op. cit.*, 220–236; Khrghian, *op. cit.*, 166–167, 219–222; E. W. Woolard, "Historical note on the deflecting influence of the rotation of the earth," *Journ. Franklin Inst.*, **233** (1942), 465–470; H. L. Burstyn, "Early explanations of the role of the earth's rotation in the circulation of the atmosphere and the ocean," *Isis*, **52** (1966), 167–187, and Burstyn, "The deflecting force and Coriolis," *op. cit.*; C. L. Jordan, "On Coriolis and the deflecting force," *Bull. Am. Met. Soc.*, **47** (1966), 401–403; H. E. Landsberg, "Why indeed Coriolis," *Bull. Am. Met. Soc.*, **47** (1966), 887–889. For references of original works on the Coriolis force see Woolard and Landsberg, *op. cit*; in particular: Laplace, *Méchanique Céleste*, Book 10, (1803) Chapter 5; Coriolis in a series of papers from 1832 to 1836, among them, "Mémoire sur les équations du mouvement relatif des systèmes de corps," *Journ. de L'École Polytechnique*, **15** cahier 24 (1835), 142–154 and *Comp. Ren.*, **2** (1836), 172–174; S. D. Poisson, "Extrait de la première partie d'un mémoire sur le mouvement des projectiles dans l'air, en ayant égard a leur rotation et a l'influence de mouvement diurne de la terre," *Comp. Ren.*, **5** (1837), 660–667.

[60] Tracy specifically noted the deficiency of Hadley's explanation. See Tracy, "On the rotary action of storms," *Am. Journ. Sci.*, **45** (1843), 65–72.

[61] In part, this may have been due to Ferrel's cumbersome and old fashioned mathematics. This becomes evident in Frank Waldo's re-edition of Ferrel's 1859/60 memoir in 1882, *op. cit.*, with an elaborate commentary that more than doubles the volume of the original treatise. Ferrel began his treatise with the equations of absolute motion in Cartesian coordinates, x, y and z, having their origin at the center of the earth (being at rest), and x corresponding with the axis of rotation. Using the $D_t x$ method of notation [*Math. Monthly*, **1** (1859), p. 141]:

$$D_t^2 x + D_x \Omega + \frac{1}{k} D_x P = 0,$$

$$D_t^2 y + D_y \Omega + \frac{1}{k} D_y P = 0,$$

$$D_t^2 z + D_z \Omega + \frac{1}{k} D_z P = 0,$$

where Ω is the potential of all the attractive forces of the earth, P the pressure of the fluid, k its density and t is time. After four pages of derivations Ferrel obtains for the general equations of motion of the fluid relative to the earth's surface in polar coordinates (p. 145, Equation 9)

$$\frac{1}{k} D_N P = -D_t^2 r + r(D_t\theta)^2 + r \sin^2 \theta (n + D_t\omega) D_t\varphi - g,$$

$$\frac{1}{k} D_{\theta'} P = -r^2 D_t^2 \theta - 2r D_t r D_t \theta + r^2 \sin \theta \cos \theta (n + D_t\omega) D_t \varphi,$$

$$\frac{1}{k} D_\phi P = -r^2 \sin^2 \theta D_t^2 \varphi - 2r \sin^2 \theta D_t\omega D_t r - 2r^2 \sin \theta \cos \theta D_t \omega D_t \theta,$$

where r is distance from the earth's center, θ is polar distance, φ, ϕ is longitude, n is angular velocity of the earth's rotation, N is the normal distance to the surface of the earth (putting cos ($\sphericalangle r, N$) $= 1$), θ' is perpendicular to N in the plane of the meridian and $\omega = nt + \varphi$.

Using more modern notation, these equations may be transformed into

$$\frac{1}{k}\frac{\partial p}{\partial z} = -\frac{dw}{dt} + \sin \theta (2n + \nu) u + \frac{v^2}{r} - g,$$

What concerns us here, however, beyond Ferrel's painstaking analysis of the influence of the deflecting force of the earth's rotation on the general circulation and the motion in cyclones, are his ideas on the origin and maintenance of midlatitude storms. He succeeded in showing some striking similarities and contrasts between cyclones and the general circulation. First of all, Ferrel regarded cyclonic circulations kinematically as being much like the general circulation, only on a smaller scale. Thus, with analogy to the general circulation, he defined cyclonic circulations as closed circulation systems. It was at this point in Ferrel's chain of reasoning that Espy's ideas became important. Accepting Espy's arguments on the role of thermal energy as "motive power" of storms, Ferrel was able to extend the analogy between the general circulation and cyclones, which he had established regarding their kinematic aspects, to energetic aspects as well. In view of the need for an internal source of energy capable of supporting the circulation in the closed cyclonic system, Ferrel was led to regard thermal energy, which was the primary source of energy in his scheme of the general circulation, as the primary source of energy in cyclones. He suggested, using modern terminology, that differential heating, for the general circulation on the global scale and for cyclones on the local scale, was the initial cause for both scales of motion:

> Besides the general disturbance of equilibrium arising from a difference of specific gravity between the equator and the poles, which causes the general motions of the atmosphere, treated in the last section, there are also more local disturbances, arising from a greater rarefaction of the atmosphere over limited portions of the earth's surface, which give rise to the various irregularities in its motions, including cyclones or revolving storms, tornadoes, and water-spouts.[62]

He concluded:

> Hence the general motions of the atmosphere are similar to those of a cyclone. For the general motions of the atmosphere in each hemisphere, form a grand cyclone having the pole for its centre, and the equatorial calm belt for its limit. But the denser portion of the atmosphere in this case being in the middle instead of the more rare, instead of ascending it descends at the pole or centre of the cyclone.[63]

Ferrel's scheme of the warm local cyclone and the cold polar vortex is illustrated in Figure 10; it is seen from the slope of the isobars that the warm local cyclone becomes weaker with altitude and finally changes into an anticyclone (above D), while the cold polar cyclone intensifies with altitude. Further, both the local and the polar cyclone are surrounded by a belt of high pressure and a closed circulation

---

$$\frac{1}{k}\frac{\partial p}{\partial y} = -\frac{dv}{dt} - \frac{2vw}{r} + \cos\theta(2n + \nu)u,$$

$$\frac{1}{k}\frac{\partial p}{\partial x} = -\frac{du}{dt} - 2\sin\theta(n + \nu)w - 2\cos\theta(n + \nu)v,$$

with x directed eastward on the parallel, $dx = udt = rd\theta$, y directed southward on the meridian, $dy = vdt = r\sin\theta d\varphi$ and z directed zenithward, $dz = wdt = dr$; and $\nu = d\varphi/dt$.

[62] Ferrel (1860), reprint, p. 41.

[63] *Ibid.*, p. 48.

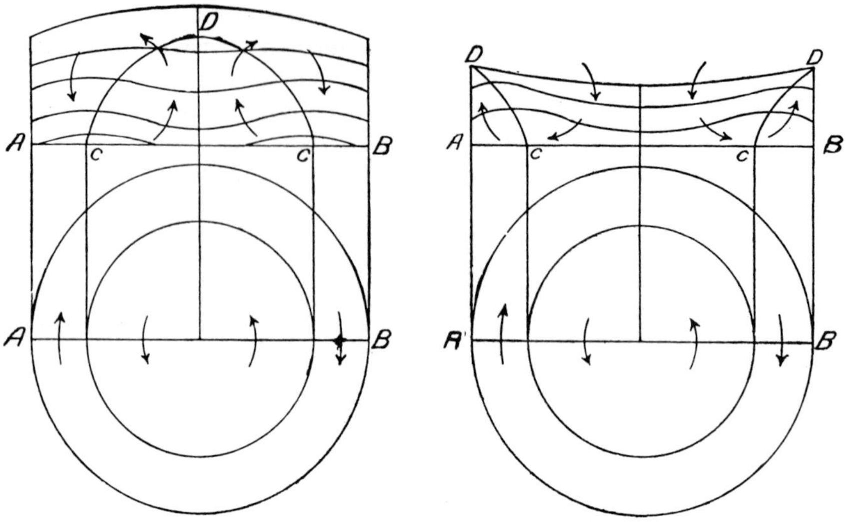

FIGURE 10. Ferrel's model of warm and cold center cyclones (1860), as illustrated by Bigelow, "Report on the international cloud observations," *Report to the Chief of the Weather Bureau,* Vol. II, 1889–1899 (Washington, 1900). Left: horizontal and vertical cross section of warm local cyclone. Right: horizontal and vertical cross section of cold polar cyclone, belonging to the general circulation of the atmosphere. Arrows indicate direction of flow, other lines are isobars; cyclonic circulation is taking place inside the spaces cDc (left) and DccD (right), anticyclonic circulation outside.

takes place between cyclone and surrounding anticyclone. The two features common to both the general circulation and the local cyclone, their mathematical similarity and, significantly, their convective nature, appear to have further unified meteorological thought and made Ferrel's views extremely attractive to Nineteenth Century scientists.[64]

In 1856, Ferrel singled out as the primary cause for localized heating the "constantly acting force furnished by the condensation of vapor ascending in the upward current . . . in accordance with Professor Espy's theory of storms and rains."[65] Elaborating on this theory, Ferrel went on,

> If, then, all the lower stratum of atmosphere over a large district were saturated with vapor, without some disturbing cause, it might remain undisturbed; but if from any cause an ascending current is produced, either by local rarefaction of air by means of heat, or by the meeting of two adverse currents, which produces a gyratory motion and

---

[64] W. M. Davis, "Ferrel's contributions to meteorology," *Am. Met. J.*, **8** (1891), 348–359. Davis remarks on page 357: "I shall not here consider the special features of this theory. The reader may find it fully stated in Ferrel's *Popular Treatise on the Winds*; but a paragraph may be given to one feature of the theory that must certainly be regarded in its favor; namely, the correlation that it establishes between convectional cyclones and the general planetary circulations; for when theoretical views bring out simple relations between apparently remotely related phenomena, this may certainly be claimed to their credit. Ferrel draws a clear comparison and a sharp contrast between the general circulation and the cyclonic circulation. Both are cyclonic, inasmuch as they whirl; but one has a cold center: the other a warm center. . . ."

[65] Ferrel (1856), reprint, p. 13.

> consequent rarefaction in the middle on account of the pressures being taken away by the centrifugal force, as soon as the air below, saturated with vapor, ascends to the colder regions above, the vapor is condensed and the caloric given out continues to rarefy it so long as the ascending column is supplied with moist air, and consequently the surrounding colder air presses in below from all sides, and thus a hurricane of more or less violence is produced and kept up for ten or twelve days, moving with the general direction of the motion of the atmosphere where it occurs.[66]

The violence and duration of a storm depended

> . . . upon the quantity of vapor supplied by the currents flowing in below. . . . it is the tropical hurricanes which originate in the Atlantic, . . . that do not abate their violence until they reach a high northern latitude where the atmosphere is cold and dry.[67]

This chain of thought was reiterated with little alteration four years later in Ferrel's mathematical paper.[68]

Of course, Ferrel could not agree with every aspect of Espy's cyclone model. Espy's view of radially inflowing currents became untenable once the deflecting force of the earth's rotation was taken into account.[69] Ferrel pointed out, however, that Espy's mistaken view of the field of motion in a storm in no way interfered with his reasoning on the origin of storms. By considering the effects of the deflecting force, Ferrel removed one further objection to the convective theory, namely the criticism that

> . . . in the rainy belt near the equator, where there are always copious rains during the day, which are succeeded by a clear atmosphere during the night, the oscillations of the barometer should be greatest, and towards the poles, where there is little condensation of vapor into rain, they should be the least; but we have seen that just the reverse of it is true.[70]

Since the deflecting force is of fundamental importance for the maintenance of the gyratory motion of large-scale cyclones, he argued, no large-scale cyclones could be expected to develop in equatorial regions, where the deflecting force vanishes. Thus it was obvious that even strong tropical rains were not accompanied normally by the development of a barometric depression.[71] Unfortunately, Ferrel's argument received little recognition in later controversies on this point.

2.4 CONCLUSIONS

Espy's theory of the role of condensational heating in storm development received support from his countrymen Loomis and Ferrel. Loomis had confirmed

---

[66] *Ibid.*

[67] *Ibid.*

[68] Ferrel (1860), reprint, p. 41.

[69] Espy had restricted his consideration of the effects of the east–west component of the deflecting force to the discussion of features of the *global* circulation, such as the Hadley cell.

[70] Ferrel (1860), reprint, p. 45. Ferrel is here referring to the fact that the mean monthly range of barometric pressure variation increases with latitude.

[71] *Ibid.*, p. 44. Ferrel noted: "Since the gyratory motion of a cyclone, and the consequent depression at the centre, depend upon a term containing as a factor cos θ, . . . , which is the sine of the latitude, according to the preceding theory of barometrical oscillations, the oscillations should be small near the equator, and increase towards the poles, somewhat as the sine of the latitude" (θ is here defined as polar distance).

Espy's views by means of synoptic studies and Ferrel had adopted Espy's ideas in the course of his dynamical studies. Consequently, Espy's view on the motive power of storms might have been regarded as firmly rooted in physical experiments, in surface observations and in theoretical studies. Nevertheless, the success of the theory was mixed. Espy's work was either praised or attacked, but both reactions appear to have amounted to only shortlived stimuli for further research on the cause of cyclones. Then, after a period of silence, Espy's fundamental proposition reappeared in the pages of meteorological journals in the 1870's. I will discuss briefly the possible reasons for this varying reception of Espy's work.

On the positive side, Espy's theory of cloud formation and large-scale precipitation was firmly grounded on his quantitative experimental analysis of the expansion and cooling of dry and moist air during ascent, on the latest available data of latent heat and water vapor pressures and on a successful contemporary theory of heat. Although Espy's theory of the thermal origin of storms, in which he utilized his explanation of the formation of clouds and large-scale precipitation, was essentially qualitative, his arguments were highly plausible and permanently directed the attention of meteorologists to the importance of adiabatic processes for certain atmospheric phenomena. Since cloud and precipitation normally occur in conjunction with storms, it was most natural for Espy and his supporters to regard adiabatic temperature changes and convection as essential for the formation and maintenance of storms. As Sir Napier Shaw remarked:

> . . . the very simple piecing together of the three parts observed in a storm [i.e., counterclockwise circulation, convergence of the circulation from high to low pressure, and convection of vertical motion, . . .] make it almost obvious that the third element, the convection is the effective cause of the whole dynamical process; . . . and it has this great advantage, that the cause which it assigns to the cyclone, namely, the convection of warmed air, has always been regarded as the cause of winds—it has been accepted as explaining the trade winds and . . . we can see in the idea a beautiful unity in meteorological theory.[72]

It is precisely this chain of thought that can be traced in the work of the proponents of the convective or thermal theory during the 1870's.

On the other hand, although Espy's explanation of the formation of cloud and rain was appreciated, there was simply not enough interest (in the 1840's) in pursuing the implications of his physical arguments. The 1840's and 1850's still belonged to the rather descriptive phase of meteorology and most of the surprisingly large number of workers in the field were observers with little training in physics. At the time of Espy the principal meteorological problem was to find the exact relationship between the wind and pressure fields for the practical purpose of navigation. Investigations of this problem naturally emphasized the horizontally distributed characteristics of storms rather than their three-dimensional structure. As discussed earlier, the debate between Redfield and Espy and their respective supporters was centered on this question: Did the wind blow parallel or

---

[72] Sir N. Shaw, "Illusions of the upper air," *Royal Institution Evening Lecture*, March 10, 1916, p. 16.

perpendicular to the isobars, i.e., in circles around the area of low pressure or directly toward the center? The assumption of radial movement toward the storm center in Espy's centripetal theory could not appear so totally wrong in Espy's time as today because no sufficiently accurate synoptic charts were at hand to disprove it. With the onset of reliable synoptic charts depicting both the pressure and wind field, it was found that Redfield's scheme of parallel isobars and wind trajectories was most easily adaptable to the pattern of inward spiralling currents. Thus, Espy's theory eventually lost out in the contest despite the backing of contemporary scientists.[73] As in the case of Dove, his theory was discarded in its entirety. Few of the early Nineteenth Century meteorologists besides Loomis and Ferrel appear to have realized that the pure radial inflow proposed by Espy was not essential to his hypothesis of the convective and thermal nature of storms, and that all that was required to assure ascending motion in the storm center was a component of radial inflow.

Espy's ideas on the formation and maintenance of storms found renewed support during the 1860's and 1870's when his experiments and conclusions were reinterpreted within the framework of thermodynamic theory. During those decades, when the significance of the first law of thermodynamics for atmospheric processes began to be explored, questions of the kind Espy had tried to answer became generally important. Scientists were then able to continue, with theoretical investigations, from the point where Espy's experiments and reasoning had come to a halt: namely, with the evaluation of the "motive power" in storms which, according to Espy, could be derived from the release of latent heat. Having available the conversion factor between heat and work—the mechanical equivalent of heat—it became possible, at least in principle, to quantify Espy's bold conclusions of the 1830's.

This latter point was already made in the Introduction. I will examine it here in more detail in order to place the emergence of the thermal theory and atmospheric energetics in its proper historical setting. It must be recalled that at Espy's time the caloric theory of heat was dominant, a theory in which *heat* was considered a substance (the caloric). In the case of adiabatic compression of a gas, it was postulated that the total amount of caloric remained invariable. The observed rise in temperature indicated that some of the "latent" caloric had become sensible. (In contrast, according to the first law of thermodynamics, the temperature increase is attributed to an energy conversion associated with the compression of the gas.) However, the theoretical concepts underlying the interpretation of adiabatic processes did not effect Espy's explanation of cloud formation. Espy's

---

[73] To this may be added the comment by Espy's friend Bache who evaluated the consequences of Espy's social appearance and scientific temperament: "His views were positive and his conclusions absolute, and so was the expression of them. He was not prone to examine and reexamine premises and conclusions, but considered what had once been passed upon his judgement as finally settled. Hence his views did not make that impression upon cooler temperaments among men of science to which they were entitled—obtaining more credit among scholars and men of general reading in our country than among scientific men, and making but little progress abroad." From A. D. Bache, "J. P. Espy," *Smith. Inst., Ann. Rep., 1859*, p. 110.

experimental results on adiabatic change were sufficient and convincing evidence. In addition, as E. Mendoza has pointed out, "the equations governing an adiabatic expansion are, in fact, independent of the model which is used for the process."[74] However, the assumption of heat as a substance did impose certain limitations on Espy's theory of storms, in particular with regard to the explanation of the source of the kinetic energy in storms. It is true that Espy compared a storm with a steam engine, but he did not and could not maintain that the thermal energy made available through the release of latent heat during condensation of water vapor was converted into the kinetic energy of the winds. During the 1830's steam engines still were regarded as machines that demonstrated that "heat could produce motion, and motion, in turn, engendered heat through friction and percussion."[75] The observed process, at this time, was not at all perceived as a conversion process.

Thus, while it was possible for Espy to determine experimentally the temperature changes and heat released during condensation of water vapor, it was not possible for him to calculate the motive power in a storm from the amount of heat available. Such calculations rest on the assumption that heat and work are interchangeable and equivalent, being connected by a constant conversion factor. The first law of thermodynamics and in particular the equivalence of heat and work were published by scientists in various European countries in the 1840's and did not gain general acceptance in the world of science until the 1850's and 1860's. During the 1870's, investigators who carried out the pertinent calculations rightly insisted on the novelty of their work. Nevertheless, recognizing the affinity between their ideas and those of Espy, they referred to his achievements on the thermal nature of storms as anticipatory of their own work, establishing in this way a link with the past.

---

[74] E. Mendoza in his introduction to the reprint of Sadi Carnot's *Reflections on the Motive Power of Fire* (New York, Dover, 1960), 19–20. In fact, Fox, *op. cit.*, p. 25, has shown conclusively that before 1840 adiabatic effects "had even appeared as strong evidence in favor" of the caloric theory.

[75] Kuhn, "Energy conservation . . . ," *op. cit.*, p. 324.

Chapter

3 Early Applications of the First Law of Thermodynamics

3.1 INTRODUCTION

Recognition of the importance of the effects of adiabatic temperature changes for atmospheric processes enabled scientists to develop new explanations for familiar phenomena which in many ways were superior to the old explanations. Pertinent investigations were discussed in Chapter 2. Now the interpretation of the process of adiabatic change on the basis of the first law of thermodynamics will be analyzed. In 1862, the subject of adiabatic change in the atmosphere was taken up in England by William Thomson, knighted Lord Kelvin. Within a few years, it was also thoroughly investigated by Theodor Reye in Germany and H. Peslin in France. These three scientists, working independently, formulated the adiabatic equations for dry and moist air and made fundamental contributions to the thermal theory of cyclones. In addition, Reye (1864) and Peslin (1868) established criteria for determining the stability of the atmosphere with regard to vertical displacements of air parcels. These criteria allowed them to predict the conditions under which convection would occur. Their work was based on graphical methods, improved tables of adiabatic temperature changes (with numerical values obtained from equations rather than experiments), and better observational material of actual atmospheric conditions in higher strata (balloon ascents and mountain observations).

Adiabatic temperature changes associated with descending air currents were evaluated correctly during the 1860's, in connection with investigations on the nature and origin of warm and dry katabatic mountain winds, the Alpine foehn. The consideration of descending currents became important for the theory of cyclones when, around 1890, the validity of Ferrel's assumption of a closed circulation between cyclones and adjacent anticyclones was questioned. The arguments used then were well known almost 30 years earlier, but were not applied to this particular problem during intervening decades.

3.2 ADIABATIC CHANGES IN ASCENDING CURRENTS: THOMSON (1862), REYE (1864), PESLIN (1868)

The new concept of the law of conservation of energy had penetrated deeply into Nineteenth Century scientific thought by the 1860's. After a period of revision and reformulation of physical theories, scientists began to assess the impact of this concept on other fields of inquiry besides physics. Meteorology was one of them. In the words of Wilhelm von Bezold, the application of the laws of thermodynamics initiated the transformation of the subject of meteorology into a "physics of the atmosphere."[1] Thermodynamics advanced meteorological research by guiding the scientists in the kind of questions asked and answers sought. It materially unified research by enabling scientists to presuppose certain assumptions and knowledge among their colleagues. Not the least important result of this trend was that well-trained and dedicated scientists were attracted to meteorology.

The scientists who first explored the applicability of the first law to atmospheric processes shared precisely this conviction: that here an avenue had opened which would lead to a significant advancement of meteorology. They were the physicist William Thomson, a co-founder of the subject of thermodynamics; the mathematician Theodor Reye, who had written his dissertation on the application of the laws of thermodynamics to the gas laws; and the mining engineer H. Peslin.[2] Their analyses of adiabatic changes represented a clear confirmation of the first law of thermodynamics from natural phenomena and was essential to the understanding of temperature changes in the atmosphere under practically all conditions.

In 1862 Thomson presented a theoretical treatment of adiabatic processes for dry and moist air.[3] He restricted his analysis to the explanation of certain observational results, in particular, the explanation of why the observed (environmental) temperature lapse rate is normally smaller than the dry-adiabatic lapse rate. Both Reye in 1864 and Peslin in 1868 attempted to show the importance of vertical motions and the presence of water vapor for a whole range of atmospheric phenomena, including the temperature lapse rate. Differences in the scope and the execution of the work of these investigators can be traced to their different outlooks and interests in the subject of meteorology. Since the absence of

---

[1] W. v. Bezold, "Die neuere Witterungskunde und die Lehre von der Niederschlagsbildung," *Himmel und Erde*, **2** (1890), p. 9. A historical analysis of this is found in J. E. McDonald, "Early developments in the theory of the saturated adiabatic process," *Bull. Am. Met. Soc.*, **44** (1963), 203–211.

[2] See biographical notes on Thomson and Reye in the Appendix. Despite extensive search I could not locate biographical information on Peslin.

[3] As noted earlier, the term adiabatic, which Rankine had introduced, began to be adopted in the physics literature during the 1870's [see, for example, Zeuner, *Grundzüge der mechanischen Wärmetheorie* (Leipzig, A. Felix, 1877)]. It became part of the meteorological vocabulary, it appears, on account of H. Hertz' influential paper of 1884 ["Graphische Methode zur Bestimmung der adiabatischen Zustandsgleichungen feuchter Luft," *Met. Zeits.*, **1** (1884), 421–431.]

a consistent terminology and method of mathematical expression makes it difficult to compare their derivations directly, I have strived to use a notation as far as possible consistent with present usage in this and the following chapters. Significant differences between the developments presented in the text and those by a particular author are described in the notes.

In a paper entitled "On the convective equilibrium of temperature in the atmosphere," Thomson proposed to investigate a suggestion made to him by his collaborator James Prescott Joule: "That condensation of vapour in upward currents of air might account, to a considerable extent if not perfectly, for the smallness of the lowering of temperature actually found going up" in the atmosphere.[4] Joule here was referring to measurements from balloon ascents indicating a smaller vertical temperature gradient than is required for convective equilibrium of dry air. According to information obtained during John Welsh's balloon ascents of 1852, as quoted by Thomson, the average environmental temperature lapse rate was 1°C per 530 feet (162 m) compared to 1°C per 330 feet (101 m) for a dry-adiabatic process lapse rate. Thomson based his analysis of the atmospheric temperature stratification on the first law of thermodynamics as applied to the expansion of gases under constant volume conditions, *viz.*

$$dQ = c_v dT + \frac{1}{J} p dv \quad [\text{cal}].$$

Here dQ[cal] denotes the heat added to the system, c_v[cal °C^{-1}] specific heat, of a pound of air at constant volume v[cm^3], J^{-1}[cal s^2 g^{-1} cm^{-2}] the thermal equivalent of work, T[°C] the temperature (Thomson used t for temperature in his paper), and p[g cm^{-1} s^{-2}] the pressure. According to this equation, Thomson argued that the work of expansion done by a quantity of air saturated with water vapor consists of two effects: in the case of adiabatic conditions, i.e., $dQ = 0$, the quantity of air "cools from temperature t to temperature $t + dt$, and it condenses a bulk $v(ds/s) - dv$ of vapour"; here "s denotes the volume of a pound of vapour at saturation at any temperature t,"[5] and the condensed volume of vapor equals the difference between the change of volume in the case of no condensation, i.e.,

---

[4] Thomson, "On the convective equilibrium of temperature in the atmosphere," *Memoirs of the Manchester Literary and Philosophical Society*, 2 (1865), read January 21, 1862, p. 127. Joule had made extensive experiments on adiabatic change and Poisson's equation was well known to him. An earlier attempt by J. C. E. Pectlet (1843) to explain the vertical temperature distribution as due to convective equilibrium had failed because he considered only dry air. Applying Poisson's formula, which is valid for dry air only, Pectlet found that the observed temperature lapse rate was much smaller than that required for the convective equilibrium. See Pectlet, "Ueber den aufsteigenden Luftstrom in der Atmosphäre," *Ann. Phys. Chem.*, **58** (1843), 655–660; extract from *Traité de Physique*, Vol. 1 (Paris, 1843), p. 576. He also suggested, but did not publish an adiabatic diagram for the atmosphere. Pectlet wrote on p. 657, *Ann. Phys. Chem.*: "If one wanted to know, e.g., to which altitude air of 100°C would have ascended on the day of the air travel of Mr. Gay-Lussac, then one would have to construct by means of the formula of Mr. Poisson a curve whose abscissa would signify the pressure (Spannkräfte) and whose ordinates the temperatures of the ascending air, and another curve whose abscissa would signify the pressure and whose ordinates the temperatures of the atmosphere corresponding to these abscissa. The abscissa of the point of intersection of the two curves would be the atmospheric pressure corresponding to the altitude sought."

[5] Thomson, p. 130.

$v(ds/s)$, and the actual change of volume dv.[6] Latent heat is liberated in proportion to the vapor condensed. Expressing pdv in thermal units, Thomson obtained an equation of adiabatic change for moist air:

$$\frac{1}{J}\,pdv = -c_v dT + L\left(v\,\frac{ds}{s} - dv\right) \quad \text{[cal]}.$$

where L [cal cm^{-3}] denotes latent heat of condensation per unit volume of water. The value for latent heat was obtained from a formula that Thomson and Joule had derived in 1854. This equation permitted the evaluation of volume changes required to produce a cooling effect $-dT$. From values for $-dv/dT$ and the hydrostatic equation, Thomson calculated the height dz "that must be reached to get a lowering of temperature, $-dt\,[dT]$, when air saturated with moisture ascends."[7] He tabulated his results for volume changes and height changes required to cool moist air by 1°C, when the air, ascending saturation adiabatically, was initially at standard pressure and for temperatures ranging from 0°C to 35°C. His theoretically derived lapse rates agreed well with Welsh's empirical data of environmental lapse rates for low temperatures (0°C to 10°), and he concluded "that at the times and places of [Welsh's] observations the lowering of temperature upward was nearly the same as that which air saturated with moisture would experience in ascending. . . . It appears, therefore, that the explanation suggested by Dr. Joule is correct."[8]

Thomson did not cite earlier studies of thermodynamic processes in the atmosphere, nor did he return to this subject in his later writings.[9] In contrast, both Reye and Peslin aimed at a broader interpretation and application of the first law and adiabatic changes to the atmosphere. They explored the role of convection of moist air in the formation and maintenance of storms and the general circulation, and they made serious and partially successful attempts to elucidate the energy budget of cyclones as will be discussed in Chapter 4. Both were well informed about contemporary meteorological theories and consequently were in a position to criticize these theories pointedly and constructively. Wherever possible, they built

[6] Thomson, p. 128.

[7] Thomson, p. 131. See also Thomson and Joule, "On the thermal effects of fluids in motion, part 2. Theoretical Deductions," *Trans. Roy. Soc.*, **144** (1854), 321–364.

[8] Thomson, p. 131.

[9] His paper must be viewed as one among the many in which he applied his ideas and results in physics to related fields and practical purposes. At a banquet given in his honor for the successful laying of the transatlantic cable in 1866 Thomson remarked: "Unless men of science pursue their studies out of a pure love of knowledge or from an abstract desire to become acquainted with the laws of nature, they will seldom carry on their labours with success; but at the same time no greater reward could crown their investigations when . . . they are means of conferring a practical service on mankind. . ." [quoted from A. P. Young, *Lord Kelvin* (London, New York, Toronto, Longmans, Green and Co., 1948), p. 25]. It should be added that humanitarian ideals indeed have influenced a number of scientists in their decision to take up the subject of meteorology, e.g., Fitzroy, Reye, Espy. Thomson's only other encounter with meteorology came 30 years later; a master in the use of analogy, he recommended that harmonic analysis be used for the identification of the atmospheric processes underlying meteorological records, since "the harmonic analyser, and the tide-predictor . . . had done such splendid service for the water" [quoted from Sir N. Shaw, "The march of meteorology," *Quart. Journ. Roy. Met. Soc.*, **60** (1934), 101–120, reprinted in the *Meteorological Papers of Sir Napier Shaw* (London, MacDonald, 1955), p. 239].

on the meager but useful observational evidence and hoped that their work would give new directions to meteorological research.

Prior to 1860, scientists repeatedly had studied the production of ascending currents and the phenomena associated with them.[10] Espy, as we have seen, provided the first generally acceptable explanation for this process. However, theoretical backing for his explanation, and, more specifically, quantitative evaluation and determination of the conditions under which vertical motion occurs, were not treated. Moreover, Espy's work found little recognition and application in Europe, after initial enthusiasm died. Reye and Peslin therefore had good reason to emphasize the need for comprehensive and thorough analysis. In the words of Reye,

> . . . in the science of clouds, the formation of hail and thunderstorms there is always much said about ascending and descending currents of air; the question, however, that is significant in this respect, i.e., under which circumstances such vertical currents are possible in our atmosphere, I have found touched upon very seldom in meteorological works and never treated thoroughly in any of them.[11]

Reye had just completed his dissertation on gas dynamics and had been appointed lecturer in mathematical physics at the Polytechnical Institute in Zurich when he proceeded to furnish the needed analysis in a paper of 1864, entitled "On vertical currents of air in the atmosphere."[12]

Reye's personal observations of cloud and storm formation dated back to his childhood years at the stormy coast of the North Sea. He retained a lively interest in meteorology throughout his career, first in Zurich and then as professor of mathematics at the University of Strassbourg, considering it in part as a diversion from his mathematical studies. He soon found "that with all its wealth of knowledge and ingenious ideas" meteorology could only profit from "some mathematical rigorosity."[13] He put this thought into practice in his critique of contemporary theories of cloud and precipitation formation, in particular the theory of Carl Friedrich Mohr, who is also known for his announcement of essential parts of the concept of energy conservation as early as 1837.[14] Mohr's popular theory implied that clouds were formed in cold descending currents of air—an explanation that was indeed a retrogression after Hutton's incomplete but nevertheless physically plausible theory and after Espy's achievements. According to Mohr's theory, the sudden condensation of water vapor in lower layers resulted in a "contraction" of volume. This "contraction," producing a partial vacuum within a storm cloud (i.e., lowering the pressure in the parcel of air affected), led to inflow of air from all sides

---

[10] W. E. Knowles Middleton, *A History of the Theories of Rain*, in the Watts History of Science Library (New York, F. Watts, Inc., 1966), 58–62, 102–106.

[11] Reye, *Die Wirbelstürme, Tornados und Wettersäulen*, (Hannover, Rümpler, 1872), preface, pp. vii–viii.

[12] Reye, "Ueber vertikale Luftströme in der Atmosphäre," *Zeits. für Mathematik und Physik*, **9** (1864), 250–276.

[13] Reye (1872), preface, p. vii.

[14] About simultaneously with William Grove, Michael Faraday and Gustav Liebig, Mohr defined a single "force," manifest in and convertible into electrical, thermal, dynamical and other forms, which could neither be created nor destroyed. See T. S. Kuhn, "Energy conservation . . . ," *op. cit.*

and violent downward currents.[15] A glaring defect in this chain of reasoning was the neglect of the effect of latent heat release during condensation that produces a volume expansion which completely offsets the volume reduction resulting from the condensation of water vapor. Using thermodynamic data extant, Reye demonstrated by a simple computation

> . . . that with normal air temperatures ranging from −10° to +35°C this [volume] expansion exceeds the [volume] reduction by more than five times the amount.[16]

This, he noted, confirmed Espy's experimental results. Reye concluded, as Espy had done, that the net effect would be the expansion of the volume of air resulting in ascending rather than descending currents. Reye substantiated his numerical results by summarizing much observational material from different places of the globe which supported his view: that ascending currents generally develop over heated areas—either unorganized or organized into a continuous stream—and that they are often associated with cloud formation and precipitation. Reye appended to his paper a thorough theoretical analysis of the dry-adiabatic and saturation-adiabatic processes, which in the words of a modern reviewer left "essentially nothing new for any later worker to add."[17] Only his deduction of the exact saturation-adiabatic equation needs to be discussed here. Reye chose a less cumbersome approach in his derivation than Thomson. In Thomson's treatment of adiabatic processes the volume of air was constantly changing during condensation. In Reye's derivation, the parcel of air consisted of two components of fixed mass, the first containing dry air only and the second water vapor and the condensation products. According to the first law of thermodynamics, he then obtained two equations for the heat needed to bring about a certain temperature change in these two components:

$$dQ_1 = mc_p dT - m\,\frac{ART}{p}\,dp,$$

$$dQ_2 = Nc_w dT + Td\left(\frac{nL}{T}\right),$$

where

dQ_1 = quantity of heat added for dry air
m = mass of dry air
c_p = specific heat of dry air at constant pressure
T = temperature
$A = J^{-1}$, the thermal equivalent of work
R = gas constant

[15] Fr. Mohr, "Über die Entstehung des Hagels," *Ann. Phys. Chem.*, **117** (1862), 89–116. See also A. Krönig's attempt to refute this theory on the basis of thermodynamic considerations in "Ueber Mohr's Hageltheorie," *Ann. Phys. Chem.*, **123** (1864), 641–650.

[16] Reye (1864), p. 251.

[17] McDonald (1963), *op. cit.*, p. 208. Reye later added this part of his paper as an appendix to his book of 1872.

p = pressure
dQ_2 = quantity of heat added for water vapor and condensation products
c_w = specific heat of water
n = mass of water vapor
$N - n$ = mass of water
L = latent heat of condensation.

The total change of heat content of moist air was then

$$dQ = dQ_1 + dQ_2 = (mc_p + Nc_w)dT - m\frac{ART}{p}dp + Td\left(\frac{nL}{T}\right).$$

For the case of adiabatic change, when $dQ = 0$, Reye integrated the equation and obtained

$$0 = (mc_p + Nc_w)\ln\frac{T}{T_0} - mAR\ln\frac{p}{p_0} + \frac{nL}{T} - \frac{n_0L_0}{T_0},$$

where p_0, T_0, L_0 and n_0 denote the initial values of p, T, L and n. Reordering, dividing by mAR ln (10) (the latter denoting natural logarithm of 10) and evaluating the constants, Reye obtained the equation for the relation between pressure and temperature for saturation-adiabatic changes:

$$\log\frac{p}{p_0} = \frac{c_p + \frac{N}{m}c_w}{AR}\log\frac{T}{T_0} - \frac{n_0L_0 - nL\frac{T_0}{T}}{mART\ln(10)}.$$

This equation enabled him to compute pressure changes as a function of temperature changes during expansion of a parcel of moist air, since the saturation pressure of water vapor and the heat of condensation were functions of temperature only. Reye summarized his computations in a table giving pressure changes associated with the saturation-adiabatic expansion of air for temperatures ranging from +30°C to −20°C.

Reye also developed a simplified saturation-adiabatic equation in order to facilitate the task of numerical solution. Here he explicitly acknowledged the pertinence of Poisson's formula (derived in 1823), which could be regarded as a special case of the general equation he derived. This general equation, Reye noted,

> . . . obviously has the form of Poisson's equation for dry air. . . . The presence of water vapor in the air thus has the same effect that an increase in the specific heat c of air would produce.[18]

Thus, for moist air, Reye let the exponent ϵ in Poisson's equation

$$\frac{p_0}{p} = \left(\frac{T_0}{T}\right)^{\epsilon}$$

increase with increasing water vapor content. Namely, ϵ was defined as $\epsilon = (c_p + \omega)/AR$, where ω represented the increase in specific heat due to the pres-

[18] Reye (1864), p. 272.

ence of water vapor as referred to in the above quotation. Thomson also had rederived Poisson's equation in his paper. Scientists appear to have fully realized the universal validity and the usefulness of Poisson's equation only when it was reinterpreted in the light of the first law of thermodynamics.

Independently of Thomson's and Reye's work, a third paper containing the equations of adiabatic change for dry and moist air was published in 1868 by H. Peslin.[19] Peslin, an engineer, pursued his strong interest in meteorology aside from his professional duties, a situation that was widespread during the Nineteenth Century, when meteorology was just emerging as a profession. He regularly took part in the weekly sessions of the Société Météorologique de France where he submitted most of his meteorological papers for discussions. In his paper of 1868 Peslin used a slightly different and somewhat less rigorous approach than Reye in the deduction of the equation for the saturation-adiabatic lapse rate. His procedure was accurate for most meteorological purposes. Because of its mathematical elegance and simplicity it has been used repeatedly in meteorological treatises.[20] From the first law of thermodynamics Peslin obtained the equation relating pressure and temperature conditions in a parcel of moist air to which no heat is added:

$$\frac{1}{J} V dp = c_p dT + L dq,$$

where

J = mechanical equivalent of heat
V = volume
p = pressure
c_p = specific heat of dry air at constant pressure
T = temperature
L = latent heat
q = specific moisture = density of water vapor divided by the density of moist air = $0.6219\, e/p$, where e denotes saturation pressure of water vapor. The quantity q is approximately the mixing ratio, which is defined as $0.6219\, e/(p - e)$, and dq is negative for condensation.

Like Reye's equation, Peslin's equation was easier to use than Thomson's because he considered a unit mass and not a unit volume of air. In addition, he expressed the water vapor content in terms of specific moisture, and in this way simplified the mathematical procedure. Introducing the hydrostatic equation, differentiating q logarithmically ($dq/q = de/e - dp/p$) and substituting in the above equation, Peslin obtained the saturation-adiabatic lapse rate

[19] Peslin, "Sur les mouvements généraux de l'atmosphère," *Bull. Hebd. l'Ass. Sci. France*, **3** (1868), 299–319.

[20] This has been pointed out by McDonald, *op. cit.* See, for example, B. Haurwitz, *Dynamic Meteorology* (New York, McGraw-Hill, 1941), p. 55; and A. Defant and Fr. Defant, *Physikalische Dynamik der Atmosphäre* (Frankfurt, Akademische Verlagsgesellschaft, 1958), 21–22.

$$\frac{dT}{dz} = -g \frac{\frac{1}{J} + \frac{Lq}{RT}}{c_p + Lq \frac{1}{e} \frac{de}{dT}},$$

where z denotes height and g gravity. Peslin furnished a small table giving the lapse rates for moist air initially at sea level pressure and for temperatures ranging from 43°C to −13°C.[21]

The equations which Peslin and Thomson derived were not exact. Both scientists introduced certain approximations concerning the condensed water vapor. Peslin suggested that water vapor and liquid were retained in the rising parcel in order to keep the unit mass constant; at the same time he assumed that their presence could be neglected in calculations of heat content. Thomson assumed that all condensation products fell from the parcel of rising air, a process that W. v. Bezold later termed pseudoadiabatic.[22] These approximations are indeed permissible for most meteorological purposes because the terms in question have small numerical values under atmospheric conditions. For this reason, Reye also introduced a simplified expression for his exact equation of adiabatic change.

Thomson, Reye and Peslin interpreted their theoretical results in significantly different ways. Thomson stated that the saturation-adiabatic lapse rate could be expected only "when the air is saturated, and when, therefore, an ascending current will always keep forming cloud."[23] He suggested that the near saturation-adiabatic lapse rate observed during fair weather with little vertical motions must be attributed to "mutual interradiation" of the warmed lower and cool upper layers of the atmosphere. On the other hand, he stressed, vertical temperature variations "in upward or downward currents in cloudless air must agree very closely" with the dry-adiabatic lapse rate.[24] He did not explore further why the environmental temperature lapse rate of the lower strata corresponded rather closely in both clear and cloudy conditions with the saturation-adiabatic process lapse rate. His primary purpose, it appears, was to substantiate the suggestion of his friend and collaborator Joule, and thereby point toward another field of science in which the first law of thermodynamics could be applied profitably. His interest in meteorology was peripheral rather than central as with Reye and Peslin.

Reye and Peslin saw the need to investigate more closely the conditions for convective equilibrium, namely, the criteria that determined the stability of an atmosphere of specified temperature stratification with regard to vertical displacement of air parcels. They realized that the establishment of these criteria was essential for the understanding and, significantly, for the prediction of the

[21] Peslin (1868), 301–303.

[22] W. v. Bezold, "Zur Thermodynamik der Atmosphäre," 1. Mitteilung, *Sitzber. Ak., Berlin*, Nr. 21 (1888), 485–522, reprinted in *Gesammelte Abhandlungen aus den Gebieten der Meteorologie und des Erdmagnetismus* (Braunschweig, Vieweg und Sohn, 1906), 109–110.

[23] Thomson, p. 131.

[24] *Ibid.*, p. 131.

atmospheric conditions under which vertical motions were likely to occur. They found that the stability of a parcel of air depended on the relationship between dry and saturation-adiabatic lapse rates and the environmental lapse rate. Reye pointed out that Espy, whose theory of storms he generally supported, had failed to consider the environmental temperature stratification when he attempted to determine the conditions under which saturation-adiabatic upward motion would tend to occur. Espy, Reye objected

> . . . assumes that in places, where water vapor condenses in accidentally lifted air masses, the heat of condensation that is liberated is sufficient to force the air mass into a vigorous, increasingly rapid ascent . . . but we now know that this effect of condensation occurs only then, when the temperature decrease during vertical ascent in the atmosphere exceeds a certain amount.[25]

Taking up this chain of thought, Peslin discussed the vertical displacement of a parcel of air in an atmosphere where the environmental lapse rate is greater than that of the ascending air.

> After the displacement the mass of air considered will be warmer than the air in the layer of the atmosphere that it has attained; therefore, it will be lighter under the same pressure, and will tend to continue its ascent under the action of buoyancy alone without the need for any new impulse.[26]

In this case, he noted, the air tends to deviate more and more from its equilibrium condition, i.e., it ascends, and the environmental lapse rate must be regarded as unstable.

In their determination of the stability criteria, both Reye and Peslin applied the so-called parcel method. This method has retained its value for the understanding of atmospheric phenomena up to modern times, even though—or perhaps because—it could lead only to simplified results due to the assumption that the moving parcel does not mix with the surrounding air. Since Reye's and Peslin's discussions of the stability criteria resemble each other closely, only Reye's work will be treated here.

Substituting $dz = -100\, dT/\tau$, where z denotes height above surface and τ denotes an environmental lapse rate (°C per 100 m), into the hydrostatic equation in the form

$$-\frac{dp}{p} = \frac{[g]dz}{RT} \quad \text{(Reye omitted } g \text{ in his derivation),}$$

Reye obtained

$$\frac{dp}{p} = \frac{100}{R\tau}[g]\frac{dT}{T}.$$

Integration of this equation yielded

$$\log\frac{p_0}{p} = \frac{100}{R\tau}[g]\log\frac{T_0}{T}$$

[25] Reye (1864), p. 262.

[26] Peslin (1868), p. 306.

or

$$\frac{p_0}{p} = \left(\frac{T_0}{T}\right)^{100/R\tau[g]}$$

describing the relationship between temperature and pressure for known environmental lapse rate τ. The temperature decrease in the parcel of air rising adiabatically was then described by

$$\frac{p_0}{p} = \left(\frac{T_0}{T'}\right)^{\epsilon},$$

where ϵ is constant for dry air ($\epsilon = 3.443$) but varies for moist air and the prime refers to conditions in the parcel of rising air. It followed that in the case of atmospheric neutrality

$$\left(\frac{T_0}{T'}\right)^{\epsilon} = \left(\frac{T_0}{T}\right)^{100/R\tau[g]}.$$

Multiplying by $(T/T_0)^{\epsilon}$ yielded

$$\left(\frac{T}{T'}\right)^{\epsilon} = \left(\frac{T}{T_0}\right)^{\epsilon-100/R\tau[g]}.$$

Accordingly, $T' > T$ for $\tau > (100/R\epsilon)[g]$ $\{$with $(100/R\epsilon)[g] = 100\cdot[g]/(29.272\cdot 3.442) = 0.993°\text{C}$ per 100 m$\}$ and $T' < T$ for $\tau < (100/R\epsilon)[g]$.[27] In his interpretation of this result Reye argued that an environmental lapse rate corresponding to the dry-adiabatic lapse rate could be regarded as the distinguishing case between stable and unstable conditions of a dry atmosphere:

> The upward displaced parcel of air is warmer and thus is specifically lighter than its new environment; therefore it rises still further when the temperature decrease for every 100 meter vertical displacement amounts to more than . . . 0.993°C; it is colder and therefore descends back to its former position, when the temperature decrease for every 100 meter is less then 0.993°. In the first case the state of equilibrium of the atmosphere is unstable, in the second stable; it is neutral when the said temperature decrease equals 0.993°.[28]

Reye applied analogous reasoning for the case of saturated air. Since the saturation-adiabatic lapse rate is smaller than the dry-adiabatic, and since the environmental lapse rate often falls between the two, instability could be expected more frequently for saturated than for unsaturated air. This explained the observation that "moist air ascends much more easily in the atmosphere than dry air."[29]

These results convinced Reye that vertical motions tended to restore the stable equilibrium in the atmosphere once it was disturbed. As an example, he cited the

---

[27] Deviating from Reye's presentation, I have included the factor g (gravity) in this expression. In general, differences in the use of g in Reye's original equations versus those presented in the text derive from differences in the definition of the equation of state. Reye defined this equation for unit weight; in current usage, this equation is defined for unit mass.

[28] Reye (1864), 274–275.

[29] *Ibid.*, p. 261.

formation of cumulus clouds on warm, clear summer days "which expand upward in immense columns" and "larger ascending air currents along the earth surface such as whirlwinds and waterspouts."[30] Similarly, Peslin concluded on account of stability considerations that the vertical temperature structure of the atmosphere as a whole (in the lower layers) must tend toward a stable equilibrium, for

> Each time that the [vertical] temperature decrease tends to exaggerate in the terrestrial atmosphere . . . the atmospheric equilibrium cannot subsist; air currents will develop which will maintain the law of temperature decrease within the limits beyond which the equilibrium would become unstable.[31]

The actual computation of simultaneous changes of pressure, temperature and moisture content for the purpose of determining the stability of the atmosphere is wearisome. Tables constructed for that purpose are cumbersome to use. Peslin, as an engineer accustomed to problems of practical application and the use of diagrams (much more so than the mathematician Reye), rendered a real service to meteorology, therefore, when he developed a graphical method which greatly facilitated the interpretation of temperature-altitude (pressure) and moisture observations in terms of stability and instability, levels of condensation, etc.[32] It will be seen in Chapter 4 how this method allowed Peslin to make fairly accurate estimates of the energy available from atmospheric instability. Peslin's diagram, whose abscissa was altitude and whose ordinate was temperature, contained lines for dry adiabats and saturation adiabats (Figure 11). The path of a parcel of air moving upward or downward adiabatically was then represented by the line of the appropriate adiabat. The stability of the temperature stratification could be judged at a glance. If the curve of the environmental lapse rate was steeper than the lines of the adiabats—dry or saturated—then the stratification was stable; if it was less steep, unstable.

During the 1860's, the few scientists who read Peslin's work apparently did not recognize how practical his diagram was, let alone the possibilities it offered; in any case, there is no record of its subsequent use. Of course, Peslin's diagram could have become fully useful only when reliable observations of conditions in the upper atmosphere became available. In the 1860's it could have been employed advantageously in thought experiments. The diagram was finally reinvented in 1884 by Heinrich Hertz, an outsider to the field of meteorology.[33]

---

[30] *Ibid.*

[31] Peslin (1868), 306–307.

[32] *Ibid.*, pp. 313–315. Peslin's diagram is only described, but not reproduced in the paper available to me.

[33] H. Hertz, "Graphische Methode zur Bestimmung der adiabatischen Zustandsgleichungen feuchter Luft," *Met. Zeits.*, **1** (1884), 421–431. See also a translation by Cl. Abbe in "The mechanics of the earth's atmosphere," A collection of translations, *Smith. Misc. Coll.*, **34** (1893), 198–211. Hertz, the great investigator of electrodynamics, wrote his purely theoretical meteorological paper while at the University of Kiel in northern Germany where he had no physics laboratory to pursue experimental studies and before he moved to Karlsruhe in 1885 where he commenced his famous experiments on electric waves in air. Hertz, who otherwise had no recognizable meteorological interests, apparently wrote his paper in obligation to the director Karsten of the physics institute in Kiel. See P. Forman, J. L. Heilbron, Sp. Weart, Physics circa 1900, *Historical Studies in the Physical Sciences*, R. McCormmach, Ed., Vol. 5 (Princeton University Press, 1975), p. 53.

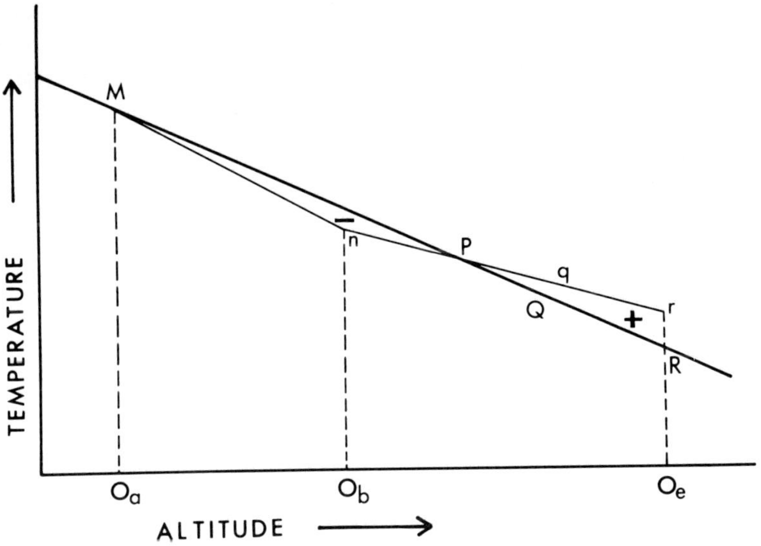

FIGURE 11. Thermodynamic diagram constructed (by the author) according to a description given by Peslin; from Peslin, "Sur les mouvements généraux de l'atmosphère," *Bull. Hebd. l'Ass. Sci. France*, **3** (1868). Symbols are explained below.

———, temperature decrease in atmosphere at rest
———, temperature decrease in rising parcel
O_a altitude at which parcel begins to rise
Mn dry adiabat
O_b condensation level
nPqr moist adiabat
O_e altitude at which parcel of air is "ejected" from the vortex.

Area MnP represents energy expended for lifting the parcel from O_a to O_b. Area PQRrq represents energy becoming available for conversion. Peslin assumes that in a storm, the area MnP is always smaller than the area PQRrq. However, it should be noted that areas are not strictly proportional to energy. For straight line adiabats (dry), as used by Peslin, the abscissa would have to be p^k. However, $h \approx \ln p$ and $dp^k \approx d\ln p$ (for $500 < p < 1000$ mb; $k = R/c_p$); therefore, energy considerations carried out with the aid of Peslin's diagram are still fairly accurate.

Of the three papers discussed, only Reye's was widely read, and then, only after he had it reprinted as an appendix to his popular book of 1872 on storms which, as Landsberg has remarked, "was on the shelf of all German meteorological institutions" at that time.[34] Thomson's paper, in fact, had no influence at all on the development of meteorology, although one should have expected his famous name to attract a readership varied enough to include a meteorologist. Apparently, not even Peslin and Reye (who were well acquainted with meteorological literature) knew of Thomson's paper until after they finished their own investigations. One can easily see how this may have happened. Thomson, like Reye and Peslin, had published in a journal that was not readily available nor ordinarily read by

[34] Landsberg, *Bull. Am. Met. Soc.*, **44** (1963), p. 511.

meteorologists. Meteorology was not yet organized as an independent field of inquiry and journals specializing in the field were not yet established. Thus the channels that would have immensely facilitated communication among scientists interested in meteorology did not exist.

3.3 THE FOEHN WIND

In their treatments of adiabatic motions in the atmosphere, Thomson, Peslin and Reye emphasized ascending currents, the formation of clouds and precipitation. In comparison, descending currents, which were far less obvious and more difficult to observe than ascending currents, had received little attention. Since the arguments involved in the analysis of the thermodynamics of descending motion became crucial for the thermal theory of cyclones during the 1890's, their first comprehensive treatment during the late 1860's will be examined.

Espy and Ferrel had suggested that areas of low pressure with inflowing surface winds and ascending currents in the central part were surrounded by areas of high pressure characterized by general descent of air and outflow in the lower layers. In supporting the view that descending and ascending currents were complementary, Francis Galton, member of the Meteorological Committee of the Royal Society, coined in 1863 the word "anticyclone" for areas of high pressure, stating

> Most meteorologists are agreed that a circumscribed area of barometric depression is usually a locus of light ascending currents, and therefore of an indraught of surface winds which create a retrograde whirl (in our hemisphere). . . . Conversely we ought to admit that a similar area of barometric elevation is usually a locus of dense descending currents, and therefore of a dispersion of a cold dry atmosphere, plunging from the higher regions upon the surface of the earth, which, flowing away radially on all sides, becomes at length imbued with lateral motion. . . .[35]

This remark makes it clear that "most meteorologists" at this time did not understand the physical processes and temperature changes taking place in descending currents. Galton, it appears, implied that the cold air, often experienced in winter during periods of high pressure, was transferred to the earth's surface from upper regions. His opinion was widely accepted. It directly contradicted Espy's conclusion derived on the basis of experiments almost 30 years earlier, *viz.*, that air must warm and become relatively dry when coming under increased pressure during descending motions in the atmosphere.[36] Apparently Espy's consideration, interspersed among the pages of his *Fourth Meteorological Report*,

---

[35] F. Galton, "A development of the theory of cyclones, *Proc. Roy. Soc.*, **12** (1863), 385–386. Galton, a cousin of Charles Darwin and gentleman scientist, devoted his life to the study of such varied fields as geography, meteorology, eugenics and fingerprints. At his own expense, he published a large work, *Meteorographia, Methods of Mapping the Weather*, illustrated by upward of 600 printed and lithographed diagrams referring to the weather of a large part of Europe during the month of December 1861 (London, MacMillan, 1863).

[36] Espy, *Fourth Meteorological Report*, 34th Congress, 3rd Session/Senate (Washington, Nicholson, 1857), pp. 13, 60, 173. Espy remarked on page 60 that "*No clouds can form in a down-moving current*; and if any clouds existed in it at first, they would soon be dissolved by the heat of compression."

had been overlooked. The fact that the same physical principles applied to descending as well as to ascending air currents was clarified during the late 1860's, when European meteorologists began to analyze a very special descending current, the Alpine foehn, in the light of the theory of adiabatic processes.

For centuries, scientists had studied the foehn. This dry, warm katabatic wind of mountain areas often brings such drastic temperature and moisture changes that plants and animals are affected adversely. From around 1850 onward, the dominant opinion among Swiss scholars was that the foehn of the Alps, because of its hotness and dryness, must have originated in the Sahara.[37] This theory won considerable support when it was employed by the geologist Conrad Escher von der Lindt in the explanation of the glaciation of the Alps. At a time when the Sahara was covered by an ocean, von der Lindt suggested, the warm foehn wind, normally a powerful snow-melting agent, failed to develop and snow and ice began to accumulate.[38] Dove was the first to oppose this Sahara hypothesis of the origin of the foehn. Instead he proposed that the Alpine foehn was an effect of equatorial currents originating in the regions of the West Indies.[39] Dove insisted that the foehn was a moist rather than a dry wind and he argued that this moisture was supplied from the tropical waters of the Caribbean Sea. He seemingly disregarded reliable, long-existing descriptions of the Alpine foehn and he showed an outspoken distrust of the newly instituted Swiss program of humidity measurements which confirmed the extreme dryness during times of foehn. The animosity that consequently developed between Dove and his Swiss colleagues found expression in a bitter polemic between Dove and Heinrich Wild, professor of physics and director of the observatory and the Meteorologische Centralanstalt in Berne.[40]

In 1866, Julius Hann, a young Austrian who had just completed his education in geography and physics, hoped to put an end to the controversy with an entirely different explanation that incorporated the principles of adiabatic change.[41] A keen observer of natural phenomena since his childhood days, he was well acquainted with the foehn. He had been puzzled by the description of a meteorological phenomenon in Greenland that appeared to be analogous to the foehn of the Alps. There was no heated continent nearby to serve as explanation for the relatively warm katabatic winds observed along the eastern slopes of Greenland:

> Greenland has a warm and apparently dry current of air which is completely analogous

[37] Otto Lehmann, "Zur Geschichte der Föhntheorie," *Mitteilungen der Naturforschenden Gesellschaft Zürich, Vierteljahrsschrift*, **82** (1937), 45–76.

[38] Julius Hann, "Zur Frage über den Ursprung des Föhn," *Wien. Met. Zeits.*, **1** (1866), p. 258. This explanation of the glaciation of the Alps was later also accepted by Charles Lyell (1864).

[39] W. H. Dove, "Ueber den Föhn," *Mitteilungen der Naturforschenden Gesellschaft Zürich, Vierteljahresschrift*, **10** (1865).

[40] Dove, *Ueber Eiszeit, Föhn und Scirocco* (Berlin, Reimer, 1867), 116 pp.; Heinrich Wild, *Ueber Föhn und Eiszeit*, Rektoratsrede (Berne, 1867), 40 pp.; Dove, *Der Schweizer Föhn*, Nachtrag (Berlin, 1868); Wild, *Der Schweizer Föhn* (Berne, 1868), 46 pp.; Wild was instrumental in the organization of the Meteorologische Centralanstalt in Berne and the Swiss meteorological station network. In 1868 he was called to Petersburg (Leningrad) to reorganize and expand the Russian meteorological service and the entire station network of the Russian Empire. Wladimir Köppen was one of his students.

[41] See biographical note on Hann in Appendix.

to the foehn of the Alps and quickly consumes snow—yet in this case it is not possible to think of a heated mainland as its place of origin.[42]

From his evaluation of the Greenland data and foehn observations in the Alps, Hann concluded that the foehn was a local phenomenon and that its salient feature was descending air associated with compression and warming and a decrease in relative humidity. Consideration of adiabatic temperature changes made it unnecessary to assume that the foehn wind was endowed with high temperatures at its place of origin in the upper strata of the atmosphere:

> Only during the descent into the lower strata, where [the air] comes under higher pressure, warming takes place due to decrease in volume according to known physical laws. A parcel of air of the equatorial current, brought quickly from great altitudes under the higher atmospheric pressure along the earth surface and compressed accordingly, should appear relatively very dry because of the substantial temperature increase, even if it had been saturated with moisture at the former temperature in the upper strata.[43]

Hann argued convincingly that the foehn of the Alps must be regarded as a local phenomenon produced when moist air masses flow over high mountains:

> A dry current of air forced to ascend to the altitude of the summits of the Bernese Alps (11–12000 feet [3400–3700 m]), for example, cools about 25°R [31.3°C]; upon descent on the other side back to its previous level, a warming of equal amount will take place. In case of a moist current of air the cooling would amount to only 16°R [20°C], and its temperature on the other side would be higher accordingly.[44]

The reduced rate of cooling and the condensation and removal of water vapor in the ascending branch of the current satisfactorily explained the extreme warmth and dryness in the descending branch. Hann found confirmation for his hypothesis in Reye's theoretical treatment of adiabatic temperature changes occurring in the atmosphere. Appointed meteorologist at the Zentralanstalt für Meteorologie in Vienna in 1868, the methodical Hann used every opportunity "to compare these conclusions, which were based on general physical laws and geographical analogies, with the pertinent observational data."[45] He published his results in the newly founded Austrian *Meteorologische Zeitschrift*. He had become co-editor of the journal during his student years in 1865, and under his leadership it soon developed into the most influential meteorological journal of the next several decades.

Initially, Hann's article did not escape Dove's attacks. In 1868, however, Dove made a complete turnabout in his position; having maintained for years that the foehn was a moist and warm wind, he implied that he could claim priority for Hann's explanation of the dryness of the foehn.[46] Hann readily admitted that, judging from early publications, Dove, the physicist, was indeed well acquainted with atmospheric convection and Poisson's equation and could certainly have applied

---

[42] Hann (1866), *op. cit.*, p. 260.
[43] *Ibid.*, p. 261.
[44] *Ibid.*
[45] Hann. "Der Föhn in den österreichischen Alpen," *Wien. Met. Zeits.*, **2** (1867), p. 433.
[46] As quoted by Wild (1868), *op. cit.*, p. 15.

these concepts toward an explanation of the foehn. It is remarkable, Hann noted, reminiscing about the controversy in 1885,

> . . . that he made no use of it at all. The Dove of the years before the mid-1850's was an entirely different [man] than the later [Dove], not yet limited by his own theories. It can hardly be disputed that Dove's completely non-physical theories retarded the progress of meteorology for a long time.[47]

Wild and other Swiss meteorologists hastened to give their support to Hann's explanation of the foehn.[48] Further synoptic investigations showed that the foehn usually occurs with high pressure to the south of the Alps and a low pressure system over northern Europe. Under such conditions moist equatorial currents moved across the Alps from south to north toward the region of lower pressure. This supported Hann's hypothesis that the foehn winds, which arrived dry and warm in the valleys, must have been moist and colder and accompanied by precipitation at the southern side of the Alps.[49]

Hann soon found other highly authoritative support of his view on the foehn. In 1865, in a short passage of his popular lecture on ice and glaciers, the celebrated physicist H. v. Helmholtz, who had always shown an interest in the weather conditions of the Alps, applied the principle of adiabatic change to the ascent and descent of moist air in regard to the foehn problem.[50] Unfortunately, as Hann remarked in 1885, Helmholtz' lecture appears to have had no effect at all concerning the controversy about the foehn raging at the time of his speech:

> . . . probably, because the question of the foehn simply did not exist for the scientific audience at large as well as for the physicist in a more narrow sense; thus this passage was not met with any special receptiveness; for the meteorologists, however, who may have read his speeches, the suggestion was too short and too general, as to give them the incentive for the formulation of a theory of the foehn.[51]

It was largely due to Hann's personal efforts that the new physical explanation of the foehn based on the principle of adiabatic change was accepted. Hann publicized the physical principles involved and provided further observational support.[52] The

---

[47] Hann, "Einige Bemerkungen zur Entwicklungsgeschichte der Ansichten über den Ursprung des Föhn," *Met. Zeits.*, **2** (1885), p. 396. See also pp. 395–396, where Hann quotes from Dove's famous Habilitationsschrift, *Die Verbreitung der Wärme auf der Erdoberfläche der Erde* (Berlin, 1852).

[48] Wild (1867), *op. cit.*, 26–27.

[49] *Ibid.*, 22–24; R. Billwiller, "Mittheilungen über den Föhn," *Mitteilungen der Naturforschenden Gesellschaft Zürich, Vierteljahresschrift*, **21** (1876), 111–113 and *Wien, Met. Zeits.*, **13** (1878), p. 317; Hann, "Neuere Arbeiten über den Föhn," *Wien. Met. Zeits.*, **3** (1868), 241–249.

[50] H. v. Helmholtz, "Ueber Eis und Gletscher," *Vorträge und Reden*, Vol. 1 (Braunschweig, 1884), 194–195. Hann remarked in "Neuere Arbeiten . . ." (1868), p. 294; "I did not regard it [explanation of the foehn process] as novel, for it appeared so simple and obvious to me that I had to suspect to find it stated in one place or another. Indeed, I repeatedly found similar views (although very implicit) . . . and while proof reading my article I obtained the speech of Helmholtz."

[51] Hann, "Einige Bemerkungen . . ." (1885), p. 396; Hann showed by means of extensive quotations that Espy had a clear understanding of the foehn process.

[52] Hann, "Die Gesetze der Temperatur-Änderung in aufsteigenden Luftströmungen und einige der wichtigsten Folgerungen aus denselben," *Wien, Met. Zeits.*, **9** (1874), 321–329, 337–346; translated by Cl. Abbe in his first collection, *Smiths. Inst., Annual Report, 1877*, 397–418. When recalling the earlier

complete agreement of observations with this explanation stood out as a beautiful confirmation of the theory of adiabatic change.

Recalling the work of Espy, it becomes clear how much had been achieved during these few years since 1860. Since observations from the free atmosphere were sparse and unreliable at Espy's time, his conclusions on adiabatic change for the most part had rested on evidence obtained from laboratory experiments. Espy's explanation of the foehn on the basis of adiabatic change, for example, differed significantly from Hann's precise physical statements, theoretical backing and abundant observational evidence. It was this kind of successful application of the first law of thermodynamics, as demonstrated in the foregoing studies of ascending and descending motion, that paved the way for its further fruitful use in meteorology. These studies were the prerequisite for a formulation of a thermal theory of cyclones that went beyond the statements of Espy and his followers and showed some degree of theoretical development. We will now consider the recasting of the thermal theory around 1870.

---

work of Reye and Peslin, Hann's discussions were not always original; it must be emphasized, however, that they were more influential than prior publications on the subject and that they helped to establish Hann's position as a leading meteorologist of his time. Later (Chapter 5) it will be seen that observations and arguments involving a comparison of adiabatic temperature changes in ascending and descending currents of air entailed serious consequences for the thermal theory. It was only appropriate that Hann, who had done so much to clarify the physics of descending motion in the foehn, was also instrumental in clarifying the implications of descending motions for the theory of cyclones and anticyclones.

Chapter

4 Emergence of the Thermal Theory of Cyclones

4.1 INTRODUCTION

Between 1867 and 1872, the hypothesis of the thermal nature of cyclones was enunciated independently by scientists in different parts of Europe: Alexander Buchan in England, Peslin in France, Henrik Mohn in Norway and Reye in Germany. Between 1876 and 1878, the hypothesis, generally referred to as the convective or thermal theory of cyclones, was reiterated and expanded by Cato Guldberg and Mohn in Norway, Hermann von Helmholtz in Germany and Ferrel in the United States. At the core of the thermal theory was the proposition that the formation and maintenance of cyclonic circulation systems depended upon the thermodynamic processes associated with the ascent of warm air and the condensation of water vapor.

According to the dates given, the emergence of the thermal theory might be interpreted as an instance of almost simultaneous discovery. Indeed, the history of meteorology offers few other examples where the same idea was formulated over such a relatively short period of time by so widely scattered scientists. The coincidence in the time of announcement of the thermal theory of cyclones, and its friendly reception and almost unanimous acceptance during the following decade by the community of meteorologists cannot be considered as truly accidental. It may be said that these events fit the often repeated observation that the time must be ripe for an idea.

The scientists who formulated the thermal theory during the 1870's approached the cyclone problem in three fundamentally different ways: 1) empirical studies of the nature and behavior of cyclones, prompted by the expanding use and improvement of synoptic charts; 2) theoretical investigations of the role of thermal energy in the energy budget of cyclones; and 3) theoretical studies in which thermal aspects of cyclone development were taken into account in mathematical cyclone models. In this chapter, we will trace the development of the thermal theory according to these three approaches.

We will begin with a summary of the advent of daily synoptic charts in relation to the establishment of national weather services during the 1860's and 1870's (Section 4.2a). This discussion sets the stage for the first comprehensive synoptic investigations of midlatitude storms in Europe by Buchan and Mohn around 1870 (Section 4.2b). Their work affirmed and extended certain results of Loomis' early synoptic investigations of the 1840's (see Section 2.3). Buchan and Mohn arrived at the conclusion that thermal processes were essential for the maintenance and propagation of cyclones. Mohn emphasized that two air currents of different thermal properties converge in a cyclone and he incorporated this observation in his empirical cyclone model.

The review of these empirical studies will be followed by a discussion of theoretical investigations of the source of energy in storms, which were carried out by Peslin, Reye and Helmholtz during the 1870's (Sections 4.3–4.5). Their works were directed toward determining the implications of the first law of thermodynamics for the cyclone process, and, in the case of Peslin and Reye, were built on their previous theoretical treatments of adiabatic processes in the atmosphere (discussed in Chapter 3). The three authors had only limited access to reliable synoptic charts. Yet, significantly, their works corroborated the empirical findings of Buchan and Mohn.

Finally, the thermal theory was further developed in the theoretical studies of Guldberg and Mohn and Ferrel during the late 1870's (Section 4.6). Guldberg and Mohn attempted to incorporate Mohn's earlier empirical findings into a mathematical cyclone model, by placing emphasis on horizontal asymmetry. Ferrel, whose indebtness to Espy concerning his view on the source of energy in storms was discussed in Chapter 2, extended his earlier kinematic description of cyclonic circulation and analyzed quantitatively how the horizontal wind field changes with height on account of horizontal temperature variations.

4.2 EMPIRICAL SYNOPTIC STUDIES

From its early beginnings the synoptic chart had been a powerful tool in the hands of meteorologists, stimulating interest in two directions: research and service. First, Loomis, in 1843, demonstrated the usefulness of the synoptic chart for clarifying and deepening the understanding of atmospheric phenomena. Since areas of low pressure appeared to be the true weather carriers on these charts, research efforts were concentrated on their description and the explanation of their formation and propagation. Second, there emerged in the 1840's and 1850's a parallel interest in the practical value of the synoptic chart. Ever since 1844 when the first telegraphic line was built between Boston and Washington, meteorologists began to press for its use for the rapid transmission and collection of data which would permit the construction of current synoptic charts. Such charts, it was hoped, would be useful not only for purposes of research but for the purpose of storm warnings and forecasts. First successes in this direction in turn intensified the interest of the public and governments in synoptic charts, and as a result government weather services began to be established which provided the necessary financial and organizational support. The development of the synoptic chart in relation to storm warnings and weather services in the United States and certain European countries will be outlined in the next section. The two subsequent sections will deal with empirical results derived from synoptic charts during the 1860's and 1870's, which played a decisive role in the rise of the thermal theory of cyclones.

a. The Beginnings of Weather Services and the Synoptic Chart

1) UNITED STATES

During the early period of weather charting, several systems of observation networks developed in the United States. The most important systems were those of Lieut. Maury, head of the Naval Observatory since 1844, and Joseph Henry, director of the Smithsonian Institution established in 1846. Maury's system was limited ultimately to marine observations. Espy's network of volunteer observers, initiated during the 1830's, was absorbed gradually into the growing system of the Smithsonian Institution. By 1849, Henry, who became one of the most successful promoters of geophysical sciences in the United States, had organized a telegraphic network for the transmission of daily meteorological observations from a selected number of stations. His weather reports and charts were published by a number of newspapers from 1854 onward, although interrupted by the Civil War in 1861. The remnants of the Smithsonian system were transferred to the federal weather service that was established in 1870.[1] The weather service was a branch of the military, the Signal Service of the U.S. Army, until it was transferred to the Department of Agriculture in 1891. Daily synoptic charts (Figure 12) and forecasts began to be published in 1871. At that time, with few observations from the western United States, isobars could be analyzed only in the eastern United States; temperature (isotherms were analyzed from 1872 onward), wind data and an indication of the appearance of the sky were given for each observation station.

2) NETHERLANDS

In Europe, the maritime and sea-faring nations developed a special interest in the possibility of storm warning and forecasting; their northern position and exposure to the sea made them particularly vulnerable to storms and dependent on

[1] M. F. Maury was an outsider to the highly influential group of scientists around Henry and Bache. Amidst a spirit of noncooperation, the two federally supported meteorological networks of Henry and Maury were never coordinated. In 1869 Cl. Abbe inaugurated a weather service for Cincinnati, Ohio. One of both Abbe's and Henry's cooperating observers, I. A. Lapham of Milwaukee, Wisconsin, initiated a petition to Congress asking for a national weather service. The federal weather service was approved in 1870. Abbe, who worked for the Weather Bureau for 45 years, made the first official forecast in 1871. Modest meteorological research was performed in what became known as the "study room," joined by Ferrel in 1888. For details see P. Hughes, *A Century of Weather Service* (New York, London,

the weather. In the Netherlands, A. C. Buys Ballot began studies using synoptic charts in 1852.[2] In 1854 he became director of the Nederlandsch Meteorologisch Instituut, which had been founded in accordance with a resolution of the first international conference of maritime nations held in 1853 upon the initiative of Maury. Buys Ballot was authorized by his government to publish telegraphic weather reports (1859) and storm warnings (1860). On his weather charts (Figure 13) he plotted wind directions and temperature deviations from normal. He indicated the distribution of relatively warm and cold air masses by different shading of areas with temperatures above and below normal; in this way, he noted, "the contrasts between elevation and diminution are sharply accentuated."[3] Upon examining the observations available from the rather small Dutch station network, he discovered in 1857 the important relationship between wind direction and speed and the barometric gradient. This relationship, which became known to a generation of European meteorologists as the Buys Ballot law (sometimes referred to as Ferrel's law in the United States), was widely used for the purpose of storm warnings.[4]

3) ENGLAND

In England James Glaisher organized a meteorological station network for the *Daily News* in 1848, and the meteorological reports appeared in that paper for two months in August 1848.[5] In 1851 a British telegraphic company published daily weather charts for a period of two months for the world exhibition in London. In 1854 Admiral Fitzroy, who had won fame as a seafarer and weather expert on his difficult voyage as Captain of the *Beagle*, was appointed head of the British Meteorological Department established by the Board of Trade. In 1859 meteorological data began to be transmitted by telegraph, and in 1861 Fitzroy began to issue daily weather forecasts in the *Times* and inaugurated a system of storm warning cones in the ports. In referring to weather charts, he soon began to use his own favorite term "synoptic chart." An example of his charts is given in Figure 14. He not only plotted wind, pressure and temperature data, but also introduced a set of symbols to depict the weather at each observation station. The ideas underlying Fitzroy's forecasts will be discussed at the end of Section 4.2c.

Paris, Gordon and Breach, 1970); R. Popkin, *The Environmental Sciences Service Administration* (New York, London, Praeger, 1967); and N. Reingold, *Science in Nineteenth-Century America* (New York, Hill and Wang, 1964).

[2] His first weather charts were published in 1852 in the *Nederlandsch Meteorologisch Jaarboek*, 1.

[3] Buys Ballot, "Erläuterungen einer graphischen Methode zur gleichzeitigen Darstellung der Witterungserscheinungen an vielen Orten . . . ," *Ann. Phy. Chem., Ergänzungsband*, **4** (1854), p. 564.

[4] Buys Ballot, "Note sur le rapport de l'intensité de la direction du vent avec les écarts simultanés du baromètre." *Compt. Ren.*, **45** (1857), 765–768. Buys Ballot found that the wind blows in general perpendicular to the pressure gradient and that the wind speed increases with increasing pressure gradient.

[5] W. Marriott, "the earliest telegraphic daily meteorological reports and weather maps, "*Quart. Journ. Roy. Met. Soc.*, **29** (1903), p. 124.

FIGURE 12. Synoptic chart of the U.S. Weather Bureau of 24 September 1872; from *Daily Bulletin of Weather-Reports*, War Dept., Office of the Chief Signal–Officer (Washington, Government Printing Office, 1873). Isobars are analyzed for every 0.1″ Hg and isotherms for every 10°F. A low pressure center is over Wisconsin. Winds, condition of sky and precipitation are indicated.

WAR DEPARTMENT WEATHER MAP.
SIGNAL SERVICE, U.S. ARMY.
Washington, Tuesday, September 24, 1872—4.35 P.M.
LOW
HIGH
REFERENCES
CLEAR
FAIR
CLOUDY
RAIN
SNOW
PUBLISHED BY ORDER OF THE SECRETARY OF WAR.
CUBA

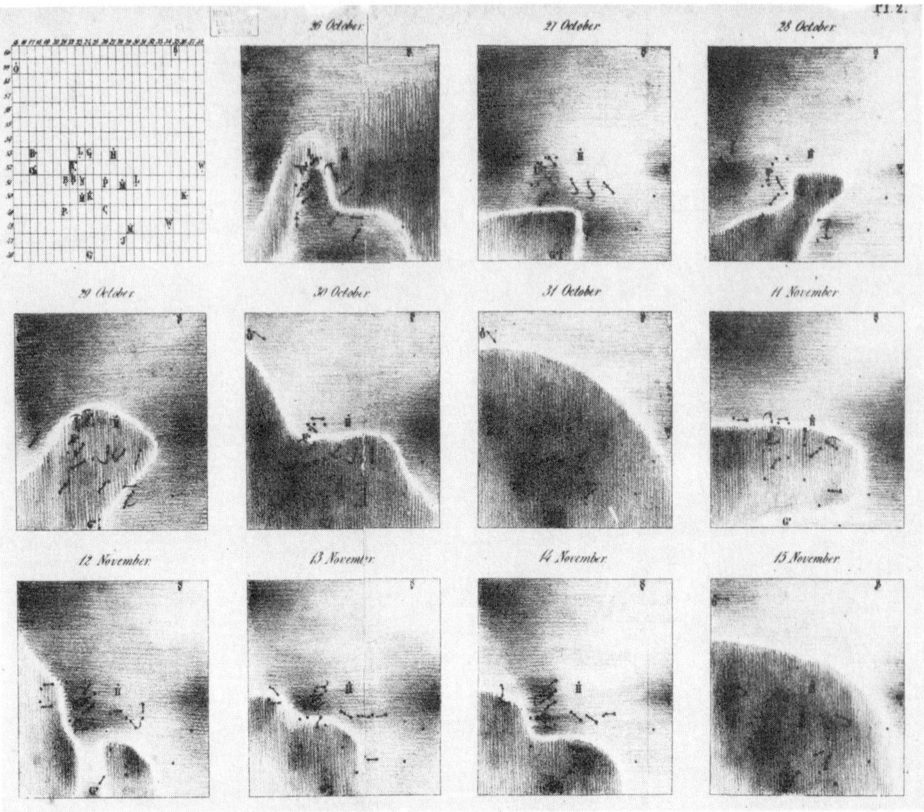

FIGURE 13. Series of weather charts from 1852 by Buys Ballot; from "Erläuterungen einer graphischen Methode zur gleichzeitigen Darstellung der Witterungserscheinungen an vielen Orten . . . ," *Ann. Phys. Chem., Ergänzungsband*, **4** (1854). Arrows indicate direction of wind; curved line at end of arrow indicates change in wind direction during course of day; horizontal hatching, temperature deviation below normal; vertical hatching, temperature deviation above normal. The shorter and denser the lines, the greater the departure from normal. Boundaries between warm and cold air are clearly defined. The charts cover most of Europe.

4) FRANCE

During the Crimean War, in 1854, the British-French fleet was destroyed by a storm in the Black Sea. The director of the Observatoire de Paris, Urbain Jean Joseph Leverrier, was asked by the French government to investigate the circumstances leading to this disaster. He found that the storm had been observed in the Mediterranean on the previous day, and could possibly have been predicted. In 1855 he was authorized to establish a storm warning system, and he consequently organized an international meteorological service.[6] He began to issue the *Bulletin*

[6] For a detailed description of these developments, see H. Landsberg, "Storm of Balaklava and the daily weather forecast," *Scientific Monthly*, **7** (1954), 347–352. The French astronomer H. Faye, who published profusely on cyclone theories, remarked pointedly with regard to the situation in France ("Trombes and tornadoes," *Am. Met. Journ.*, **7** (1890), p. 296.): "And the laws of storms were so completely forgotten seventeen years after (the publications of Redfield and Espy), at the time when the

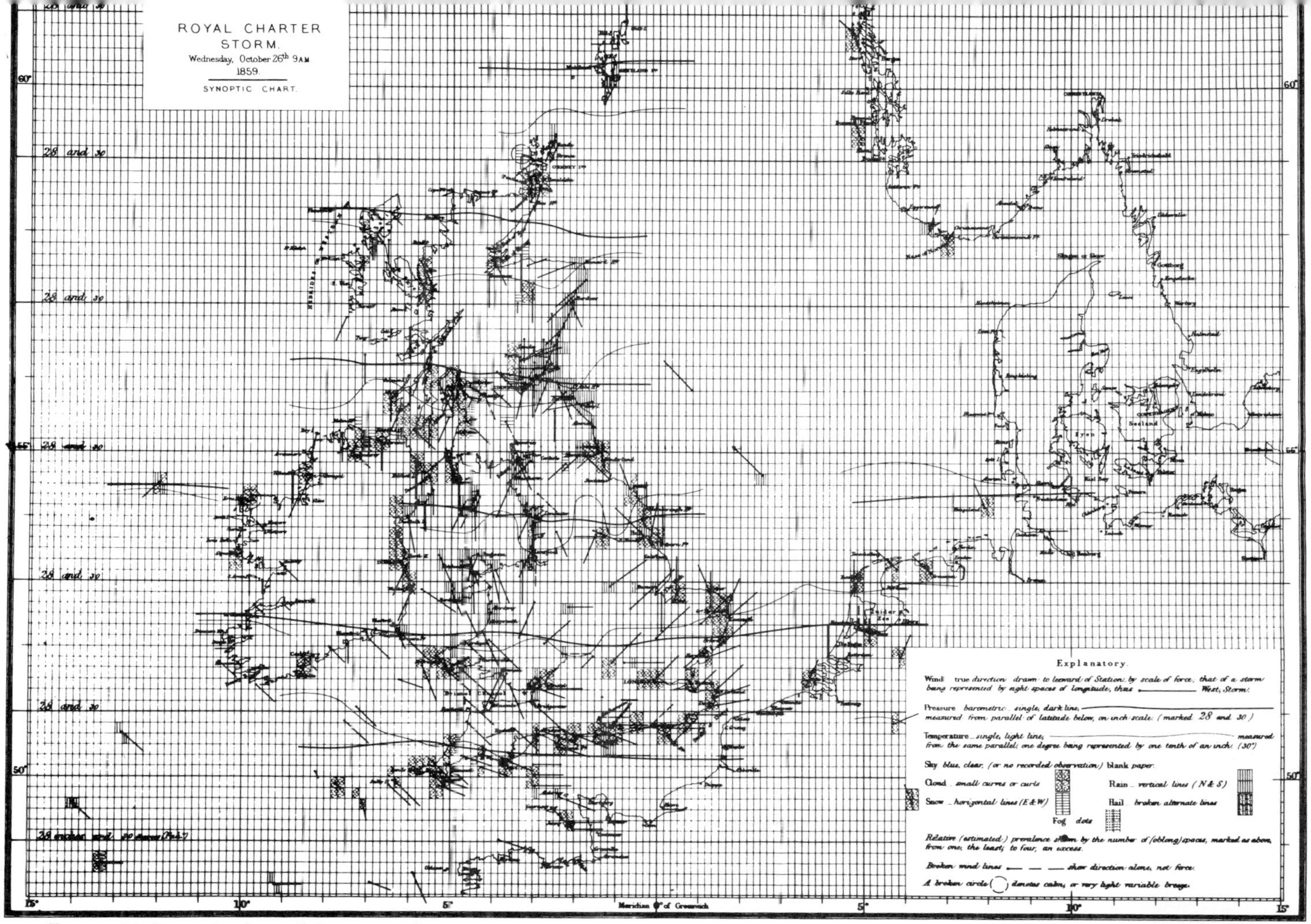

FIGURE 14. Synoptic chart of the storm of 26 October 1859 (in which the British vessel *Royal Charter* was destroyed) by Fitzroy; from Fitzroy, *The Weather Book* (London, Longman, Green, 1863). Thick lines are barometric pressure, thin lines are temperature. Short straight lines indicate winds and hatched boxes show weather conditions.

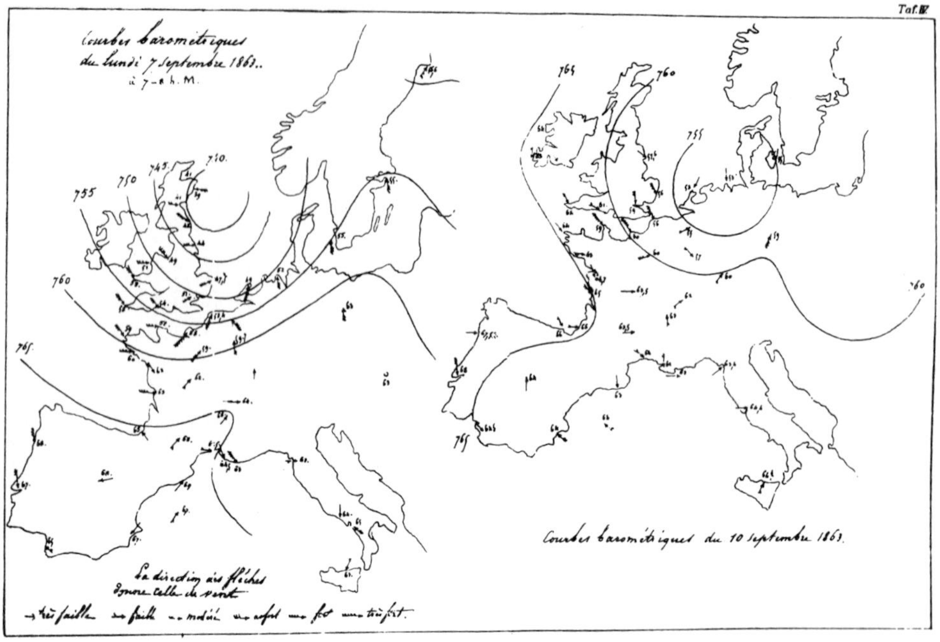

FIGURE 15. Weather charts of the *Bulletin International de l'Observatoire de Paris* of September 1863; reproduced from G. Hellmann, *Neudrucke von Schriften und Karten über Meteorologie und Erdmagnetismus*, No. 8, Meteorologische Karten (Berlin, Asher & Co., 1897). Solid lines indicate isobars (mm Hg); numbers at stations refer to barometric pressure; wind direction and force are indicated by arrows with feathers. The charts are for the 7th and 10th September 1863.

International de l'Observatoire de Paris in 1857 and daily charts in 1863. These charts depicted the pressure distribution and wind data (Figure 15). In the following year, the chart boundary was extended westward to cover the Atlantic, and a set of symbols was introduced to indicate the state of the current weather at each observation station.

5) FURTHER DEVELOPMENTS

Other European countries soon followed with the introduction of synoptic charts in conjunction with the establishment of weather services and storm warning systems.[7] Examination of the synoptic charts (Figures 12–15) indicates that the principles used in their construction were far from uniform. Buys Ballot's charts show only the temperature field and wind, the others give isobars and wind data and in two cases isotherms. The representation of current weather and the appearance

---

hurricane of November 14, 1854, struck our fleet in the Crimea, that it was a revelation to the whole world. What! Storms travel, and cross Europe with such velocity! We must study that, said Marshal Vaillant to the director of the Paris Observatory, and Leverrier, with his great intelligence and his no less great force of will, set himself at work, without suspecting that this storm had only followed the laws discovered long before in the United States."

[7] See also Table 1.

of the sky, conditions which are difficult to chart, shows greatest variation. It became customary at most weather services, when preparing weather reports and forecasts, to plot the various meteorological elements on separate charts rather than on one single chart. This procedure saved time, but it had the disadvantage that a certain amount of information was lost to the viewer. Synoptic charts prepared for research purposes, however, generally incorporated the maximum amount of information available.[8] They were thus constructed according to the principles established by Loomis in 1846, when he published his first synoptic charts: to present "nearly every circumstance essential to a correct understanding of the phenomena of a storm . . . to the eye at a single glance."[9]

During the 1860's, the charting of the weather provided a great challenge for meteorologists. As Sir Napier Shaw has pointed out, the coordination of measurements at different places and times and of different kinds into a picture that gave insight into atmospheric processes and their causes required more than merely the designing of instruments or the accumulation of observations.[10] One of the most important conditions for success was the uniformity of observations in every respect. Uniformity consequently became the guiding principle of cooperation between the meteorological institutions of the world. Pertinent rules and procedures were laid down at international meetings. The first meeting in Leipzig, Germany, in 1872 was followed by an international congress in Vienna in 1873.[11] Before these international efforts took place, it was a cumbersome and lengthy process to procure the necessary and comparable observations for the construction of reliable, large-scale synoptic charts.

b. Buchan's Synoptic Studies on the Role of Latent Heat (1868)

A superb example of early and laborious synoptic analysis is the series of synoptic charts for 1863 published by Alexander Buchan, secretary of the Scottish Meteorological Society since 1860 and chief contributor to its journal.[12] The difficulties he faced may be estimated from the fact that he quoted seventeen sources for the meteorological data collected from "135 places scattered over Europe."[13] The observations had to be corrected for time differences; pressure

---

[8] This is evident from charts of Buchan (Figure 16) discussed in the following. The famous Hoffmeyer charts, prepared specifically for research purposes by the director of the Danish weather service from 1868 onward, contained all information received by telegraph and mail. Köppen continued the edition of the Hoffmeyer charts after 1878, for selected periods, in the volumes of the *Archiv der Deutschen Seewarte*. These charts contain the same type of data information as modern charts, using almost identical symbolism.

[9] Loomis (1846), *op. cit.*, p. 164.

[10] Shaw, *Manual, op. cit.*, pp. 157–162.

[11] The first international conference of the seafaring nations with the intent to discuss problems of marine meteorology was held in Brussels, Belgium, in 1853 upon the initiative of M. F. Maury, then American naval lieutenant. For a detailed discussion of efforts in international meteorology see H. G. Cannegieter, "The history of the International Meteorological Organization, 1872–1951," *Annalen der Meteorologie*, Neue Folge, **1** (1963), 280 pp.

[12] Buchan, "Examination of the storms of wind which occurred in Europe during October, November and December 1863," *Trans. Roy. Soc., Edinb.*, **24** (1865), 191–205. See biographical note on Buchan in Appendix.

[13] *Ibid.*, p. 192.

observations were reduced to sea level; and temperature deviations from the mean instead of absolute values were used in order to eliminate irregularities due to the use of different instruments.[14]

Buchan's charts incorporated observations of pressure, temperature and wind and contained data on cloud cover and precipitation for a 24-hour period (Figure 16). Examination of 18 charts containing 32 depressions revealed a close relationship between the isobaric field associated with a storm and its wind, temperature and precipitation patterns.

> The temperature rose as the barometer fell, and fell as the barometer rose. Generally, the temperature in advance of a storm was above average, and in the rear of the storm below it. But if it was considerably above the average in advance of the storm, it was still above the average when the storm had passed, though lower than it was before.[15]

Buchan described the weather experienced during the passage of a cyclone:

> When the barometer fell, the sky began to be obscured, and rain to fall at intervals; and as the central depression advanced, the rain became more general, heavy and continuous. After the center of the storm had passed, or when the barometer had begun to rise, the rain generally became less heavy, falling more in showers than continuously; the clouds began to break up, and fine weather, ushered in with cold breezes, ultimately prevailed.[16]

This description of the sequence of phenomena associated with the passage of a cyclone seems rather vague, primarily, perhaps, because Buchan did not distinguish clearly between air currents and their boundaries. It is this distinction that makes Loomis' work and even Buys Ballot's rudimentary weather charts so appealing to the modern reader. Buchan most probably would have regarded the station network as too sparse to reveal the existence of distinct boundaries between air currents.[17]

Buchan's charts proved beyond doubt what Buys Ballot, Loomis and Ferrel had expounded more than ten years earlier: that the wind in a cyclone turned

---

[14] Buchan strongly advocated the use of observed barometric pressure values reduced to sea level in the construction of synoptic charts, rather than deviations from the mean, a practice which could result in distorted and misleading pictures of the actual pressure distribution (Buchan, *Handybook of Meteorology*, Edinburgh, Blackwood, 1867, p. 140).

[15] *Ibid.*, p. 200.

[16] *Ibid.*, p. 201.

[17] Elsewhere Buchan clearly distinguished two air currents of different properties and geographical origin. He stated emphatically in his critique of Dove's system: "That storms often occur between these two great currents [polar and equatorial] is undoubted; for in such cases the dry, heavy polar current, by flowing under the moist, warm equatorial current, and thus thrusting it into the higher regions of the air, produces that disturbance in the atmospheric equilibrium which constitutes a storm." Buchan, however, objected to Dove's view "that storms are produced by the mutual lateral interference of two currents of air flowing in opposite directions. It is very difficult to imagine how the polar and equatorial currents could be brought to affect each other as they flow in opposite directions, so that between them an atmospheric eddy or whirl 1200 miles in diameter could be formed rotating round its axis at the rate of 50 or 70 miles an hour" (*Handybook*, p. 163). For similar reasons Buchan must have rejected Fitzroy's storm model (although he did not state so). Buchan's book contains carefully selected, adequate references to older works, but Fitzroy's famous book of 1863 is ignored; Buchan did praise Fitzroy's introduction of the storm warning system in England (p. 9).

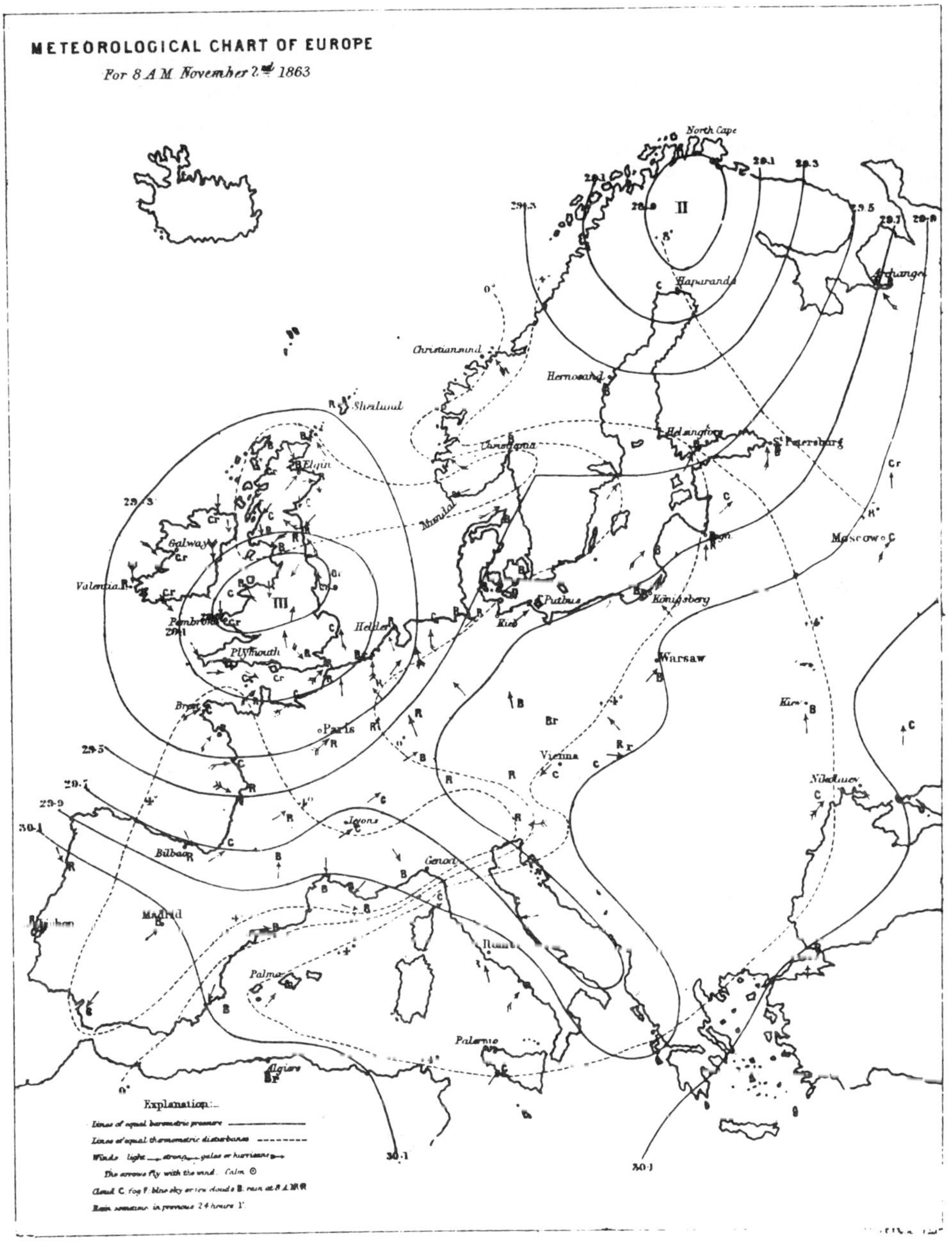

FIGURE 16. Synoptic chart of Europe (Buchan, 1865), from Buchan, "Examination of the storms of wind which occurred in Europe during October, November and December 1863," *Trans. Roy. Soc., Edlnb.*, **24** (1865). Isobars (mm Hg) are indicated by solid lines; isotherms (deviations from mean) are dashed lines; wind: calm ⊙, light →, strong ⇝, gale »›; C denotes clouds; B, clear or fair skies; F, fog; R, rain at 8 a.m., r, rain during the past 24 hours.

counterclockwise with respect to the cyclone center.[18] The vortical nature of a cyclone's wind field, as depicted on synoptic charts, constituted a clue for the explanation of the low pressure center. Along with Loomis and Espy, Buchan concluded in his *Handybook of Meteorology* (1867) that the low pressure center was maintained against the continuous inflow of new converging air currents by strong ascending currents in the central part of the storm and upper outflow. Buchan remarked

> . . . we are compelled to the conclusion that from a large area within and about the centre of the storm a vast ascending current must arise to the upper regions of the atmosphere.[19]

Upon examining these ascending currents as far as surface data and cloud observations permitted, Buchan began to recognize convection as essential for the formation and maintenance of cyclones. He thought that latent heat released in convective currents of moist air in the front part of a storm produced pressure fall and should be regarded as the "motive power" of storms:

> Now all observation shows that in front of storms the air is warm and moist, and it is there that most of the rain accompanying storms falls. Thus far observation; but may we not go a step further, and say that it is the heat of condensation into rain of the vapor of the warm moist air in front of the storm when it has been drawn up into higher regions of the atmosphere, which relieves the barometric pressure and thus forms the motive power of the storm?[20]

The formulation of this last statement illustrates Buchan's approach. Expressed in the noncommittal form of a question, it nevertheless constitutes a hypothesis that conveys the impression of an inductively arrived-at conclusion concerning the convective nature of storms.

In the introductory chapters of his book, Buchan took care to explain in detail the physical processes taking place during adiabatic changes of dry and moist air. As a former student of the physicist P. G. Tait in Edinburgh, Buchan was intimately acquainted with the first law of thermodynamics and its applications. Furthermore, he was aware of the efforts of some of the earlier workers on this subject in meteorology. He specifically quoted Espy in support of his hypothesis. Although he invoked the principles of thermodynamics more explicitly in his later publications than here, he never went so far as to call his views a theory. He regarded available observations as too incomplete to warrant the formulation of a theory. Lacking trustworthy facts a theory could remain only "vague and unsatisfactory."[21] This stringent view of total dependence of theory on facts was common during the

---

[18] Buchan presented this conclusion as diametrically opposed to Dove's view that the wind in a storm turns with the sun. Dove's statement, however, applied to a given place rather than the storm center and did not contradict counterclockwise rotation, at least in the southern part of a storm (see Figure 19b). This confusion of points of view illustrates the decline and loss of appreciation of Dove's system.

[19] Buchan (1867), p. 158.

[20] *Ibid.*

[21] Buchan, *A Handybook of Meteorology* (Edinburgh, Blackwood, 1868), p. 291.

second half of the Nineteenth Century and contributed much to the popularity of the synoptic chart. After the overthrow of the edifice of the old physics in mid-century, a great number of scientists doubted the possibility "of a systematic structure of science on deeper, not directly evident foundations."[22] Analyzing the scientific attitudes of these Nineteenth Century physicists, the physicist and historian of science Rosenberger remarked:

> Only the description of directly observed processes was considered possible by those physicists, and only a rule derived by induction from many observations was regarded as probably certain; under all circumstances, hypotheses on the causes of phenomena constituted for them only aids of construction for a better synopsis of the results and for facilitating the induction of laws; but in all cases they [hypotheses] were without any objective validity.[23]

In 1868, Buchan published a second edition of his *Handybook* that had quickly become the standard English textbook in meteorology. Knowledge had increased so markedly within the time span of a year that Buchan felt it necessary to recast the greater part of his work. On comparing the two editions one finds the chapter on storms greatly extended. By 1868 Buchan had become firmly convinced of the importance of the presence of water vapor in the atmosphere, and he concluded the chapter on its global distribution with the statement—using capital letters—that "THE CHIEF DISTURBING INFLUENCES AT WORK IN THE ATMOSPHERE ARE THE FORCES CALLED INTO PLAY BY ITS AQUEOUS VAPOUR."[24] A new study of European and American storms also strengthened Buchan's hypothesis of the convective nature and origin of storms.[25] In 1868 he stated firmly what he previously had only suggested:

> . . . the saturation of the atmosphere with vapour often over a most extensive region . . . must be considered as the necessary precursor of storm.[26]

Buchan did not claim to be in possession of a complete theory of cyclones. He believed that the detail and accuracy of weather charts had to be greatly improved for attaining this goal and he did his share in supplying the factual information that was necessary. He was in a position to do so since his work as the secretary of the Scottish Meteorological Society not only included meetings, discussions and the publication of scientific papers, but also the collection of data and the organization and supervision of the station network. In the ensuing years climatology increasingly claimed Buchan's attention, and he began the collection of data on a global scale. In 1868 and 1869 he prepared the first world charts of mean atmospheric pressure.[27]

---

[22] F. Rosenberger, *Die Geschichte der Physik*, Vol. 2 (Leipzig, F. Vieweg, 1884), p. 327.

[23] *Ibid.*, pp. 327–328.

[24] Buchan (1868), p. 55.

[25] Buchan, "On two storms which passed over the United States between the 13th and 22nd March 1859," *Scott. Met. Soc. Journ.*, **2** (1868), 198–213.

[26] Buchan, *Handybook*, 2nd. ed. (1868), p. 282.

[27] Buchan, "The mean pressure of the atmosphere over the globe for the months and for the year," Part I, *Proc., Roy. Soc. Edinb.*, **6** (1868), 303–307; Part II, *Trans., Roy. Soc. Edinb.*, **25** (1869), 575–637.

c. Mohn's Empirical Thermally Asymmetric Cyclone Model (1870)

The results of Buchan's investigations on the temperature and pressure distribution in midlatitude cyclones were soon confirmed and expanded by Henrik Mohn in Norway. While an observer at the astronomical observatory in Christiania from 1861 to 1866, Mohn developed a strong interest in meteorology and became instrumental in the establishment of the Norske Meteorologiske Institut.[28] In 1866 he was appointed professor of meteorology at the university and director of the Institut, which post he held until his retirement in 1913. Considering Norway's long coast line and its exposure to storms arriving from the Atlantic, Mohn thought it imperative to embark on an extensive study of cyclones.[29] Having studied the weather charts of Fitzroy and Leverrier, he choose Leverrier's method of analysis as the basis for the construction of synoptic charts. In 1870 Mohn published a major treatise, entitled *Det Norske Meteorologiske Instituts Storm-Atlas*, in which he proposed explanations of some of the most prominent features of cyclones.[30] This treatise formed the basis for his widely read and influential book of 1872, *Om Vind og Vejr*.[31] In his *Storm-Atlas* Mohn also presented a qualitative cyclone model, which he offered several years later in mathematical form in collaboration with his friend the mathematician Cato Guldberg (see Section 4.6).

As in the case of Buchan's studies, the quality of the weather charts was of great importance for the outcome of Mohn's investigations. There were four charts per day in the *Storm-Atlas*, two pressure charts, one chart depicting pressure variations and one chart of temperature variations. Water vapor content was analyzed on separate charts.[32] In addition, Mohn included in the *Storm-Atlas* a lengthy interpretation of these charts. He gave special attention to the contrast in meteorological elements between the front and rear portion of cyclones, such as is evident in his analysis of the storm of 7 February 1868 (Figure 17). The upper chart of Figure 17 shows a large barometric depression approaching Norway. The lower chart shows clearly a tongue of warm and moist air extending into the front part of the advancing cyclone. The warm air was also associated with extensive cloud cover and precipitation. On the basis of this and numerous other cases Mohn concluded that different types of air currents continuously converged in cyclones.

It is recalled that Buchan had used the temperature and moisture contrast between the front and rear of a cyclone in his explanation of the maintenance of cyclones. Mohn attached even greater importance to this feature. He concluded

---

[28] See biographical note on Mohn in the Appendix.

[29] Mohn, "Les lois des tempêtes," *Bull. Hebd. l'Ass. Sci. France*, **3** (1868), 53–56.

[30] Mohn, *Det Norske Meteorologiske Instituts Storm-Atlas*, (Christiania, Bentzen, 1870). Written in Norwegian and French.

[31] Mohn, *Om Vind og Vejr* (Christiania, Mallings Bogtrykkeri, 1872). The book, written in Norwegian, was translated into six languages, but not into English, and had gone through five regularly revised editions by the turn of the century.

[32] It appears that Mohn had also analyzed the actual isotherms and lines of equal water vapor pressure, but he did not publish these charts in the *Storm-Atlas*, except for one example of water vapor distribution. In his book of 1872 he introduced maps of water vapor distribution for all storms discussed. Three years later, in the German edition of his book, he added the analysis of the actual temperature distribution (rather than variations, as in the *Storm-Atlas*), thereby acknowledging the growing interest in detailed analyses of the observed temperature field in storms.

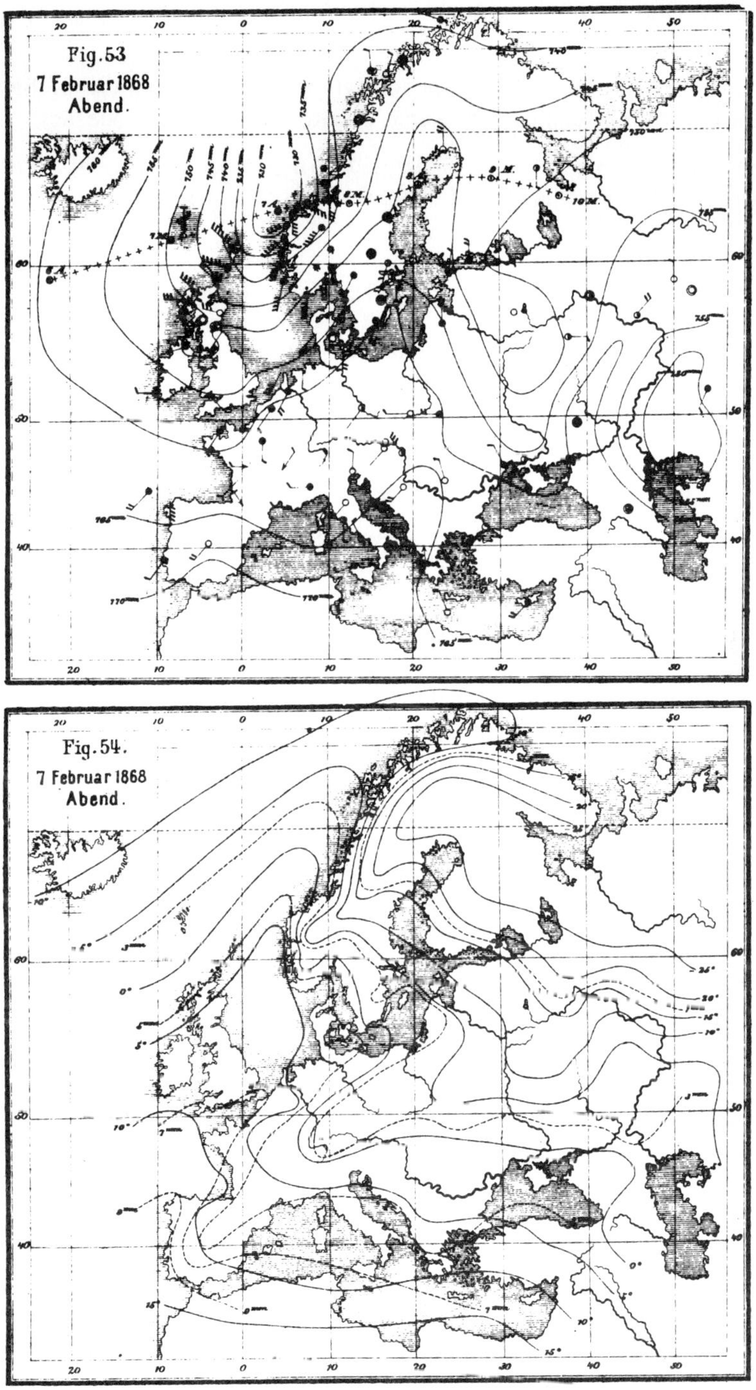

FIGURE 17. Synoptic charts of pressure, temperature and water vapor distribution over Europe in the storm of 7 February 1868 by Mohn, from Mohn, *Grundzüge der Meteorologie* (Berlin, Reimer, 1875). Top: Solid lines are isobars (mm Hg); arrows indicate wind direction. Wind force is given on scale from 0 (calm, circle around station) to 6 (orcan, 6 feathers); (●) rain, (∗) snow; degree of cloud cover is indicated by shading of station circle; ++++, path of storm center. Bottom: solid lines are isotherms (°C), dashed lines are lines of equal water vapor pressure (mm Hg).

that the propagation as well as the formation and maintenance of barometric depressions were the result of the same essentially thermal processes:

> The movement of translation of the center of the depression is caused by the contrast in properties of the currents [winds] between the front part and the back part.[33]

He added:

> The translation of the centers of depressions consists in an incessant formation through barometric [pressure] fall in the front part of the cyclone [mouvement tournant]. One has to assume that the same causes that are acting here are present at the formation of the origin of a depression center.[34]

In a more detailed description of this process Mohn outlined carefully the role played by atmospheric water vapor content. He proposed that latent heat released during condensation of water vapor in ascending currents of air had to be regarded as a major source of localized heating and therefore pressure fall:

> The winds blowing at points located to the east of the center are from south and south-east. . . . These winds thus belong to regions warmer than where the cyclone brings about its currents; they come from regions, we have seen, that form reservoirs for water vapor, and thus they are winds which . . . are most efficient for the production of low barometer when they ascend to a suitable altitude. . . . The air flowing at the back side toward the center of the depression comes from more northern regions; thus it is relatively cold and can hold only a small quantity of water vapor. . . . The winds at the back side thus lack most of the conditions which produce the low barometer and, at this side of the center, the depression can fill up on account of the inflowing air. The trajectories of the air currents grow tighter towards the center, and it is likely that here an ascending motion becomes established.[35]

Mohn summarized his conclusions graphically in horizontal and vertical diagrams of an idealized cyclone (Figure 18). The upper diagram shows the inward spiralling wind circulation near the surface and lines of equal temperature and pressure variations. The warm moist air entering the "front" leads to pressure fall and the cold dry air entering the rear causes pressure increase. The lower diagram, depicting the vertical circulation, indicates that ascending motion associated with cloud formation and precipitation takes place in the front part of the cyclone ahead of the center of low pressure.[36] This asymmetry of the vertical circulation with respect to the horizontal pressure distribution contrasted strongly with Ferrel's earlier cyclone model which featured the vertical circulation as symmetrical to the center of low surface pressure.

---

[33] *Storm-Atlas*, p. 21.

[34] *Ibid.*, p. 22.

[35] *Ibid.*, 20–21. The word trajectory is used in the French original. Sir Napier Shaw defined and firmly established the term trajectory for the actual path of the air in "Meteorological aspects of the storm of February 26–27, 1903;" *Quart. Journn. Roy. Met. Soc.*, **29** (1903), p. 240.

[36] Important information, such as the nature of the transition between two types of air currents in storms, was not included by Mohn in this simple model.

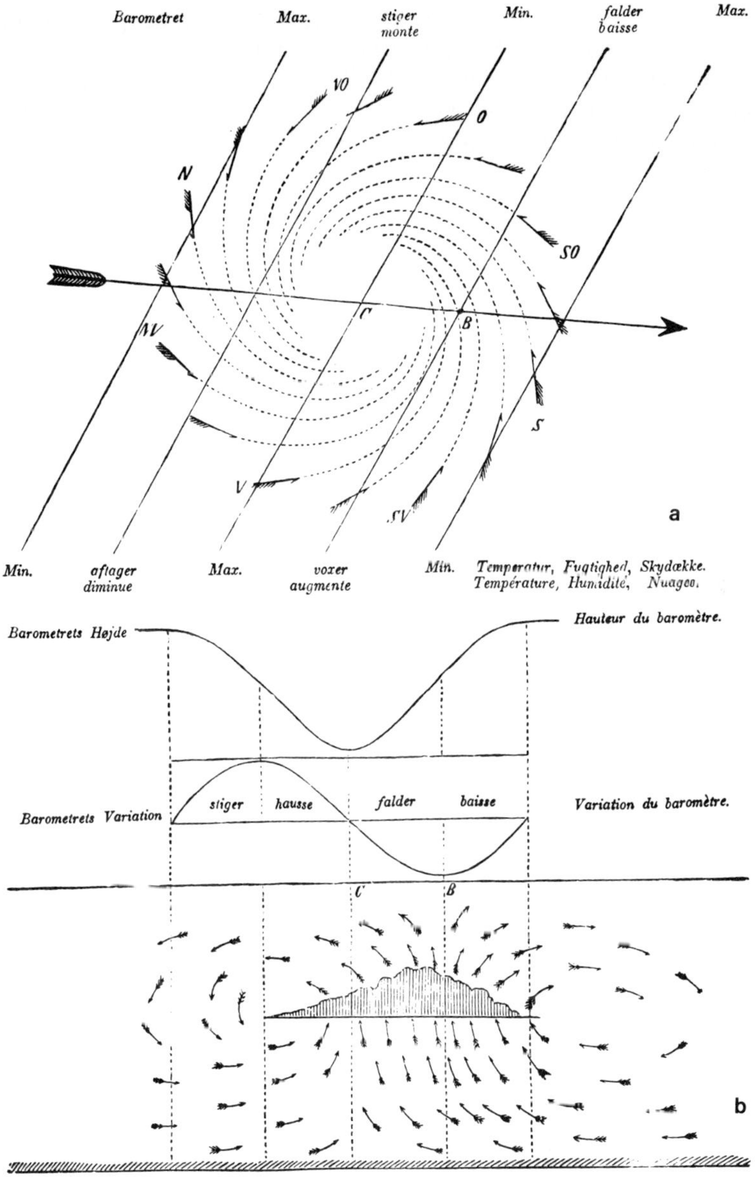

FIGURE 18. Mohn's empirical cyclone model (1870); from Mohn, *Det Norske Meteorologiske Instituts Storm-Atlas*, (Christiania, 1870). Top: field of surface winds associated with a cyclone; long straight arrow indicates direction of propagation; slanted lines indicate tendencies of pressure, temperature, humidity and clouds. Bottom: corresponding vertical circulation and curve of pressure and pressure variation.

In his discussion of the physical processes taking place in cyclones, Mohn pointed out the significance of the Scandinavian mountain ranges for the formation of precipitation and the deepening and retarding of cyclones. He explained the change in the direction of propagation and the gradual "filling up" of cyclones over continents by the smaller water vapor supply over land, i.e., small compared to the oceans. Over land the water vapor had to be carried to the center of the cyclone from regions further and further away.

According to Buchan, a large fraction of the cyclones arriving in Europe originated in the vicinity of Newfoundland. In agreement with modern views, Mohn considered this region as a natural breeding ground for cyclones because here "the warm air currents and the large quantity of water vapor from the Gulf Stream encounter the cold currents from the Baffin Bay."[37] Assigning an important role to the Gulf Stream in the formation of cyclones, he proposed that the centers of cyclones should be expected just north of the Gulf Stream so that the water vapor reservoir feeding the cyclone would be located in its southern part.

> The warm air and the vapors are transported by the winds from south and from south-west of the Gulf Stream to the eastern side of the cyclones [mouvements tournants], where the incessant fall of the barometer draws the center of the depression along the northern side of the Gulf Stream toward east. For that reason one should look for the greatest number of cyclones . . . in higher latitudes.[38]

Thus, Mohn seems to have noted that cyclones tend to propagate at right angles to the horizontal temperature gradient with higher temperatures to the right. This feature of cyclone movement played an important part in the further development of the theory of cyclones as discussed in Chapter 6.

Frequent references to contemporary meteorological literature in the *Storm-Atlas* indicate that Mohn was thoroughly acquainted with the work of his colleagues. His wide knowledge allowed him to select references that would support and strengthen his position, i.e., the publications of Buchan, Loomis and Peslin. As Buchan had done before, Mohn specifically identified the warm and cold air currents entering the cyclone with Dove's polar and equatorial currents.[39] Dove's schematic description of 1828 of the changes in temperature, clouds and precipitation during the passage of a storm over a single observation station was, in important aspects, the same as Mohn's derived from synoptic charts (Figure 19).[40] In Dove's graphical representation, series of observations recorded at an individual

---

[37] *Storm-Atlas*, p. 23.

[38] *Ibid.*

[39] *Ibid.*, p. 18. Later in the text (p. 23), Mohn also acknowledged that Dove's "Drehungsgesetz" (law of the "turning of the wind") applied to the southern part of the cyclonic circulation. This reference to Dove may serve as an illustration that Dove's views were not yet entirely erased from meteorological memories.

[40] Figure 19a was first published by Dove in 1828 and again in 1837 in *Meteorologische Untersuchungen* (Berlin, Sanders), with description, on pp. 140–141; it was not used in the second edition of Dove's *Gesetz der Stürme*. With regard to transitions between air currents, Dove remarked in this second edition [transl. by Scott, *The Laws of Storms* (London, Longman, Green, 1862), 215–216]: "It follows on account of colder winds commencing at low levels on the west side, that commencement of wind, formation of clouds, precipitation as rain or snow and rising of the barometer will coincide, and frequently the wind will start before the other phenomena; on the east side, on the other hand, cloud formation will be earlier than the wind noticeable below. Cloud formation proceeds from lower to upper strata on the west side, from upper to lower strata on the east side. The end of cloud formation, when the northern wind becomes more and more dominant, is called the breaking of clouds . . ."

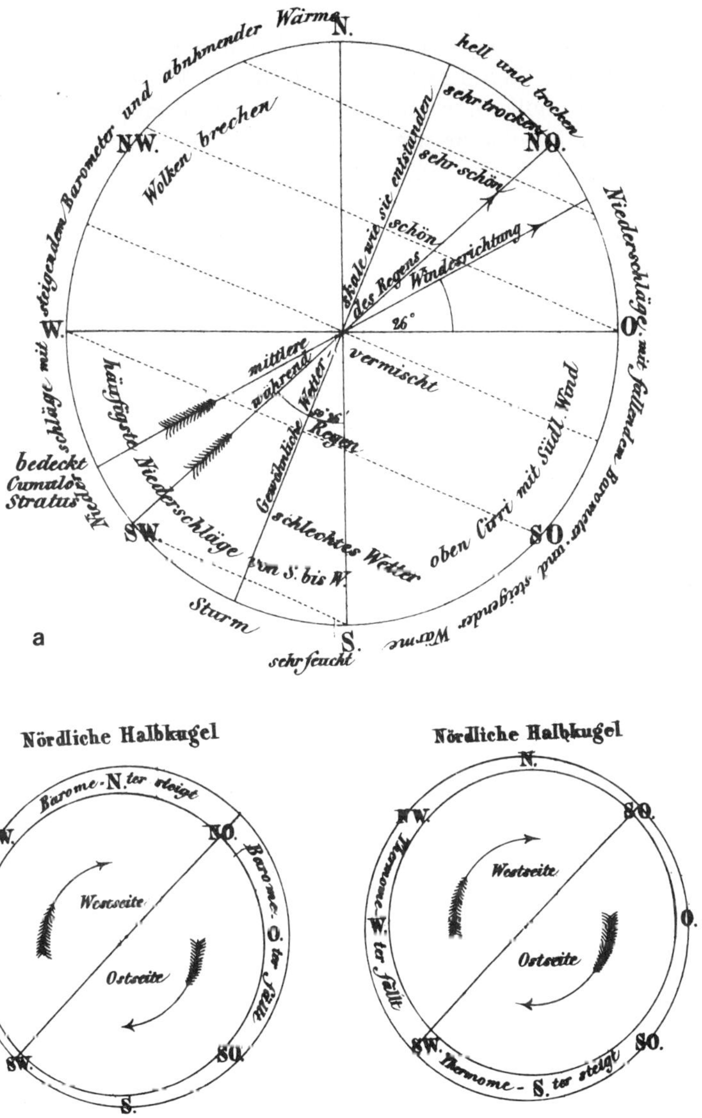

FIGURE 19. Wind roses of single observation stations during passage of storm in Northern Hemisphere according to Dove. (a) Wind rose for changes in temperature, pressure, clouds and precipitation during passage of storm; from "Ueber den Zusammenhang der Hygrometeore mit den Veränderungen der Temperatur und des Barometers," *Ann. Phys. Chem.*, **13** (1828). (b) Wind roses for changes in pressure (left) and temperature (right) during passage of storm; from *Meteorologische Untersuchungen* (Berlin, Sanders, 1837).

station were summarized, i.e., the arrows indicate the locally observed veering of the wind rather than direction of circulation with respect to the storm center. It is significant that both Mohn and Dove emphasized the role of different air currents and their characteristics in their empirical storm models. This similarity in their ideas reflected, of course, the undeniable and obvious fact that southerly winds in Europe are most often warm and moist and that northerly winds normally are relatively cool and dry. In contrast to Dove, however, Mohn did not view the origin and propagation of midlatitude cyclones as a result of the mechanical conflict of these two currents; instead, he stressed that the inflow of air currents of different thermal properties was responsible for the continuous reformation of the cyclone in advance of its center. He proposed that the entire process was analogous to the propagation of a wave. Mohn's work set the stage for investigations dealing with the role of thermal contrasts in the formation and propagation of cyclones.

Mohn's emphasis on physical processes might explain the fact that he did not refer to Fitzroy's storm model of 1863, which so beautifully illustrated the confluence of polar and tropical air currents in vortical storms and which for that reason has often been quoted as a forerunner of the polar front theory of cyclones. In order to clarify this point, a brief discussion of Fitzroy's storm model (Figure 20) is necessary.

Fitzroy was perhaps the most famous follower of Dove. Their admiration was mutual, for Dove dedicated his major work, *Gesetz der Stürme*, to Fitzroy. By 1863, when Fitzroy published his *Weather Book* containing his storm model, it was, of course, well established that midlatitude storms formed vortices; thus Fitzroy simply disregarded Dove's proposition that storms were normally associated with linear currents of air, but he retained the concept of polar and tropical currents of air. Taking into account the influence of the earth's rotation, Fitzroy concluded that

> currents from a pole move towards the equator and towards the west also, . . . and those from the equator move towards the east while going towards a pole. Their mutual approach occasions a movement of the intermediate air, rotary, in one direction only.[41]

In Figure 20, the straight arrows indicate the average direction of polar and equatorial currents as defined by Dove. Several cyclonic vortices are shown at different stages of development. The vortex over the British Channel is based on Fitzroy's analysis of the so-called *Royal Charter* storm of 26 October 1859 (see Figure 14) in which the *Royal Charter* was wrecked. Mohn apparently regarded Fitzroy's model (and for that matter Dove's system) and the system of the "new" meteorology as mutually exclusive, even though the concept of air currents was a key element in both of them. Thus, whereas Dove and Fitzroy regarded storms solely as the result of the mechanical interference of the two currents, this mode of thinking was alien to Mohn who treated the cyclonic process as a problem of dynamics. Aside from alluding to the mechanical force of the wind in the two major currents, Fitzroy said nothing about the source of energy in storms, or energy conversions. To him that question was irrelevant. In fact, Fitzroy's book was one of the last major meteorological treatises that did not incorporate the new concepts of energy conservation and conversion. Fitzroy also did not incorporate Espy's

---

[41] *Weather Book*, p. 63. Although Fitzroy referred to Ferrel's work in several places—Dove had quoted Ferrel as early as 1861—Fitzroy had only a limited understanding of the effect of the deflecting force of the earth's rotation. Apparently, the importance of Ferrel's work was sensed to a certain degree but not clearly understood at the time.

FIGURE 20. Fitzroy's storm model, illustrating the meeting of polar and tropical currents, from *The Weather Book* (London, Longman, Green, 1863). Blue refers to polar air; yellow to tropical air; straight arrows indicate average directions of polar and tropical currents. According to Fitzroy, features on the map may be regarded as illustrative of the *Royal Charter* storm of 26 October 1859 (see synoptic chart in Figure 14).

explanation of precipitation by adiabatic cooling in rising currents of air. In contrast, one of Mohn's principal aims was to promote the new physical basis of meteorology. Viewing this "new" meteorology as a rather abrupt break with the past, he made no attempt to include in his book a discussion of the earlier mechanical tradition of storm theories.[42]

[42] Mohn, *Grundzüge der Meteorologie* (Berlin, Reimer, 1875), Preface.

4.3 EARLY STUDIES OF THE ENERGETICS OF STORMS: PESLIN (1868)

The convective or thermal theory of cyclones was almost universally accepted during the 1870's. A combination of two factors appeared to provide it with solid support. First, Buchan and Mohn furnished convincing empirical evidence, derived from the examination of the most complete and meticulously evaluated collection of observations summarized in synoptic charts. Second, almost simultaneously with Buchan's and Mohn's studies, Peslin and Reye (Section 4.4) published important theoretical investigations that supported the thermal theory. Their conclusions were corroborated and extended by Helmholtz (Section 4.5). Significantly, these three authors, Peslin, Reye and Helmholtz, derived their results largely on the basis of physical reasoning without the benefit of daily synoptic charts.

The development of the laws of adiabatic change formed only the introduction to Peslin's paper of 1868 discussed in Section 3.2. Its main purpose, as the title "Sur les mouvements généraux de l'atmosphère" suggested, was the investigation of large-scale atmospheric motions with emphasis on midlatitude cyclones. Peslin first defined what he regarded as the crucial problem that any cyclone theory must address. He noted that the explanation of the center of low pressure and the wind field (essentially questions about mechanics and kinematics) had formerly been regarded of paramount importance, and that now, under the impact of the law of conservation of energy, emphasis had shifted to aspects of dynamics and energetics. Accordingly, Peslin acknowledged that contemporary theory, i.e., French theory, appeared to explain satisfactorily the barometric depressions which accompanied cyclones, as well as the inward motion towards the center of the cyclone, but he emphasized that this was not enough.[43] It was equally important, he argued, to investigate the energy balance requirements of a cyclone and, in particular, the source for the kinetic energy of the winds continuously dissipated by friction:

> But the current theory of storms [tempêtes], which connects all the known facts, is incomplete from one point of view: it does not give an account of the causes that develop and maintain the cyclone [mouvement tournant] in the atmosphere. The storm is always accompanied by a great display of kinetic energy [forces vives]. . . . This mechanical power of the storm is used up, in proportion to its propagation, by the effects of all the resistances which the terrestrial surface and that of the ocean set up against the motion of the air; it is necessary, however, that it creates and assimilates new kinetic energy along its path; it is necessary that the propagation of the storm in the terrestrial

---

[43] The prominent French meteorologist Edme Hippolyte Marié-Davy, for example, proposed in 1866 that a storm consisted of a large rotating air disc at some altitude. Centrifugal forces, resulting in outflow of air and subsequent diminution of pressure at the center, were supposed to be compensated by inflow of air at the lower and upper end of the cyclone axis. In the second edition of his popular textbook, Marié-Davy acknowledged that in addition "the condensations of water vapor . . . are the source of a special motive force;" *Météorologie Générale* (Paris, G. Masson, 1877), 226–227. The influential astronomer Hevré Faye for over three decades defended a theory of cyclones according to which cyclones form in the upper strata of the atmosphere. Kinetic energy supposedly was propagated downward by descending motion accompanied by gyration around a vertical axis. See Faye's numerous articles in the *Comp. Ren.* from the 1860's onward, and *Nouvelle Étude sur les Tempêtes, Cyclones, Trombes ou Tornadoes* (Paris, Gauthier-Villars, 1897), 140 pp.

atmosphere gives rise to the development of motive power equivalent to the frictional forces . . . It is from this point of view that I will attempt to complete the theory of storms: I will search for those conditions which must be fullfilled in that the movement of the atmosphere, as determined by the storm, gives rise to motive power.[44]

Peslin proposed to solve this problem by clarifying the effect of variations in the vertical temperature gradient on vertical and horizontal motions. As discussed previously, Peslin established the criteria of stability regulating the development of vertical motions. The employment of these criteria allowed him to ascertain the sign of vertical accelerations—whether increasing or decreasing—but not their magnitude. Peslin now attempted to calculate the kinetic energy that would be generated once vertical motion had commenced in an unstable atmospheric stratification. This was a complex problem. Espy's attempts to estimate the magnitude of vertical motions solely on the basis of surface pressure differences between the column of ascending air in the central part of the storm and the surrounding area had yielded the astonishing and obviously unrepresentative value of 240 feet per second (73 m s^{-1}) for a one inch (34 mb) barometric depression.[45] Obviously, estimates of vertical motions had to be related more intimately to the temperature conditions of the warm rising air and the cooler surrounding air.

Peslin simplified the problem by applying what is now referred to as the parcel method. Quantifying the qualitative arguments used in stability considerations, he introduced the energy balance equation in differential form; setting changes of the kinetic energy of a parcel of air equal to the sum of changes in gravitational potential energy and the work done by the pressure force, he obtained

$$m \frac{d(w^2)}{2} = -mgdz - Vdp,$$

where w denotes vertical motion, m the mass, V the volume (mass/density), p the pressure, z the height and g the gravitational acceleration. This equation represents the first attempt to formulate an energy balance equation for a cyclone.

Peslin attempted to link mechanical forms of energy to thermal energy (which he regarded as the source of kinetic energy exhibited in storms). Assuming hydrostatic conditions for the environment surrounding the parcel (environmental parameters denoted by primes) he rewrote the above equation as

$$\frac{d(w^2)}{2} = \frac{dp'}{\rho'} - \frac{dp}{\rho}$$

and, using the equation of state, obtained

$$\frac{\rho_0 T_0}{p_0} \frac{d(w^2)}{2} = \frac{T'dp'}{p'} - \frac{Tdp}{p},$$

where ρ denotes density, T temperature and the subscript indicates environmental conditions at a reference level. Then, integrating this equation from the

[44] Peslin (1868), p. 309.
[45] Espy (1841), 304–308. Espy applied Bernoulli's equation in this computation.

pressure level where the parcel was entrained into the storm vortex ($w_0 = 0$ at $p' = p_0$) to the pressure level (p_l) where it was finally ejected, and assuming equal pressure for the rising parcel and the environment, he obtained for the kinetic energy per unit mass acquired by the rising and accelerating parcel

$$\frac{w^2}{2} = \frac{p_0}{\rho_0 T_0} \int_{p_0}^{p_l} (T' - T) \frac{dp'}{p'} = g \int_{z_0}^{z_l} \frac{T - T'}{T'} \, dz.$$

The changes in vertical velocity, and therefore kinetic energy, thus depended upon the temperature difference between environment and air parcel. Peslin's studies on adiabatic ascent of dry and moist air (Section 3.2) had shown that of all causes, the release of latent heat during condensation of water vapor in ascending moist air was most effective in increasing the temperature difference ($T - T'$). He concluded that the thermal energy driving a cyclone must be attributed to the release of this latent heat. This implied a relationship between differential heating and the production of kinetic energy in the vertically accelerating parcel. He proposed that the thermal energy and the gravitational potential energy that became available to the parcel must be regarded as the source of the kinetic energy in storms and were sufficient to maintain them against frictional dissipation. This chain of thought was developed decades later by Vilhelm Bjerknes (1898) and J. W. Sandström (1916) whose circulation theorems related two-dimensional motions (both vertical and horizontal) to the thermodynamic cycle. Peslin's approach was strictly applicable for small-scale processes and did not allow him to make explicit statements pertaining to the field of horizontal motions associated with large-scale storms. A more suitable method of analyzing the energy budget of storms was eventually provided by Margules (1901–1906) as described in Chapter 6.

The integral in the energy equation for the rising parcel was difficult to evaluate. Peslin made his theoretical results practical by employing his thermodynamic diagram (Figure 11). This diagram made it possible to evaluate the integral by a simple graphical procedure. The kinetic energy available was determined by measuring the area between the curve of environmental lapse rate and the adiabat, moist or dry, followed by an ascending parcel in the altitude-temperature diagram.[46] Areas on the diagram where the rising air was warmer than the environment were taken to be positive, since they were proportional to the gain in kinetic energy of the parcel. Areas where the moving parcel was colder than the environment were denoted negative, being proportional to the energy required to lift the parcel to the altitude where parcel curve and environmental curve intersect.

Peslin found it difficult to obtain observational evidence for his view of the source of energy in cyclones. He deplored the fact that the synoptic charts then published by the French weather service did not contain sufficient information to either deny or confirm his theory conclusively. They provided information about

[46] In Peslin's diagram the areas were not strictly proportional to energy because of his choice of coordinates, altitude and temperature. For further explanation see Figure 11.

pressure, wind field and the path taken by a cyclone, but not about temperature and humidity, let alone observations of the free atmosphere (Figure 15). Had he known about Buchan's charts he would have found in them much to support his theoretical, yet speculative considerations. In 1868 Buchan's synoptic charts appear to have been almost the only ones that contained information on temperature (Figure 16). Mohn's *Storm-Atlas* of 1870 also contained daily temperature analyses, but inconveniently on separate charts instead of combined with the pressure and wind analyses.

Nevertheless, Peslin could point to at least one well known observation favoring his ideas. Although the atmosphere normally tends toward stable equilibrium, as he noted in the beginning of his paper,[47] the likelihood of atmospheric instability was considerably enhanced in air over warm ocean currents such as the Gulf Stream; "The mariners," he noted, "have said for a long time passed that the Gulf Stream is the father of the storms of the northern Atlantic," the explanation being that

> The atmosphere over the Gulf Stream is warmer and more saturated with water vapor in the lower regions than the atmosphere which extends either to the north or to the south of the Gulf Stream: A proof of this are the fogs which generally cover the Gulf Stream in winter. On the other hand, the upper regions of the two atmospheres must be almost in the same state, as the influence of the Gulf Stream cannot extend toward a very great altitude in the presence of the constant currents of the trades and the anti-trades. However, we find combined above the Gulf Stream the two principal conditions which favor the passage of storms and which maintain their motion: the rapid decrease of temperature and the hygrometric state of the air near the point of saturation.[48]

It is recalled that Mohn had also analyzed the role of the Gulf Stream in cyclone formation and development. Both Peslin and Mohn stressed that the air over the Gulf Stream was warm and moist. Peslin viewed as most important for kinetic energy production the vertical instability of the atmosphere due to vertical temperature and moisture gradients. In addition to this factor, however, Mohn underlined the role of strong horizontal temperature and moisture contrasts for the formation and propagation of storms. Peslin did not employ the concept of the meeting of air currents of different thermal properties in storms, perhaps because he lacked sufficient observations. The difficulties which Peslin encountered in generalizing and idealizing from only partially known conditions will also be seen in Reye's theoretical studies on the thermal theory of cyclones.[49]

---

[47] See Chapter 3.

[48] Peslin (1868), p. 319.

[49] This situation was pointedly described by A. Sprung (*Lehrbuch der Meteorologie*, Hamburg, Hoffmann & Campe, 1885, p. 273), when alluding to Dove's ideas as well as to the difficulties encountered by Ferrel, Peslin, Reye and others who had little or no access to synoptic charts: "For very long one has known that on the average the barometer in middle and northern Europe is lower with south-western winds than with polar winds." Without the benefit of the synoptic chart "it was natural to explain this difference on account of the higher temperature and the greater moisture content of the south-western winds originating over the ocean, assuming equal heights of the air columns. Presently one can see from almost every weather chart that the lowest pressure is not found *within* the south-western air current as proposed by Dove but along its edge, *between* the south-western and north-western current."

4.4 REYE'S QUANTITATIVE INVESTIGATIONS ON THE ROLE OF LATENT HEAT IN STORMS (1872)

The investigations of Peslin, Buchan and Mohn represented a new direction in European meteorological thought. Their theory on the nature of storms found immediate acceptance in Scandinavian countries and Great Britain, partly because of its appealing simplicity and the favorable evidence produced by surface observations, and partly, it appears, because there was no recognized authority present who would have effectively opposed it. Both Buchan and Mohn were directors of meteorological services. In England, Fitzroy had died in 1865 and as the attitude of the scientific community toward his forecasts had grown increasingly critical much of his reputation and esteem for his views on the nature of storms were lost.[50] The remaining members of the Meteorological Office and the meteorological committee of the Royal Society welcomed the results of Buchan's seemingly inductive approach to the cyclone problem. In France and Germany, however, where mechanically-oriented theories developed during the first half of the Nineteenth Century still dominated the scene, the thermal theory encountered strong resistance. Peslin's work in particular was met not merely with indifference but with outspoken hostility from the established French authorities on the subject of meteorology.[51]

During the 1870's, the situation in Germany became somewhat more favorable for the reception of the "new" meteorology. The "old" mechanically-oriented meteorology had been associated primarily with one person, H. W. Dove, whose overpowering influence now began to decrease. With advancing years this patriarch of German meteorology had developed a strong intolerance toward opinions that did not conform to his own. For example, he boycotted the use of the synoptic chart in the Preussische Meteorologische Institut and stressed instead the use of his own local (i.e., one station) method. As described earlier, this method was based on the assumption that weather characteristics at a certain location, including barometric pressure, depended principally upon the direction of the wind. Under the influence of Dove, therefore, research concentrated on statistical investigations of the relationship between the wind direction at a particular location and other meteorological variables, summarized in so-called wind roses.[52] In addition, Dove

---

[50] Shaw remarked in his historical article, "The march of meteorology," *op. cit.*: "Notwithstanding the vivid interest in weather maps, there were serious misgivings in the highest scientific circles about making forecasts from mere maps, without the light which the recording instruments might throw on the events of weather and their approximate causes" (see *Selected Meteorological Papers*, 1955, *op. cit.*, p. 236).

[51] The Observatoire de Paris and the Société Météorologique de France were essentially ruled by Leverrier, E. H. Marié-Davy, director of the Observatoire Montsouris in Paris since 1873, and the influential astronomer Hevré Faye.

[52] Examination of synoptic charts carried out elsewhere, however, appeared to indicate that the pressure distribution was the primary cause of all weather changes, including changes in wind direction. "Thus," pointed out Mohn, "the *primary task* of [the new] *meteorology* will be to establish the *laws* which apply to the *distribution and changes of barometric pressure*" (*Grundzüge* . . . , 1975, p. 169). The local method advocated by Dove produced, however, valuable knowledge; it was an important factor in the early development of the air mass concept, and continued to be used even by Dove's critics. Mohn, who made important contributions to the physical understanding of the role of air currents in the

accepted neither the vortical nature of midlatitude storms nor the baric wind relationship that had proved so fruitful in the prediction of storms.[53] The difference between the "old" and the "new" meteorology were so great that no compromise appeared possible. Thus, in 1875 Mohn remarked in the preface to the German edition of his widely read textbook on meteorology:

> The readers who are acquainted with the presentation of older meteorological textbooks, will find that the presentation of various subjects in this book differs from earlier ones. Wherever such deviations from older points of view occur, I would like to recommend that the reader examine the reasons for these contrary views and then choose between them rather than attempt to reconcile them; for this cannot be done.[54]

Dove began to transfer his meteorological duties to younger men during the 1870's (he did not retire officially until 1879), and German-speaking meteorologists began to free themselves from Dove's ideas that had dominated their thinking for a period of four decades. The turnabout came as quickly as the synoptic chart proceeded on its victorious advance. The Austrian weather service, out of reach of Dove's official power, introduced weather charts in the late 1860's. Hann, who was the first to object openly to Dove's writings, and others found that even superficial inspection of these charts disclosed severe contradictions to Dove's theory of the wind field in midlatitude storms. In contrast, little was known in Germany about synoptic charts. When the Deutsche Seewarte in Hamburg was founded in 1875, the first director, Georg von Neumayer, a zealous organizer and promoter of meteorological work, immediately "imported" the German-born Wladimir Köppen from the Central Physical Observatory in St. Petersburg to introduce synoptic meteorology. It was Neumayer who had persuaded Mohn to prepare a German edition of the textbook mentioned above. Publication of Mohn's book in

---

cyclonic circulation, devoted more than ten pages in his book to the discussion of wind roses of meteorological elements, as an introduction to the theory of cyclones.

[53] See Köppen, "Die Stellung von H. W. Brandes und H. W. Dove, 1820 und 1868, zum barischen Windgesetz," *Met. Zeits.*, **2** (1885), 415–416: ". . . between 1820 and 1863 is the reign of L. von Buch and Dove in meteorology, and how far Dove was removed from the views of modern meteorology until the end, stands out most clearly in his short note in the *Sitzung Beilage der Akademie* of Dec. 1868 . . ." According to this note, in 1868 Dove still opposed the vortical nature of storms in midlatitudes and continued to promote his linear current theory. On the other hand, he acknowledged that the pressure field associated with most storms consisted of closed isobars around a center of low pressure. It must be concluded that he did not fully appreciate Buys Ballot's law which described the interdependence of pressure field and wind. See also, Köppen, "H. W. Dove und wir," *Met. Zeits.*, **38** (1921), 289–292. It should also be noted that despite his official stand against synoptic analysis, Dove included synoptic charts depicting isobars in the third edition of *Gesetz der Stürme* (1866).

[54] H. Mohn, *Grundzüge der Meteorologie* (Berlin, Reimer, 1875), 1st German edition, Preface, vii–viii. In the early 1920's, after the appearance of the polar front theory of cyclones, Dove frequently was cited as a precursor of this theory with the implication that adherence to the study of polar and equatorial currents as defined by Dove would or could have led much sooner to the formulation of the polar front theory of cyclones. One of the first assertions of this kind may be found in O. Myrbach, "Die Polar-front und—Dove," *Met. Zeits.*, **38** (1921), 129–134. This interpretation, however, appears too simplified in view of the issues involved. Dove opposed the use of the synoptic chart primarily because evidence derived from them was incompatible with his meteorological system. Thus meteorologists were forced to make a choice between his system and the new synoptic approach, as indicated by Mohn. They chose the latter. Since the discoveries of the Bergen School of meteorologists emerged from the study of highly detailed synoptic charts, it may be argued that meteorologists made the "right" choice.

1875 considerably facilitated the introduction of the "new" meteorology in Germany.[55]

Under these circumstances, it perhaps was not surprising that in Germany the first effective refutation of Dove's theory of storms was founded not so much on observations as on physical reasoning. In 1872 the mathematician Reye, who had developed his conception of atmospheric processes independently of Dove's meteorological edifice, published the first detailed and carefully reasoned physical objections to Dove's theory of storms.[56] At the same time he attempted to replace Dove's theory with his formulation of the convective or thermal theory of storms. Reye's view of storms, based on his earlier theoretical investigations of adiabatic processes, found many followers among German speaking meteorologists.

By the 1870's the concept of conservation of energy had attained such prominence that, whenever possible, its implications for a theory were examined. Any basic contradictions that arose were regarded as making that theory untenable. Thus Reye felt, just as Peslin had, that the most important drawback of existing theories, including Dove's, was their failure to explain the source of kinetic energy displayed in storms:

> The main reason why all older views on the development and maintenance of whirlstorms [Wirbelstürme] do not satisfy us is that they do not provide a sufficient explanation for the enormous mechanical power exhibited in these storms.[57]

The German term Wirbelstürme (whirlstorms or vortical storms), which Reye employed throughout his book, applied to cyclonic wind systems of the tropics as well as midlatitudes. Reye noted that velocities in opposing currents generally were not strong enough to produce the high velocities observed in these storms. The kinetic energy associated with such currents indeed is generally not sufficient to account for the kinetic energy observed in cyclones. Scientists realized only later that such air currents, when of different temperatures, may store potential energy that upon conversion can account for the kinetic energy displayed in midlatitude cyclones. It appears that Reye excluded this explanation because he developed his theory for tropical cyclones where temperature differences are small, and he presented only a qualitative extension of the theory to include midlatitude cyclones. He suggested instead, after an exhaustive study of Nineteenth Century storm literature, that vortical storms tended to develop in regions of weak winds or calms.

Reye postulated ascending currents of warm and moist air as a necessary condition for the development and maintenance of vortical storms. Once the ascending current was initiated—and there must be certain conditions, he asserted, "which under favorable circumstances cause the first ascending of the warm and moist lower layers of air on a large scale"[58]—water vapor was condensed in the rising column and latent heat released. Since temperatures were higher in the

[55] W. Köppen, "Nachruf für Georg v. Neumayer," *Met. Zeits.*, **26** (1909), p. 405.
[56] Reye (1872), 151–159.
[57] *Ibid.*, p. 160.
[58] *Ibid.*, p. 137.

ascending air column than in the surrounding air and because of outflow from the column in the upper layers

> . . . the atmospheric pressure [at the bottom of the column] must be lower than all around. Air flows towards this place of rarefaction from all sides, yet following the existing spirals of the storm wind, first slowly then faster and faster, because it is driven by higher atmospheric pressure in the outer regions.[59]

Reye suggested here that inflow, or cross-isobaric flow, was taking place in the outer regions of the storm where the pressure gradient was only partially balanced by the deflecting force of the earth's rotation. Thus the inward spiralling air was accelerating. Reye then invoked the concept of the centrifugal force: as the parcel of air approached the center of the storm, the centrifugal forces became increasingly effective in establishing circular flow around the center of low pressure.[60] The gradual increase in the angle between pressure gradient and wind direction with approach to the center of the storm constituted convergence of air, and, assuming mass continuity, the air was forced to ascend. The ascending current continued as long

> . . . as sufficient quantities of water vapor are carried along to warm the air when condensed and thus to push it upwards; for the moving force in whirlstorms is that of the heat which is liberated during condensation of atmospheric water vapor. . . . This force makes it conceivable why cyclones occur preferably during the summer months and are most violent over oceans and in the hot zone; for here and during those months the lower air layers receive the largest amount of water vapor.[61]

Here, Reye referred to tropical cyclones. Reye thought it artificial to erect boundaries between different classes of storms because

> . . . one can arrange a complete series with regard to magnitude not only from whirlwinds and waterspouts to the larger tornadoes, but also from these to the true whirlstorms.[62]

Reye applied the term whirlwind to small-scale, rotating columns of air such as dust devils. He added:

> . . . the vertical, in most cases ascending air current is the primary cause in the whirlwinds and tornadoes, producing the inflow of air at the base, the decrease of atmospheric pressure, the rapid formation of rain and thunderstorm clouds, and the greatest mechanical effects: it is likewise in the whirlstorms.[63]

Reye thus proposed that vortical wind systems of all sizes were convective in nature. The scale size, Reye felt, led to significant but nonetheless tolerable

---

[59] *Ibid.*, p. 132.

[60] In some cases, Reye argued in his explanation of the so-called eye of the storm, the centrifugal force becomes so strong (as the wind speed increases towards the center) "that the inflowing air, even before it has actually reached the cyclone-axis, starts to ascend, thereby leaving a central area storm free, with calm or only weak and irregular winds" (p. 133).

[61] Reye (1872), p. 134.

[62] *Ibid.*, p. 130.

[63] *Ibid.*

differences between them in two respects, namely, in the wind field and in the stability of the air stratification. He acknowledged that in large-scale cyclones the deflecting force of the earth's rotation came into action and determined the sense of rotation in the storm;[64] he conceded that one cannot assume atmospheric instability to exist over the extended area of a large-scale midlatitude cyclone:

> while in the case of [whirlwinds and waterspouts] it is permissible and necessary to proceed from the presupposition of instability in the atmosphere, it is not possible to make this assumption for the many thousands of square miles of ocean surface that are affected by a large whirlstorm simultaneously or by and by. . . . However, it is permissible and necessary to assume that the lowest layers of air in the whirlstorm and all around are strongly impregnated with water vapor and, during the summer months, are relatively strongly heated.[65]

He thought that cyclones must move in the direction of moistest and warmest ascending air. Here he agreed with Mohn, whose *Storm-Atlas* he had studied, and he cited earlier supportive papers by W. Redfield, Alexander Thom and others.[66] Contrary to Mohn, however, and clearly because he lacked Mohn's synoptic experience, Reye viewed most midlatitude cyclones as an outgrowth of tropical cyclones. While Mohn regarded the Newfoundland area as a major breeding ground for North Atlantic cyclones (because cold and warm, moist currents tended to meet there), Reye felt that midlatitude cyclones often resulted from modifications of tropical cyclones, once their course had been inflected in the Caribbean from a northwest to a northeast path due to the influence of the Gulf Stream.[67] Reye attributed their loss of strength during this transition to the fact that less warm and moist air was drawn into the cyclone in higher than lower latitudes. In addition, the cyclone covered a larger area in middle and high latitudes than in the tropics.[68] This latter statement seemed to imply his use of the assumption of constant angular momentum, an important concept later applied quantitatively in the analysis of atmospheric motions.

The view that midlatitude cyclones originated from tropical cyclones entailed further significant consequences. Contrary to Mohn, Reye did not specify that the vertical circulation in midlatitude cyclones was asymmetric with respect to the horizontal pressure distribution, i.e., that the warm, moist air was ascending in the leading portion of the storm rather than the center. In analogy to the symmetrical

---

[64] Reye (1872), 137–138. Reye noted, "Without doubt, the vertical movement which arises in this way furthers the continuance and growth of the central rarefaction of air and hence simultaneously the duration of cyclones for weeks." Reye referred to several articles in the *Comp. Ren.*, **49** (1859) on the deflecting force of the earth's rotation. On pp. 658–660 and 685–693, this question is discussed by J. Bertrand, J. Babinet and Morin and C. E. Délaunay, and includes a review of the work of Léon Foucault and G. G. Coriolis.

[65] Reye (1872), p. 131.

[66] Redfield, "Remarks on the prevailing storms of the Atlantic Coast of the North American Seas," *Am. Journ. Sci.*, **20** (1831), 17–51; Alexander Thom, *An Inquiry into the Nature and Course of Storms in the Indian Ocean South of the Equator* (London, 1845), 351 pp.

[67] Reye (1872), p. 143. Here he was following Redfield and other meteorologists of the early Nineteenth Century.

[68] *Ibid.*, p. 144.

circulation assumed to take place in tropical cyclones, Reye assumed conditions for midlatitude cyclones resembling those of the convective theory as illustrated in Figure 1 or Ferrel's warm core cyclone model. Clearly, asymmetry was a feature that was introduced into cyclone theory largely on account of increasingly detailed synoptic experience.

Like Peslin, Reye attempted to quantify his theory in its most important aspect, *viz.*, the production of kinetic energy from thermal energy. In his 1864 paper he had indicated the possibility of computing the vertical velocities that could develop if the air stratification was unstable. The kinetic energy associated with these velocities could be regarded as a measure of the thermal energy converted. In an appendix to his book of 1872, he supplied the necessary equations and calculated a specific example. Like Peslin, he employed the parcel method for obtaining an equation for vertical accelerations. Whereas Peslin used his thermodynamic diagram for obtaining final estimates of kinetic energy production in conjunction with vertical motions, Reye developed an equation to make similar estimates.

The acceleration of the rising parcel, Reye argued, depended on the difference between the specific volume of the rising parcel, V', and the environmental air, V. The acceleration per unit mass of rising air, dw/dt, could then be expressed as

$$\frac{dw}{dt} = \frac{wdw}{dz} = g\left(\frac{V'}{V} - 1\right),$$

where w denotes the vertical velocity, t the time, z the height and g the acceleration of gravity. Substituting from the equation of state with the further assumption that parcel pressure equaled environmental pressure such that $V'/V = T'/T$, he obtained

$$\frac{dw}{dt} = w\frac{dw}{dz} = g\left(\frac{T'}{T} - 1\right). \qquad (1)$$

Reye assumed equal temperature T_0 for parcel and environment at the height z_0, and, with the assumption of equal pressure for the rising parcel and environment, he was able to obtain a relationship between parcel and environmental temperature based upon the use of Poisson's equation for the rising parcel and an assumed environmental lapse rate τ [see Reye's work on lapse rates (Section 3.2)] so that

$$\frac{p_0}{p} = \left(\frac{T_0}{T}\right)^{100[g]/R\tau} = \left(\frac{T_0}{T'}\right)^{\epsilon}. \qquad (2)$$

Reye approximated the vertical temperature structure by assuming a constant dry-adiabatic lapse rate for the environmental air and a saturation-adiabatic lapse rate for the rising parcel. Reye's analytical formulation of the vertical temperature conditions was more restrictive than Peslin's graphical formulation which allowed for differing temperatures in parcel and environment at height z_0 and for a varying lapse rate in the rising parcel (dry-adiabatic until the condensation level was reached and saturation-adiabatic thereafter).

A simple transformation of Equation (2) yielded

$$\frac{T'}{T} = \left(\frac{T}{T_0}\right)^{(100[g]/\epsilon R\tau)-1}. \tag{3}$$

Substituting Equation (3) into Equation (1) and considering that

$$dz = -\frac{100}{\tau}\,dT,$$

Reye obtained

$$\frac{w\,dw}{dT} = -\frac{100}{\tau}\,g\left(\frac{T}{T_0}\right)^{(100[g]/\epsilon R\tau)-1} + \frac{100}{\tau}\,g$$

and upon integration

$$\tfrac{1}{2}w^2 = \text{constant} - \epsilon R T_0\left(\frac{T}{T_0}\right)^{100[g]/\epsilon R\tau} + \frac{100g}{\tau}\,T.$$

Denoting the vertical velocity at height z_0 with w_0, the temperature being T_0, the constant of integration was determined as

$$\text{constant} = \tfrac{1}{2}w_0^2 + \epsilon R T_0 - \frac{100g}{\tau}\,T_0,$$

so that

$$w^2 = w_0^2 - 2\epsilon R T_0\left[\left(\frac{T}{T_0}\right)^{100[g]/\epsilon R\tau} - 1\right] + 2\,\frac{100g}{\tau}\,(T - T_0).$$

Expanding

$$\left(\frac{T}{T_0}\right)^{100[g]/\epsilon R\tau} \quad \text{or} \quad \left(1 - \frac{T_0 - T}{T_0}\right)^{100[g]/\epsilon R\tau}$$

into a binomial series, since $T_0 - T < T_0$, and retaining only the first two terms, this equation reduced to

$$w^2 = w_0^2 + \frac{g}{T_0}\,\frac{\epsilon R\tau - 100[g]}{100\epsilon R}\,(z - z_0)^2,$$

since

$$T_0 - T = \tau\,\frac{z - z_0}{100}.$$

With known surface temperature T_0, this equation[69] yielded quite satisfactory results for kinetic energy production associated with vertical accelerations in cases where the parcel method was approximately applicable, i.e., in cases of little mixing and entrainment of environmental air. Thus, "if the initial velocity [w_0] of the ascending air were equal to zero," Reye argued for the simplest case, "then its velocity for every thousand meter altitude traversed . . . would increase 13 meter [13 m s^{-1}]" for $p_0 = 1013$ mb and $T_0 = 30$°C.[70] Reye obviously referred to the vertical

[69] *Ibid.*, 227–230.

[70] *Ibid.*, p. 230. The coefficient ϵ depended on the water vapor content of the parcel, and thus assumed different values corresponding to different T_0 and p_0 at the saturation level z_0.

motions in dust devils, thunderstorms, tornadoes, and also hurricanes. He argued that for these phenomena the value of 13 m s^{-1} still was rather small:

> In reality, however, the initial velocity $V_0[w_0]$ of the lower air masses, which enter the ascending current of waterspouts and tornadoes over land, is much higher . . . in many cases it was gale-like and can be assumed to be 40 to 50 meters per second.[71]

Reye assumed here that the horizontal velocities of the inflowing air could be viewed as the initial velocities of the rising air. It appears doubtful whether Reye realized that typical vertical motions in midlatitude cyclones were more than two orders of magnitude less than his estimates.

Although he insisted that vortical wind systems of all sizes were convective in nature and derived their kinetic energy from buoyancy associated with the release of latent heat, Reye never attempted to analyze precisely how this principle would work in the case of large-scale cyclones of midlatitudes which may extend over a million or more square kilometers. Nevertheless, he chose the specific example of the great Cuba storm of October 1844 to show quantitatively that latent heat release can be sufficient to supply the kinetic energy exhibited in a tropical storm. His calculation represents the first estimate of kinetic energy production in a storm from actual data.

Assuming a storm radius of 100 miles, an average wind speed of 40 m s^{-1}, cross-isobaric inflow at an angle of 6°, 100 m for the depth of the inflow layer, and an average density of 1.29×10^{-3} g cm^{-3}, Reye calculated an inward mass flux of approximately 490×10^9 g sec^{-1}.[72] Again, using 40 m s^{-1} as the average wind speed, he obtained a value of 3.995×10^{18} g cm^2 s^{-2} for the rate of addition of kinetic energy to the storm volume per second. He showed that this energy production rate was equivalent to the thermal energy liberated during condensation of 1.5809×10^8 g of water vapor per second. If one assumes that the condensation rate equaled the precipitation rate, the latter would

> . . . result only in the insignificant precipitation of 17/100 millimeter or 1/16 line in the course of 24 hours. . . . Thus, also in this respect our explanation of whirlstorms fullfills all requirements.[73]

---

[71] Reye (1872), p. 230.

[72] *Ibid.*, 120–121, 160. Reye used here the value which Redfield had determined as the average for the angle of inclination (angle between isobars and wind direction) in the Cuba storm of 1844. This value of 6°, Reye maintained, "is certainly much too low." Nevertheless, Reye remarked, "despite this small angle of inclination of only 6 degrees the inflowing mass of air [Luftmasse] is so large that 5 hours and 19 minutes are sufficient to fill this enormous storm cylinder." (p. 120). On pp. 79–80, Reye noted that Redfield had obtained this angle by plotting on charts the wind arrows indicating wind directions for 20 different times (using 165 reports of the storm) and then adding concentric circles (to make the revolving character of the storm winds more obvious). Redfield did not analyze isobars. Evaluating these charts, Reye remarked, "I would have estimated [the angle] of inclination higher." As indicated in Chapter 1, contemporary data by Buchan, Ley and others gave on the average an angle of inclination between 10° and 30°; but these estimates were apparently not available to Reye at the time he wrote his book.

[73] Reye (1872), p. 160.

$$\text{Precipitation (mm m}^{-2}\text{ day}^{-1}) = \frac{(\text{g water vapor s}^{-1}) \times (\text{s day}^{-1})}{\text{area of storm}} \approx 1.7 \times 10^2\ \frac{\text{g water vapor}}{\text{m}^2\text{ day}},$$

These results convinced Reye that the amount of precipitation observed in ordinary midlatitude cyclones indicated a release of latent heat sufficient to explain the observed kinetic energy. His example found wide recognition in the literature and was viewed as proof of the soundness of the thermal theory.[74]

4.5 HELMHOLTZ' CONVECTIVE THEORY OF STORMS (1876)

Reye's book on storms soon became widely known and exerted a notable impact on meteorological thought, especially in Germany. His ideas certainly impressed Hermann v. Helmholtz who, throughout his life, showed a lively interest in meteorology and contributed significantly to the advancement of that science.[75] A co-founder of the field of thermodynamics, Helmholtz explored—just as his long-time friend Thomson had—the applicability of the new concepts of physics to other areas of knowledge including meteorology. Helmholtz pursued many of his meteorological studies while on vacations in Switzerland. It was on his long walking tours in Pontresina in Engadin that his attention was drawn to the foehn phenomenon. Similarly, he began his investigations on the nature of storms after witnessing the formation of a thunderstorm on the summit of the Rigi. Reflecting on this spectacular thunderstorm in a lecture of 1876, entitled "Whirlstorms and thunderstorms,"[76] he raised the question: What is the origin and the cause for the release of such vast amounts of energy? How is it possible, he wondered,

> . . . that the weak pressure differences in the atmosphere which are caused by temperature variations and which normally reveal themselves only in insignificant differences of the position of the barometer can produce such terrifying discharges and such violent motions. It appears to me that, particularly with regard to answering this question, considerable progress has been made through the aforementioned paper of *Reye*, who really gives us an insight into the variable nature of the weather phenomena. What matters essentially is the concept of unstable equilibrium.[77]

Here Helmholtz singled out the importance of Reye's work on stability criteria for answering the question of kinetic energy production in the atmosphere. Noting that the state of the atmosphere may change gradually from stability to instability, Helmholtz discussed the significance of one special case of atmospheric instability

---

or 0.17 mm m^{-2} day^{-1}. Assuming a rainfall of about 10 mm per day for the storm investigated by Reye, his calculation indicates an efficiency of about 1% for the conversion of thermal energy derived from the conversion of latent heat into kinetic energy. Reye himself made no efficiency estimate.

[74] See, for example, Margules, "Zur Sturmtheorie," *Met. Zeits.*, **23** (1906), p. 482.

[75] See biographical note on Helmholtz in Appendix.

[76] Helmholtz, "Wirbelstürme und Gewitter," *Deutsche Rundschau*, **6** (1876), 363–380. See also L. Koenigsberger, *H. v. Helmholtz, Vol. 2* (Braunschweig, 1903), 65–68, 230. Gillispie has described Helmholtz as the perhaps "most gracious personality of nineteenth century science." Devoting much thought and effort to his brilliant lectures on popular science, Helmholtz began a process of "civilizing science by passing it through a cultivated mind, alive with a sense of cultural responsibility." (Gillispie, *The Edge of Objectivity*, Princeton, Princeton University Press, 4th printing, 1967, p. 382).

[77] Helmholtz (1876), p. 372.

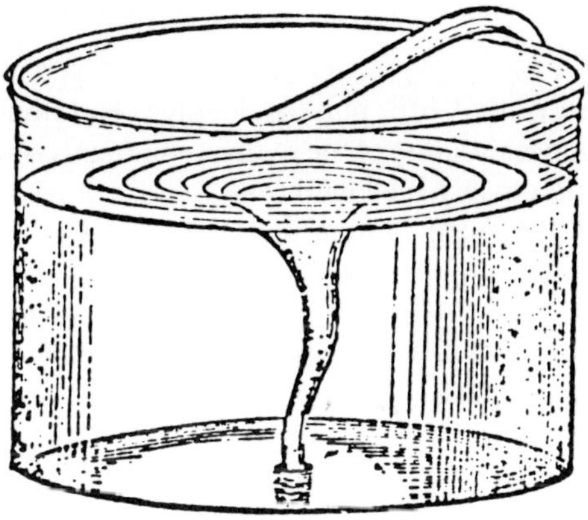

FIGURE 21. Helmholtz' "bath tub" experiment; from Helmholtz, "Wirbelstürme und Gewitter," *Deutsche Rundschau*, **6** (1876), p. 377.

for the development of tropical storms, or whirlstorms [Wirbelstürme].[78] Given the unstable condition of a layer of cool air spread out above a layer of warm moist air (over the ocean), then a small disturbance at some place will act as a trigger for a convective current. This current, forming a narrow vertical channel into the upper cool layer, is enhanced through latent heat release during condensation of water vapor. Once this process is initiated, a system of winds will develop in which air converging horizontally takes the place of air transported upward by convection. The cool dry upper layers of air surrounding the warm channel are simultaneously sinking. A vortex forms in the converging and ascending flow due to the deflecting force of the earth's rotation.

Helmholtz likened this vortical wind system to the process in a draining bath tub in the vicinity of the drainage pipe (Figure 21). When the water is set into rotation in a container with an opening in the bottom, he explained, it will flow in the form of spirals toward this opening, and

> close to the center the centrifugal force of these vigorously rotating rings becomes so large that the water pressure is unable to contract them any further. Then, as shown in the Figure, a vertical air-filled pipe is formed through the mass of water which reaches down to the lower opening, expands upward in funnel shape and normally is striped along its wall in the form of a screw. These pipes have exactly the shape that is used in illustrating waterspouts.[79]

Referring to his theoretical investigations on vortex motion, he continued

> I have pursued theoretical investigations in the year of 1858 on the theorems of motion of

[78] These unstable meteorological conditions, Helmholtz emphasized, are responsible for the difficulties in weather prediction: when small causes can produce great effects, then normally computations fail; for it is normally assumed that small errors in the beginning statement lead to only small errors in the result. A century later, difficulties in weather prediction are still being traced to the large effects of small causes, as Helmholtz so concisely stated.

[79] *Ibid.*, p. 377.

such vortices, the results of which can be confirmed by experiment in a few, more simple cases.[80]

Even within the context of a popular lecture, Helmholtz' conclusions were based on a superior understanding of the hydrodynamical conditions in a vortex and were more precise and closely reasoned than Reye's representation of the field of motion associated with a storm. In particular, Helmholtz applied the principle of conservation of angular momentum to vortex motion. Ferrel had taken this important step earlier, but at that time his work was unknown in Europe. Helmholtz proposed that once a vortex was formed due to the deflecting force of the earth's rotation, velocity changes depended on variations of the vortex radius. As a particle approaches the center of the vortex, its angular velocity increases if the angular momentum remains constant. Helmholtz also used the concept of the centrifugal force in the discussion of the equilibrium of forces that permitted circular flow about a center of low pressure. He specifically discussed the effect of centrifugal forces in conjunction with frictional forces on the convective current; in the center of the storm, Helmholtz reasoned,

> . . . we may assume that it is primarily the powerful centrifugal force which delays the ascending of the warm air. It will be possible for the air to ascend only in the proportion that the mighty rotation decreases due to friction along the earth surface, and it will continue to rotate in the upper strata, but, due to the decrease in rotation, it will gradually expand its circles in the proportion that new air follows.[81]

Thus, according to Helmholtz, friction reduces the wind speed at the surface and cross-isobaric flow toward low pressure results. Assuming mass continuity, he noted, the frictional convergence near the surface will then result in ascending motion in the center of the vortex. Reye also had considered these effects of centrifugal forces. Reye had regarded extremely high values for vertical velocities as reasonable. Although Helmholtz did not cite values for vertical velocities, it is clear that he took them to be small.

More clearly than Reye, Helmholtz recognized and emphasized the necessity and importance of simultaneous sinking motion in the surroundings once an ascending current was initiated. In the discussion of his tropical cyclone model he stressed that descending motion would tend to increase the stability of the air concerned. Around the place of "breakthrough [Durchbrechung]," as Helmholtz described it, where the lower moist air intrudes into the upper cool layer, the equilibrium becomes increasingly more stable "due to the depletion of the moist air and the lowering of the upper boundary surface [Grenzfläche]."[82] In other words,

---

[80] *Ibid.*, p. 378. Assuming friction is effective only near the earth's surface, he felt that a vortex, once formed "can continue for a long time, even when the causes cease to act that have produced it." (p. 378). Helmholtz is here referring to a paper of 1858, "Ueber Integrale der hydrodynamischen Gleichungen, welche den Wirbelbewegungen entsprechen," *Journal für die reine und angewandte Mathematik*, **55**, 25–55, translated in Cl. Abbe's second collection, *op. cit.*, (1891), 31–57. In this paper, which was important both for its results and mathematical methods, Helmholtz treated vortex motion in water, assumed to be homogeneous and incompressible.

[81] Helmholtz (1876), p. 377.

[82] *Ibid.*, p. 375.

the descending cool air, warming adiabatically, is taking the place of the ascending air which is cooling saturated adiabatically. During the process the mass of the warm moist air at the bottom is depleted, the layer of cool air is lowered and the moist air which has ascended forms a third layer above the layer of cool air. These considerations led Helmholtz to conclude that

> The entire process can lead to a standstill and to a new equilibrium only when the upper dry air has descended so far that the channel of moist air positioned in the center of the vortex, which connects the lower and the ascended upper layer of moist air, contains air of the same weight, on the average, as the drier layers which it is breaking through.[83]

In the paragraph cited, Helmholtz indicated a process in which potential energy is converted into kinetic energy. It is clear, although Helmholtz did not mention it, that once the process of rearrangement of warm moist air and cool dry air is completed, the center of gravity of the whole system has descended. This idea was not investigated in detail until more than three decades later when Max Margules, in one of his so-called chamber models, approximated the process and calculated the energy conversions taking place.

It is important to note that Helmholtz' discussion of "large atmospheric vortices" referred to tropical storms and did not include midlatitude cyclones. In contrast to Reye, he regarded midlatitude storms as a different nonvortical class of storms. Following the tradition of Dove, he thought that the weather of midlatitudes was based on the "mutual displacement of cool and dry polar winds and warm, moist equatorial winds."[84] Helmholtz obviously regarded Dove's observational material as reliable evidence. At least at this time he apparently was not acquainted with the accumulating evidence, from contemporary studies of synoptic charts, that the extensive storms of midlatitudes were characterized by systems of closed isobars and inward spiralling winds. It is unfortunate that Helmholtz was so little acquainted with the results of synoptic meteorology. Otherwise he might have attempted to apply his stability considerations, and more important, his hydrodynamic equations for vortex motions, to large-scale extratropical cyclones. Reye's book represented only a meagre source of information on this type of storm.

4.6 DYNAMIC CYCLONE MODELS

The storm treatises discussed thus far encompassed two approaches to the cyclone problem: first, the empirical investigation of cyclones, based on synoptic charts, and second, studies on the energy budget of storms in conjunction with the theoretical analysis of atmospheric stability and convection. Convective currents were thought to be produced by local inequalities of temperature and water vapor content or warm air flowing upward over colder air. The release of latent heat was considered essential for the maintenance of convection on a large scale, and for the production of kinetic energy in a cyclone. However, no attempt had been made to analyze quantitatively, and within a dynamical framework, the relationships

---

[83] *Ibid.*, p. 376.

between the vertical and horizontal motions. For the solution of this problem it was first necessary to describe mathematically the motion of air in terms of the forces acting on it. The developments in dynamic meteorology in relation to the thermal theory will therefore be discussed.

During the 1870's, a number of innovative papers on atmospheric dynamics were published, some of which were authored by prominent exponents of the thermal theory. In this section, we will discuss the outstanding contributions of Guldberg and Mohn and of Ferrel. In a memoir of 1876, entitled, *Études sur les Mouvements de l'Atmosphère*, Guldberg and Mohn presented the equations of motion for a cyclone model based on a central convective current.[85] It was primarily this memoir which determined the development of dynamic meteorology in Europe during the following decades. In 1878 Ferrel published a paper "On cyclones, tornadoes and waterspouts," in which he extended his earlier theoretical analysis (1859/60) of cyclonic circulations by relating horizontal temperature variations to the field of motion at different height levels.[86]

Before proceeding with the discussion of Guldberg and Mohn's work, a few remarks are appropriate on the communication of results of meteorological research during the 1870's and 1880's. As noted several times, important papers had remained unknown or unavailable for years after publication. During the 1870's, meteorologists recognized that communication was inadequate, especially at the international level. There were several attempts to improve this situation. Of particular importance in the United States were Cleveland Abbe's English translations of European publications. The first of three collections was published in 1877. It contained important papers of Hann, Reye, Colding and Peslin. The papers of Helmholtz, Oberbeck, Hertz and Bezold (see Chapter 5) were translated in the second collection of 1891. In addition, during the 1880's and 1890's Abbe regularly reported on advances in meteorological research in Europe and the United States in the Smithsonian Institution's *Annual Reports*. As editor of the *Meteorologische Zeitschrift* Julius Hann published translations into German of several papers during the 1870's; also, extensive summaries and reviews of foreign meteorological papers became a significant part of the journal. For example, Hann summarized Ferrel's work and requested and obtained from Guldberg and Mohn a shortened German version of their memoir for the journal. It is certain that these efforts facilitated international communication of ideas among Nineteenth Century meteorologists.[87]

---

[84] Helmholtz (1876), p. 368.

[85] Guldberg and Mohn, *Études sur les Movements de l'Atmosphère*, Part 1 and 2 (Christiania, A. W. Brøgger, 1876 and 1880), 39 and 53 pp. Translated in Abbe's third collection (1910), *op. cit.*, pp. 122–248.

[86] Ferrel, "Meteorological researches for the coast pilot," Part II, *U.S. Coast and Geodetic Survey, 1878*, Appendix No. 10, (Washington, 1881), 175–267.

[87] At the second meteorological congress of 1879 in Rome it was proposed for the first time to establish an international meteorological bibliography. A first step in this endeavor was the *Bibliography of Meteorology*, a catalogue of printed literature in meteorology with more than 50,000 entries and an author index, prepared under A. W. Greely and edited by O. L. Fassig (Washington, Signal Office, 1889), which incorporated the catalogue of Cl. Abbe. 20,000 of the entries were furnished by George Symons (1838–1900), the first assistant of Fitzroy in the Meteorological Department of the Board of Trade and

a. Guldberg and Mohn—Role of Convective Current and Thermal Asymmetry (1876–1880)

Mohn's investigations of the dynamics of cyclones were the direct outcome of earlier synoptic studies of the 1870's that had convinced him of the thermal origin of cyclones. At that time he gave thought to the close relationship observed between the wind and the pressure distribution, then known as Buys Ballot law. He continued to work on this problem during subsequent years.[88] In the course of his studies he became acquainted with two papers by the engineer L. A. Colding of Copenhagen: one on the motions of water (1870), and another (1871) in which formulas developed for the motions of rotating cylinders in water were applied to the motion of the air in tropical cyclones (neglecting the effect of the deflecting force of the earth's rotation).[89] Colding's analysis of the dynamics of air in motion appeared to be a promising approach to the cyclone problem. For this reason, Mohn drew the attention of his friend Guldberg, an applied mathematician at Christiania, to Colding's articles. Guldberg developed independently the equations of atmospheric motion for a rotating earth and found, as had Colding before, that numerical solutions based upon these equations agreed well with the wind and pressure observations for a particular storm.[90] Mohn further adapted these equations for meteorological purposes. In the midst of these activities Guldberg and Mohn received a paper of Ferrel (1874), "On the relation between the barometric gradient and the velocity of the wind," in which Ferrel summarized his earlier work. Guldberg and Mohn found to their surprise and satisfaction that Ferrel had derived formulas and obtained numerical results corresponding to their own.[91]

---

founder of *Symons Monthly Meteorological Magazine* (1866). Symon's meteorological bibliography amounted to about 60,000 entries [See Symon's obituary in *Quart. Journ. Roy. Met. Soc.*, **26** (1900), p. 158.]

[88] See also Peslin, "On the relation between barometric variations and the general atmospheric currents," translated in Abbe's first collection, *Smiths. Inst., Annual Report* (1877), 465–478, *Bull. International de l'Obs. de Paris et de l'Obs. Phys. Cent. de Montsouris*, 1872. In a supplement to this paper, Peslin noted that in the *Storm-Atlas* of 1870 Mohn had "independently" of his work "and probably anterior thereto . . . recognized the law of inverse ratio between the velocity of the wind and the distance of the isobars" (p. 477). The main body of Peslin's paper was presented in 1869 to the Academy of Science in Paris. Peslin's mathematical treatment of the deflecting force of the earth's rotation, pressure gradient and centrifugal force was the first investigation of this kind in Europe. However, Peslin's paper was not appreciated, just as Ferrel's early work on the equations of motion on a rotating earth had not been followed up by contemporary scientists.

[89] Mohn related this information in a letter to the editor of the *Met. Zeits.*, "Bemerkungen über das Luftdruckminimum im Centrum eines Sturmfeldes," *Wien, Met. Zeits.*, **10** (1875), 92–94. The respective papers of Colding are "Om Stromninsforholdene i almindelige Ledninger og i Havet," *Danske Videnskabernes Selskabs Forhandlinger, Skrifter*, Ser. 5, **9** (III), (1869), 81–214, submitted 1870 and "Nogle Bemaerkinger om Luftens Stromningsforhold," *Danske Videnskabernes Selskabs Forhandlinger, Oversigt* (1871), 89–108. Both of these articles were partially translated into German by Hann ["Einige Bemerkungen zu den Strömungsverhältnissen der Luft," *Wien, Met. Zeits.*, **10** (1875), 133–142, 151–155], and into English ("Some remarks concerning the nature of currents of air") in Abbe's first collection (1877), *op. cit.*, 447–462. Hann also published an enthusiastic review of the work of Colding and of Ferrel's 1874 paper in "Ueber die Beziehungen zwischen den Luftdruckdifferenzen und der Windgeschwindigkeit nach den Theorien von Ferrel und Colding," *Wien, Met. Zeits.*, **10** (1875), 97–106, translated in Abbe's first collection, *op. cit.*, pp. 426–444.

[90] C. M. Guldberg, "Theorien for vandets og luftens strominger pa jordens overflade," *Polyteknisk Tidsskrift*, **19** (1872), 68–76.

[91] Ferrel, *Am. Journ. Sci.*, **8** (1874), p. 263. It was largely through this article that Ferrel's work

In their memoir of 1876, Guldberg and Mohn introduced a simple kinematic model of a cyclone. They determined the horizontal motion of air in the case of circular isobars around a barometric minimum in which the horizontal motion fed a permanent vertical current and the low central pressure was maintained by upper level mass divergence. Guldberg and Mohn did not assume a closed circulation for the cyclone system, as Ferrel had done in his model of 1859/60; air was permitted to flow toward the cyclone center from a distance, i.e., new air currents constantly converged in the cyclone and its growth depended on the properties of these currents. During the 1890's, when the assumption of a closed circulation was shown to be untenable, this view became highly important for the continuance of the thermal theory.

An important step in their analysis, going beyond Ferrel's earlier work, was the introduction of the condition of mass continuity into their system of equations. For a given vertical motion in their model, the velocity of the inflowing air was determined by means of this condition. Ferrel had implied this condition in the descriptive part of his work, but had not incorporated it into his theoretical analysis. In addition, Guldberg and Mohn introduced a simple frictional coefficient still in use today. Assuming that air flowing over the earth's surface experiences a resistance proportional to its velocity and in the direction opposite to the motion, they equated kv (where k is the friction coefficient and v the velocity) with the frictional force.

Guldberg and Mohn stressed that on the basis of observational and theoretical evidence, a major distinction was required between tropical cyclones and cyclones of midlatitudes. This distinction constituted a definite shift away from the earlier view, as maintained by Reye, that rotary or vortical wind systems of all scales belonged to one group of phenomena explainable by a single principle, while other differences played a subordinate role. In contrast, Guldberg and Mohn considered it necessary to classify wind systems according to the relative importance of the forces acting in them. Variations in the effectiveness of these forces under the different conditions of tropics and midlatitudes, they noted, were so pronounced that minimizing them for the sake of a "unifying" principle could only result in confusion and would impede a deeper understanding of both types of storms. They concluded (here following Cleveland Abbe's translation from the French original):

> We divide the systems of wind into two classes. The systems of the *first order* are those which extend only over quite a limited part of the surface of the earth, and which at the same time exhibit variations of velocity so great that we can neglect friction and the

became known in Europe. See Hann, "Ueber Beziehungen zwischen Luftdruckdifferenzen . . . ," (1875), *op. cit.* Subsequently, Ferrel's work was reviewed by Sprung, "William Ferrel's Untersuchungen über atmosphärische Wirbel," *Wien, Met. Zeits.*, **17** (1882), 161–175, 276–282, and in his excellent textbook, *Lehrbuch der Meteorologie* (Hamburg, Hoffmann and Campe, 1885). In the United States, Ferrel's work became widely recognized after 1870, largely due to efforts of Cleveland Abbe. Abbe introduced his fellow American meteorologists to Ferrel's ideas in a popular circular, *Practical Use of Meteorological Reports and Weather-Maps*, (Washington, Government Printing Office, 1871), p. 73. "It is fair to say," Abbe remarked in an obituary of Ferrel, "that in the absence of actual experience my predictions of the first years were mainly of a deductive character based upon my confidence in the truth of the principles developed by Espy and Ferrel." [Abbe, "Ferrel's influence in the Signal Office," *Am. Met. Journ.*, **8** (1891), 344–345].

> deflecting force of the rotation of the earth. For example, we mention tornadoes, waterspouts, whirlwinds of smoke, etc. The systems of wind of the *second order* are those in which all the acting forces have some importance. As example we mention cyclones, the trade winds, the sea breezes and land breezes.[92]

Guldberg and Mohn now could discuss tropical and midlatitude cyclones separately and in this way opened the door to several important conclusions on midlatitude cyclones.

Specifically, they sought to explain the large variation in the magnitude of vertical motions in tropical and extratropical cyclones. Although they agreed with the authors of cyclone models discussed earlier, namely that vertical motions must be regarded essential for the development and maintenance of both types of storms, they viewed it a significant factor that vertical motions in extratropical cyclones were generally small compared to vertical velocities in tropical cyclones and that in both systems the vertical velocities were small compared to horizontal velocities.

With regard to midlatitude cyclones, they attempted to account for the spatial variation in the magnitude of vertical motions. Assuming vertical motions to be strongest in the storm center, Guldberg and Mohn refined their simple symmetrical model by subdivision into two parts:

> . . . distinguishing between two zones of motion: the outer zone in which the horizontal air current can be thought of as moving with variable vertical extent, and the inner zone in which the air essentially has an ascending motion and can thus be compared with a horizontal flow of steadily increasing vertical extent. We will approximately determine the transition between the outer and inner zone by interpolation.[93]

Thus, the field of horizontal motion in the inner vortical zone and the outer zone was represented by different functions, resulting in a discontinuous change in the angle between pressure gradient and wind direction and consequently a velocity discontinuity along the boundary of the two zones. Such a discontinuity, however, was unrealistic; thus, Guldberg and Mohn's solutions for the equations applying to the inner and outer zones of the cyclone could not be combined to provide a useful solution for the entire cyclone. Guldberg and Mohn attempted to surmount this difficulty by offering a graphical method for interpolation of conditions in the transitional zone between inner and outer zone.[94]

Within Guldberg and Mohn's cyclone model the forces acting on air in horizontal motion were identified as the pressure gradient force $(\mu/\rho)dp/dn$, positive from higher to lower pressure, the deflecting force of the earth's rotation $2\omega \sin \varphi v$, the centrifugal force v^2/R, the tangential acceleration $v dv/ds$ or dv/dt, and the frictional force kv, where

---

[92] Guldberg and Mohn (1880, from Abbe's translation), p. 182.

[93] Guldberg and Mohn, "Die Bewegung der Luft in aufsteigenden Wirbeln," *Wien, Met. Zeits.*, **12** (1877), p. 257.

[94] Improving on Guldberg and Mohn's model in this respect, the German meteorologist Anton Oberbeck in 1882 introduced the further requirement that changes in pressure and wind velocity may only be continuous. See Anton Oberbeck, "Ueber Bewegungen der Luft an der Erdoberfläche," *Ann. Phys. Chem.*, **17** (1882), 126–148, translated in Abbe's second collection, *op. cit.*, pp. 151–170.

r = radius of isobars
n = distance along r
ρ = density
μ = conversion factor, converting the dimensions of the pressure gradient from mm Hg per degree of meridian to kg/cm^2
ω = angular velocity of the earth's rotation
φ = latitude, assumed to be constant for the entire barometric depression
p = pressure
v = velocity
R = radius of the curved trajectory s associated with the cyclone
k = coefficient of friction
t = time.

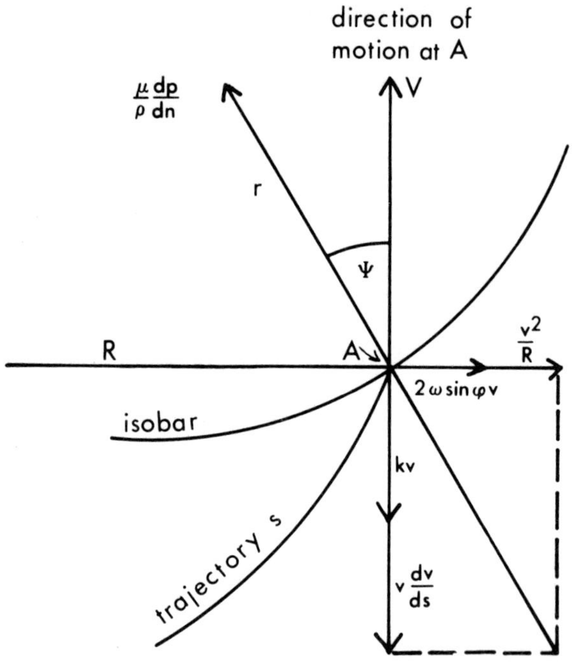

Illustration of forces acting in horizontal flow (adapted from Guldberg and Mohn).

The resulting equations for the two components of horizontal motion, radial and tangential, were

$$\frac{\mu}{\rho}\frac{dp}{dn}\cos\psi = kv + v\frac{dv}{ds}, \qquad (4)$$

$$\frac{\mu}{\rho}\frac{dp}{dn}\sin\psi = 2\omega\sin\varphi v + \frac{v^2}{R}, \qquad (5)$$

where ψ is the angle between pressure gradient and wind direction.

In the outer zone, where the vertical component of motion was assumed to be zero, the condition of mass continuity required that a constant volume of air per unit time was flowing through the cross section $2\pi rh$, where h denotes the height of the layer of inflow being considered. Since the radial component of the velocity, i.e., $v \cos \psi$, denotes the velocity of the inflowing air, it followed

$$2\pi rhv \cos \psi = \text{constant}. \tag{6}$$

Assuming that the angle between wind direction and pressure gradient was constant over the entire outer zone of the barometric depression, it followed that

> . . . the wind trajectories [become] logarithmic spirals, since these curves have the property that the angle between the tangent and the radius is constant.[95]

From Equations (4), (5) and (6), they obtained for the angle ψ in the outer zone

$$\tan \psi = \frac{2\omega \sin \varphi}{k}, \tag{7}$$

which was the same as for straight, equidistant isobars.[96]

Vertical motions could not be neglected in the inner part of the cyclone. They were taken into account by assuming that the height of the inflow h was a function of the distance from the center of the barometric depression r;

---

[95] Guldberg and Mohn, "Die Bewegung der Luft . . . ," (1877), p. 259.

[96] The assumption of φ = constant made it necessary to consider the deflecting force of the earth's rotation as uniform over the entire barometric depression. Since $2\pi h$ was the same for all cross sections, Equation (6) could also be written (following Guldberg and Mohn (1877))

$$vr \cos \psi = \text{constant}.$$

Differentiation of this equation yielded, since ψ = constant,

$$rdv + vdr = 0,$$

$$\frac{dv}{dr} = -\frac{v}{r},$$

Since $ds = -(dr/\cos \psi)$, it follows that

$$\text{(a)} \quad \frac{dv}{ds} = \frac{v \cos \psi}{r};$$

furthermore

$$\text{(b)} \quad R = \frac{r}{\sin \psi}.$$

Substituting (a) into (4) and (b) into (5) yields

$$\frac{\mu}{\rho}\frac{dp}{dn} \cos \psi = kv + \frac{v^2 \cos \psi}{r}, \tag{4a}$$

$$\frac{\mu}{\rho}\frac{dp}{dn} \sin \psi = 2\omega v \sin \varphi + \frac{v^2 \sin \psi}{r}. \tag{5a}$$

Multiplying (4a) by $\sin \psi$ and (5a) by $(-\cos \psi)$ and adding the resulting equations, one obtains

$$0 = kv \sin \psi - 2\omega v \sin \varphi \cos \psi,$$

or, Equation (7) of the text,

$$\tan \psi = \frac{2\omega \sin \varphi}{k}.$$

specifically, the height h was made inversely proportional to the square of r. In this case the equation of continuity was

$$2\pi r \frac{h}{r^2} v \cos \psi = \text{constant}. \tag{8}$$

This equation, in conjunction with Equations (4) and (5), yielded for the angle between pressure gradient and wind direction in the inner zone

$$\tan \psi = \frac{2\omega \sin \varphi}{k - 2c}, \tag{9}$$

where c is a constant and ψ is considered constant over the entire inner zone of the cyclone.[97] The trajectory again became a logarithmic spiral, but was now larger than in the case of the outer zone (see Figure 22).[98]

---

[97] See Guldberg and Mohn (1877), 260–261. For motions in the inner part of the cyclone, described by Equations (8) and (9) in the text, they obtained, dividing Equation (8) by $2\pi h$,

$$\frac{v \cos \psi}{r} = \frac{\text{constant}}{2\pi h} = c, \quad \text{considering} \quad \psi = \text{constant}.$$

Differentiation yields

$$\frac{rdv - vdr}{r^2} = 0,$$

$$\frac{dv}{r} - \frac{v}{r^2} dr = 0,$$

$$\frac{dv}{r} + \frac{v}{r^2} ds \cos \psi = 0, \quad \text{since} \quad \frac{v}{r} \cos \psi = c.$$

It follows $dv/ds = -c$.

Substituting the last expression into Equation (4) and the relation $R = r/\sin \psi$ into Equation (5), one obtains

$$\frac{\mu}{\rho} \frac{dp}{dn} \cos \psi = v(k - c), \tag{4b}$$

$$\frac{\mu}{\rho} \frac{dp}{dn} \sin \psi = 2\omega v \sin \varphi + \frac{v^2}{r} \sin \psi = 2\omega v \sin \varphi + v \frac{\sin \psi \cdot c}{\cos \psi}. \tag{5b}$$

Multiplying (4b) by $\sin \psi$ and (5b) by $(-\cos \psi)$ and adding the resulting equations, one obtains

$$0 = \sin \psi v(k - c) - 2\omega v \sin \varphi \cos \psi - vc \sin \psi,$$

$$\sin \psi(vk - vc - vc) = 2\omega v \sin \varphi \cos \psi,$$

or, Equation (9) of the text,

$$\tan \psi = \frac{2\omega \sin \varphi}{k - 2c}.$$

In 1880 Guldberg and Mohn wrote Equation (8) in terms of horizontal and vertical velocities.

[98] During the second half of the Nineteenth Century, numerous statistical studies were carried out on the determination of the angle ψ. It is important to note that the angle ψ, often called angle of deviation, refers to the angle between *pressure gradient* and wind direction. On the other hand, the older term, angle of inclination, signifies the angle between *isobars* and wind direction. This latter term was used by Redfield and others during the 1840's and corresponds to departure from geostrophic flow. During the 1870's and 1880's, Ley, Hoffmeyer, Loomis, Hildebrandsson and others showed that the angle of deviation ψ varies considerably; ψ was found to be greater in summer than in winter, greater over the ocean and at shorelines than over land, increasing with increasing wind velocity, and to some extent, with distance from the center of a barometric depression. In addition, ψ showed marked variations in the different sectors of a cyclone, with largest values found for southwest and west winds. Nineteenth Century investigations on the angle of deviation were summarized extensively by Hann in *Lehrbuch der Meteorologie* (3rd ed., Leipzig, Tauchnitz, 1915), 512–516.

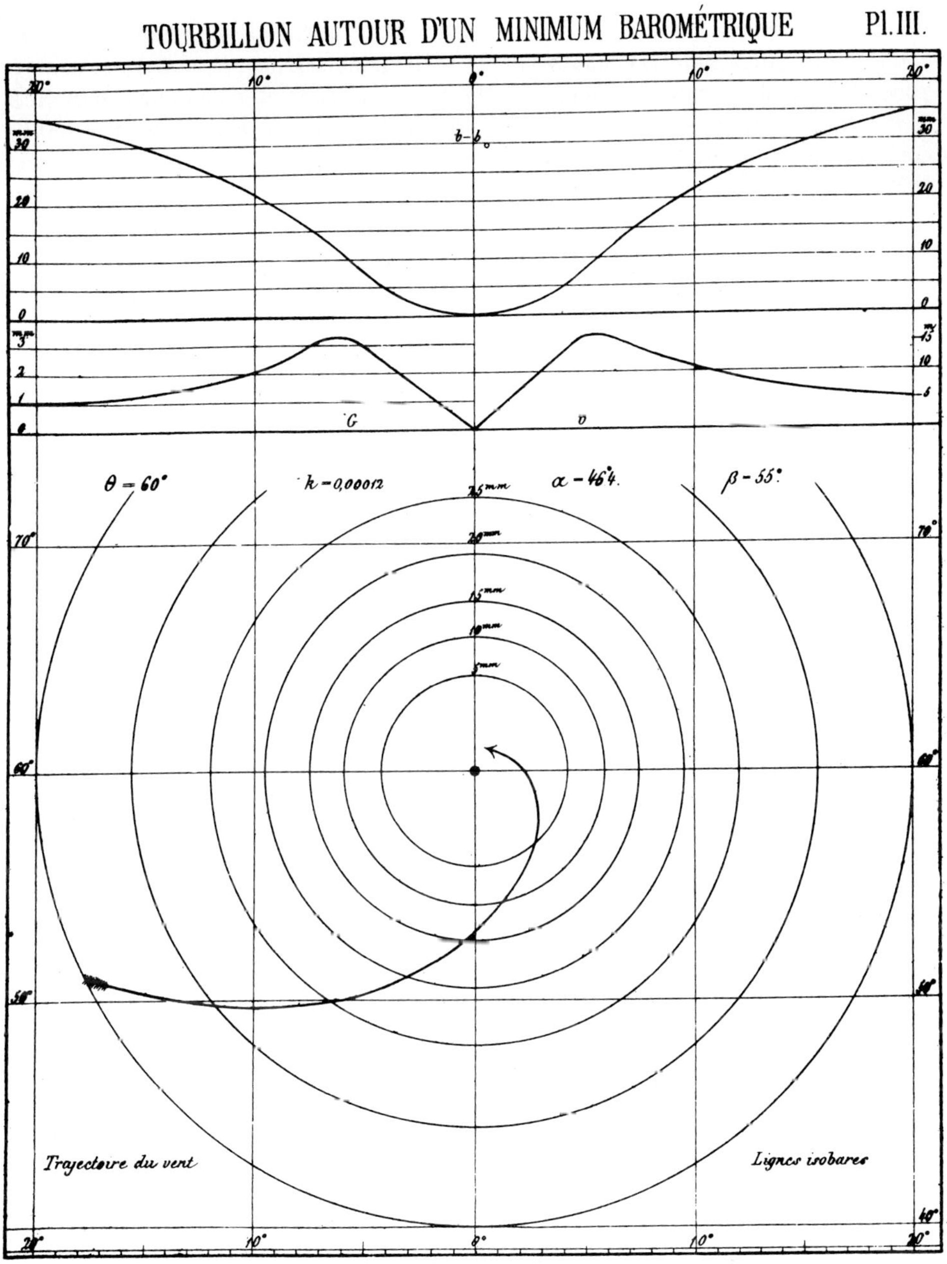

FIGURE 22. Guldberg and Mohn's mathematical model of wind spirals around a barometric depression, from *Études sur les Mouvements de l'Atmosphère* (Christiania, Brøgger, 1876). $b - b_0$ indicates pressure increase with distance from cyclone center where the pressure equals b_0 (mm Hg). G denotes pressure gradient (mm Hg per meridional degree). v is horizontal velocity (m s^{-1}); v_{max} is 16 m s^{-1} at a distance of 6° from the center. The barometric depression is located at latitude 60°, the friction coefficient is $k = 0.00012$, α is the angle between pressure gradient and wind direction in the outer zone, and β is the corresponding angle in the inner zone of the cyclone.

It is seen from Equations (6) and (8) that v decreases with distance from the center in the outer zone, while it increases with distance from the center in the inner zone of the cyclone model so that v and the pressure gradient must have a maximum in the zone of transition (see Figure 22). Aside from the uncertainties imposed by simplifying assumptions in this model, the authors concluded "that a stationary cyclone . . . is completely determined by the magnitude and position (distance from the center) of its maximum velocity of the wind."[99] In other words, for known values of maximum wind velocity in a stationary symmetrical cyclone (i.e., magnitude and position of v_{max} specified) it was possible to determine the pressure gradient curve, the corresponding system of isobars and also the horizontal wind trajectories. The results of such calculations for the case of a midlatitude cyclone are illustrated in Figure 22. Guldberg and Mohn stressed that real cyclones would hardly conform to the conditions introduced in their mathematical model. They suggested that the transition zone between interior and exterior zone might extend over the entire cyclone.[100] Thus they acknowledged that real cyclones rarely showed a well-defined wind maximum as was required in their model.

Reflecting further on the quality of their cyclone model, Guldberg and Mohn stressed that, although attractive in itself, it was rather artificial when compared with actual midlatitude cyclones. The assumption of incompressibility of air and the essentially two-dimensional dynamic analysis imposed severe restrictions on their model. Much depended upon the assumptions concerning vertical motions, about which little was known from observations. Guldberg and Mohn's cyclone model showed that vertical motions depended not only on the vertical temperature stratification and the moisture content of the air, but also on horizontal pressure differences. This complicated the numerical estimation of vertical motions, since observations of pressure, temperature and moisture from the free atmosphere were not available.

Nevertheless, through the combination of the results of these dynamical investigations and Mohn's previous synoptic studies, the authors arrived at several important conclusions. Synoptic experience and theoretical considerations of the conditions for ascending motion convinced them that differences in the temperature

---

[99] Guldberg and Mohn (1877), 262; assuming throughout the cyclone the same geographic latitude, friction coefficient and density.

[100] *Ibid.*, p. 267. Oberbeck continued these calculations in 1882 in a numerical example for a cyclone ("Ueber die Bewegungen der Luft an der Erdoberfläche," *op. cit.*, translated in Abbe's second collection, pp. 167–170). He applied the equations of Guldberg and Mohn and, in addition, introduced the condition that changes in the wind velocity are continuous throughout the area of the cyclone. As a specific example, Oberbeck chose a cyclone with a wind velocity of 10 m s^{-1} at 1000 km distance from the center of the depression. His results indicated that the cyclone would contain a broad band of storm winds (15–25 m s^{-1}) between 200 and 500 km from the center and that vertical motions would be very low, on the order of 0.1 m s^{-1}. In Oberbeck's model, the angle of deviation was assumed to be 45° throughout the outer zone, and increasing in the inner zone from 45° to 78° at the center. In 1885, Sprung compared the values Oberbeck had obtained for pressure gradients in his model with observed values of pressure gradients in four cyclones of about equal size and with approximately circular isobars (*Lehrbuch . . .* , *op. cit.*, 149–151). The curves of average pressure gradients for these four cyclones, as plotted on a diagram with pressure gradient and distance from the depression center as coordinates, showed good agreement with Oberbeck's theoretical values; the latter tended to be on the high side, largely, according to Sprung, because of the high value assumed for the frictional coefficient.

and moisture conditions of the ascending air and the environment primarily determined the magnitude of vertical currents in cyclones. (This result was reminiscent of that obtained by Peslin and Reye from the parcel method.) Thus it appeared to be of utmost importance to consider what kind of current was entering a storm.

It is recalled that empirical investigations had shown repeatedly that two different currents of air were discernible in a storm. Prominent examples were Loomis' storm charts of the 1840's, Dove's two current model and Fitzroy's analysis of storms. By the 1870's, this storm characteristic had been confirmed in numerous investigations (see also Section 5.2). The empirical cyclone model of Mohn (Section 4.2c), in particular, featured the confluence of two currents of different origin and thermal properties as essential in cyclone development. In view of this evidence, Guldberg and Mohn attempted in Part II of their dynamic investigation a theoretical analysis of the role of these two currents for the maintenance and propagation of midlatitude cyclones. Thus, the concept of air mass became increasingly important in cyclone theory during the last decades of the Nineteenth Century. Guldberg and Mohn, here quoting from Abbe's translation of the French original, called the air that entered a cyclone and "has such a physical state that it can produce or sustain a vertical current . . . the *alimentary air*," and air "which cannot sustain a vertical current the *supplementary air*."[101] Considering the pressure changes resulting from the density changes in the incoming air, they arrived at the conclusion

> . . . that the supplementary air is colder and dryer than the alimentary air. If then the air flowing into a stationary cyclone changes its physical state and becomes colder and dryer, the horizontal barometric depression diminishes little by little and the cyclone is destroyed after a certain time.[102]

The concept of alimentary and supplementary air was used as well to explain the propagation of cyclones. The reasoning was practically the same as Mohn had put forward in his *Storm-Atlas* in 1870, namely, that the propagation of cyclones was the result of the same processes essential for their origin and maintenance.

> At the front of the cyclone the alimentary air whose temperature is τ [sic—should read τ_1] enters and produces a lowering of the pressure that we denote by δ_1. At the rear of the cyclone the supplementary air whose temperature is τ_2, enters and produces an increase of pressure whose value is δ_2. The air of the central part has the temperature τ and we have $\tau_1 > \tau > \tau_2$.[103]

With reference to the mean position of the isotherms, they wrote "we must expect the cyclone to be formed on the south of the supplementary air and on the north of the alimentary air and also that they move in general from west to east."[104] This

---

[101] Guldberg and Mohn (1880, from Abbe's translation), p. 208.
[102] *Ibid.*, pp. 208–209.
[103] *Ibid.*, p. 217.
[104] *Ibid.*, p. 200.

conclusion agreed with Mohn's earlier opinion that centers of cyclones moving across the Atlantic should be expected just north of the warm Gulf Stream.

After 1880, Guldberg and Mohn's fruitful cooperation did not continue. Guldberg turned from the field of meteorology, and Mohn became increasingly occupied with administrative work in his position as director of the Norwegian Weather Service. According to V. Bjerknes, Mohn became overly despondent after the first enthusiasm of the "new meteorology" had gone without providing the success anticipated and turned gradually from dynamic and synoptic meteorology to climatology.[105]

Bjerknes' comment merits further interpretation. During the last two decades of the Nineteenth Century the development of meteorology appears to have been plagued by the failure of progress in weather prediction. The great enthusiasm which had accompanied the introduction of the synoptic chart gradually gave way to an attitude of indifference, especially in the maritime nations where the continued loss of men at high sea stood witness to unsuccessful forecasts of storms. This indifference and at times pessimism on the part of meteorologists had serious consequences. It led to a preoccupation with statistical meteorology and climatology at some national weather services. For example, D. Brunt remarked with regard to the situation in England,

> . . . until the early years of the twentieth century it is not an unfair criticism to say that in general the only treatment to which the observations were submitted was a statistical or arithmetical treatment.[106]

More material, Brunt suggested, was collected than the few workers available could deal with, and for the remainder of the Nineteenth Century no serious advance in the understanding of the processes in weather was made in Britain. A similar situation prevailed in other countries, including Norway, France and the United States, making it less attractive for young talented scientists to enter the field of meteorology. Thus, although Guldberg and Mohn's novel and exciting dynamic studies were widely publicized and admired, there were relatively few scientists who carried on the study of dynamic meteorology.

b. Ferrel—The Thermal Wind Concept (1878)

Almost simultaneous with the appearance of Guldberg and Mohn's memoirs, Ferrel published an expanded version in two parts (1875 and 1878) of his 1859/60 memoir (discussed in Chapter 2).[107] At this time, Ferrel was working in Washington for the Coast and Geodetic Survey. His meteorological investigations had become well known, and in recognition of his achievements he was soon to be appointed professor of meteorology in the Signal Service (in 1882). The cyclone model

---

[105] V. Bjerknes, *Professor H. Mohn* (Kristiania, 1917), 7–8.

[106] D. Brunt, "A hundred years of meteorology," *The Advancement of Science*, **30** (1951), 114–124.

[107] Ferrel, "Meteorological researches for the use of the coast pilot," Part I: "On the mechanics and the general motions of the atmosphere," *U.S. Coast and Geodetic Survey, 1875,* Appendix No. 20 (Washington, 1877), 369–412, and Part II: "On cyclones, tornadoes and waterspouts," *Ibid., 1878,* Appendix No. 10 (Washington, 1881), 175–267.

presented by Ferrel in Part II of his new treatise was completely symmetrical with respect to the low pressure center. This procedure, which had also been followed by Guldberg and Mohn in 1876, facilitated the theoretical analysis. Ferrel thought it permissible because, in his view, the assumption of symmetry appeared to be in basic agreement with the physical processes taking place in the cyclonic system, namely, that a buoyant central region of heated air was rising and maintaining the cyclonic circulation.

Despite these similarities, the two cyclone models, Guldberg and Mohn's and Ferrel's, were otherwise strikingly different—and these differences, no doubt, arose in part from the varied scientific backgrounds of the authors. In Part II of their memoir (1880), Guldberg and Mohn stressed the notion that new air currents constantly converge in a cyclone, and that the growth as well as the propagation of cyclones depends on the properties of these air currents. In contrast to Mohn, who was director of a national weather service, Ferrel had few detailed observations of cyclones at his disposal, at least during the time span when he first formulated his theory in 1859/60. He proceeded from largely theoretical considerations of the general circulation of the atmosphere and applied these to cyclonic systems. In Ferrel's model of the general circulation the cold polar cyclone was linked by what is now referred to as a direct thermal circulation to a belt of high pressure surrounding it, i.e., warm air was rising in the anticyclonic belt and cold air sinking in the polar cyclone. Reaffirming his position of 1859/60, he proposed in 1878 that analogous to the cold core polar cyclone, the warm core cyclones of midlatitudes were surrounded by a belt of anticyclonic circulation and formed with them a self-maintained closed system; as in the general circulation model, a direct thermal circulation took place, but in this case it was associated with warm air rising in the cyclone and cold air sinking in the anticyclonic belt (Figures 10 and 23).

Ferrel limited his dynamic analysis to the field of horizontal motions near the earth's surface, as Guldberg and Mohn had done. His equations for horizontal motion were "obtained upon the hypothesis of no friction between the air and the earth's surface, and are independent of any form of the disturbing function"[108] that maintained the circulation. In the real atmosphere, he argued, friction could not be neglected and a disturbing force in the form of heat sources and sinks was necessary "to keep up an interchanging motion between the interior and exterior portions" of the cyclone against friction.[109]

While the effect of friction was treated only qualitatively, Ferrel attempted to analyze quantitatively the effect of horizontal temperature differences on the horizontal pressure field at various levels. In this way he was more successful than Guldberg and Mohn in relating thermal and dynamic aspects in the cyclonic process. Specifically, Ferrel proposed that "the function expressing the temperature upon which the disturbance of static equilibrium and the maintenance and the activity of the cyclone depend was symmetrical with respect to the pressure

[108] Ferrel (1881), p. 4.
[109] *Ibid.*, p. 14.

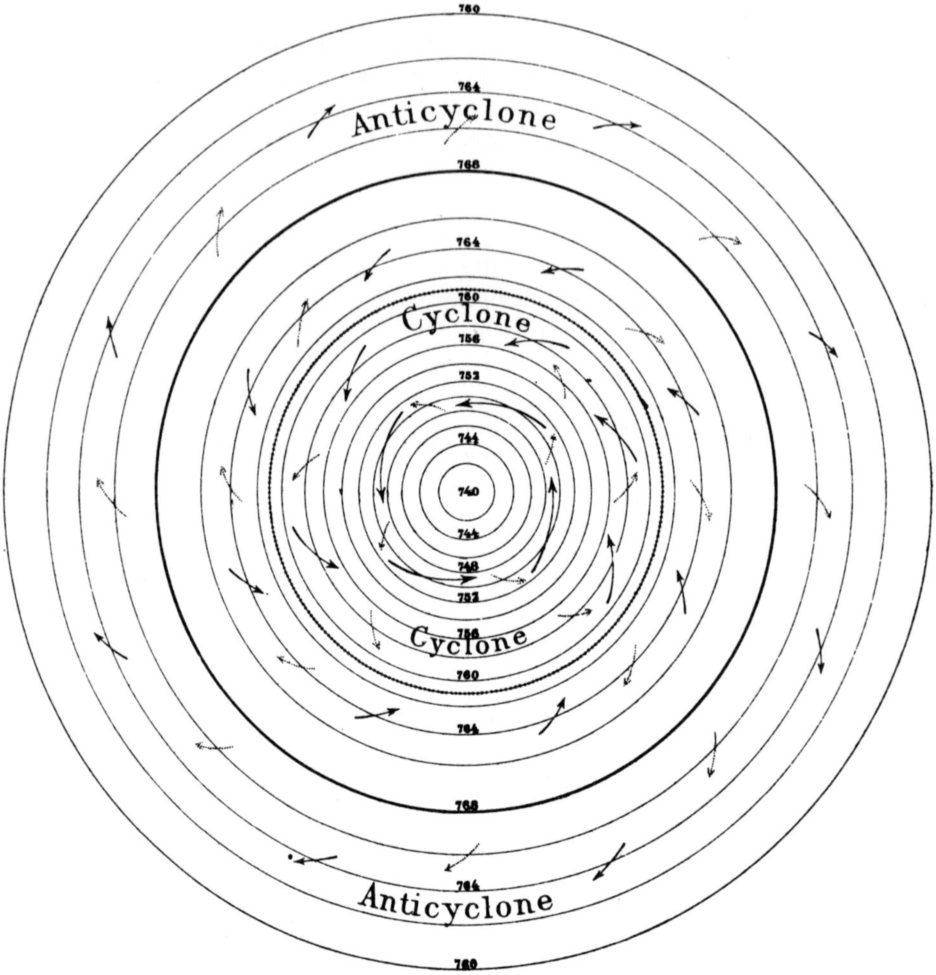

FIGURE 23. Ferrel's cyclonic circulation model (1878); from Ferrel, "Meteorological researches for the use of the coast pilot, Part II, cyclones, tornadoes and waterspouts," *U.S. Coast and Geodetic Survey, 1878* Appendix 10, (Washington, 1881). Surface isobars (mm Hg) are shown as thin solid lines; surface winds are solid arrows; upper level winds are dotted arrows; surface pressure gradient reversal is shown by the heavy solid line; upper level pressure gradient reversal is shown by the dotted line.

distribution,"[110] i.e., that circular isotherms ran concentric to the isobars around a barometric depression. In the ensuing analysis, Ferrel derived the important concept of the thermal wind which indicates the relationship between the horizontal temperature gradient and the changing of the wind with elevation.

He proceeded from derivations of the equations for horizontal motion in polar coordinates—the polar coordinate system being appropriate for a circular cyclone

[110] *Ibid.*, p. 19.

model. Only his equation for the radial accelerations will be considered here since it alone enters into his derivation of the thermal wind relationship.[111] His equations (here presented in a modified terminology) are as follows:

At the surface, corresponding to pressure p',

$$\frac{1}{p'}\frac{\partial p'}{\partial r} = \alpha'\left[fv' + \frac{v'^2}{r} - F_u' - \frac{du'}{dt}\right], \tag{10}$$

and at height h, corresponding to pressure p,

$$\frac{1}{p'}\frac{\partial p'}{\partial r} - gh\frac{\partial \alpha'}{\partial r} = \alpha\left[fv + \frac{v^2}{r} - F_u - \frac{du}{dt}\right], \tag{11}$$

where r = radial coordinate

u, v = radial and tangential components of the wind

$\alpha = \dfrac{1}{RT}$, where R is the gas constant and T temperature

$f = 2\omega \sin \varphi$, where ω is the angular velocity of the earth's rotation, φ the latitude

F_u = friction term

$\dfrac{du}{dt}$ = radial acceleration.

The pressure gradient term in the equation for level h is expressed in terms of the surface pressure gradient and temperature gradient, the latter using the hypsometric equation. In the simplest case discussed, he allowed α to vary with r only and set $\alpha' = \alpha$. Then, subtracting Equation (11) from (10), and assuming that inertial and friction terms were small in comparison with the remaining terms, he obtained

$$\left(f + \frac{v'}{r}\right)v' - \left(f + \frac{v}{r}\right)v = gh\frac{\partial \ln \alpha}{\partial r}.$$

Furthermore, he assumed that except near the center where r was very small, the terms v'/r and v/r would be small in comparison with the parameter f and could therefore be set equal to each other, and thus arrived at the approximate relationship for the wind shear with height

$$v' - v = \frac{gh\dfrac{\partial}{\partial r}\ln \alpha}{f + \dfrac{v'}{r}} = -\frac{gh\dfrac{\partial}{\partial r}\ln T}{f + \dfrac{v'}{r}}.$$

In this equation (now called the thermal wind relationship) Ferrel had developed a tool that allowed the construction of an upper level wind field on the basis of a lower level wind field and temperature field. Since aerological data were practically

[111] *Ibid.*, p. 14.

nonexistent at his time, it was necessary to make appropriate assumptions about the horizontal temperature distribution at various levels. Ferrel assumed that the horizontal temperature function was of the form

$$T = T_0 + C + C \cos \frac{r}{R_0} \pi,$$

so that

$$\frac{dT}{dr} = -C \frac{\pi}{r} \sin \frac{r}{R_0} \pi,$$

where R_0 denotes the maximum value of r, $C = \frac{1}{2}(T_c - T_0)$, and subscripts c and o denote conditions at the center and outer limit of the system, respectively. Finally, although the equation was derived assuming an isothermal layer, he noted that it could be applied to a layer of constant lapse rate by setting α (hence T) equal to the midpoint or mean value for the layer.

Since pressure decreases faster with height in cold air than in warm air according to the hydrostatic equation, Ferrel could conclude that

> . . . in a cyclonic system, with a warm center, the gyratory velocity v decreases algebraically with the altitude, or, in other words, decreases in the cyclone and increases in the anticyclone. . . . In the system, therefore, with a warm center, the distance from the center at which the gyrations are reversed from the cyclonic to the anticyclonic decreases with the increase of altitude, and the more so the greater the value of C, so that at a considerable altitude, and with a large temperature gradient, or value of C, the gyratory velocity v may become negative at all distances from the center, however small, although it may have a large positive value at the earth's surface, and thus above that altitude the gyrations at all distances from the center are anticyclonic.[112]

Accordingly, with a sufficiently large horizontal temperature gradient the warm surface cyclone could be replaced by an anticyclone above a certain altitude. The transition from cyclonic to anticyclonic circulation in upper layers is indicated in Figure 23 by the dotted circle. This scheme enabled Ferrel to account theoretically and quantitatively for the barometric maximum and divergence assumed to prevail above the surface cyclone, a circumstance which Guldberg and Mohn could explain only in general qualitative terms.[113] Thus, the introduction of the thermal wind concept made it possible to offer informed and objective statements about the upper wind field on the basis of surface wind and temperature observations, at a time when few upper air observations were available.[114]

Ferrel's model of a stationary symmetric cyclone constituted a closed

---

[112] *Ibid.*, pp. 15–16.

[113] Nineteenth Century meteorologists generally believed (according to the thermal theory) that an anticyclone in the upper strata was necessary to ensure the maintenance of low pressure near the surface. Although no particular altitude was given, it was implied that the anticyclone occurred in cirrus level or slightly above (see Section 5.4).

[114] In his paper of 1878 Ferrel dealt with the special case of concentric isobars and isotherms. Actually Ferrel had first employed the thermal wind concept in his model of the general circulation, characterized by a polar cyclone. The term thermal wind was introduced by E. Gold in 1917; see Gold, "The Meteorological Office and the First World War," *Met. Mag.*, **84** (1955), p. 173.

circulation system where the air "ascends in the central part, or cyclone, and descends in the anticyclone" surrounding the interior part.[115] As noted in the discussion of Ferrel's cyclone model in Section 2.4, such a circulation system required an energy source that was located within its boundaries. Ferrel assigned this role to surface heating and latent heat release during condensation of water vapor, regarding the former as "primary" and the latter as a "secondary" source of heat:

> The first give[s] rise to the initial cyclonic motions of the air, and the latter can only come into play after these initial motions take place.[116]

Differences in incoming and outgoing radiation, he stated, produced inequalities of air temperature

> . . . which give rise to temperature gradients. If the isotherms be somewhat circular, as they frequently may be, we have approximately the condition of a cyclone.[117]

Latent heat release, he argued, played "an important part in cyclonic disturbances," for

> . . . the effect of the cold of expansion, or loss of sensible caloric, in the ascending currents is opposed to that arising from the primary disturbances, but the latent caloric set free in the condensation of the aqueous vapor in part replaces the loss of sensible caloric by expansion, more than one-half generally.[118]

In order that the cyclonic circulation be maintained, it was necessary that the body of the cyclone remained warmer than the environment, i.e., a continuous addition was required of a

> . . . reasonable amount of primary disturbance, although the ascending currents should be continually supplied below with air saturated with aqueous vapor . . . for if the ascending currents have been kept up long enough . . . and there has been no accession of temperature meanwhile from the primary causes, the temperature of the air above becomes so reduced, and the density consequently so great, that the atmospheric pressure, even of the lower strata, so far as it depends upon the temperature, becomes as great in the interior as in the exterior part of the disturbed area, and then the power of the cyclone and all motion must cease.[119]

Ferrel did not refer here to the self-limiting process in a closed vertical circulation system, where the descending branch, warming dry adiabatically, gradually becomes warmer than the ascending branch, cooling saturation adiabatically. Rather, consideration of observed temperature lapse rates forced him to his conclusion. The results of James Glaisher's balloon ascents, reported by Hann in a 1874 paper from which Ferrel adopted much of the basic material for his general discussion of atmospheric stability criteria, showed that on the average the

---

[115] Ferrel (1881), p. 29.
[116] *Ibid.*, p. 19.
[117] *Ibid.*
[118] *Ibid.*, p. 29.
[119] *Ibid.*, p. 26.

observed lapse rate approached the saturation adiabatic lapse rate of the rising air above 200m. Average lapse rates, of course, did not necessarily represent conditions in a cyclonic system. Ferrel felt that the actual lapse rate might often be larger than Glaisher's average values, especially in summer, thus favoring ascending motions. Ferrel believed that in the absence of exceptionally large initial and continuing temperature differences due to primary causes, latent heat release had to be regarded not only as an important but as a necessary condition for the maintenance of cyclones. Here he referred to

> . . . progressive cyclones of long continuance, and travelling over long distances. . . . The temperature disturbance due to the primary causes which first originate the cyclone must soon be lost, and then the cyclone must depend for its support upon the caloric of condensation.[120]

As in his early paper of 1859/60, Ferrel proposed in 1878 that "the progressive motion of a cyclone depends mostly upon the general motions of the atmosphere."[121] In addition, he stated, that the increase of the deflecting force with latitude resulted in a tendency for cyclones to propagate toward the pole. His model of a symmetric cyclone, representing a closed circulation system, was in accord with this view, for such a system could not at the same time "harbor a cause" that would enable it to propagate in a particular direction. In 1878 Ferrel emphasized, however, that the propagation of cyclones also depended on "other strong modifying influences, and perhaps among these the principal are the distribution of the aqueous vapor and the positions of the general isothermal lines."[122] In his discussion of these influences, Ferrel closely followed arguments put forward during the early 1870's by Mohn and the Reverend Clement Ley (whose meteorological work will be discussed in the following chapter). Ferrel suggested that in an eastward traveling cyclone of midlatitudes the condensation of water vapor mostly along "the east or northeast side of the cyclone . . . gives rise to a tendency to form a new center of a cyclone continually in advance of the old one, so that the progressive motion of the cyclone is rather"[123] a continuous reformation of the cyclone in advance of its center. It should be noted that this aspect of asymmetry in storms played a subordinate role in Ferrel's cyclone theory; it was dictated in part by observations and their interpretation in the current meteorological literature. From Ferrel's later publications it is seen that he continued to view cyclones as entities almost completely separate from the general circulation of the atmosphere.

In contrast, Guldberg and Mohn's view of the development of cyclones implied an intimate connection between cyclones and the general circulation. They emphasized that the real cyclone necessarily had to be asymmetric in order to allow

---

[120] *Ibid.*, p. 67. Similarly, of course, the original moisture supply must soon be exhausted if the assumption of a closed circulation was to be maintained. Ferrel was aware of these limitations of a closed circulation model, but he did not attempt to account for them in his theoretical cyclone model.

[121] *Ibid.*, p. 32.

[122] *Ibid.*

[123] *Ibid.*, pp. 32–33.

for the influx of alimentary warm, moist air needed for its maintenance, while at the same time initiating the propagation of the storm. They proposed that the entire process was analogous to the propagation of a wave. The notion that the ascending warm air in the cyclone did not form a central core but that the vertical circulation was asymmetric with respect to the center of low pressure at the surface became a focal point of cyclone research during the 1880's, as will be discussed in Chapter 6.

In summary, Ferrel as well as Guldberg and Mohn had analyzed the field of horizontal motions in their cyclone models by applying the hydrodynamic equations. They treated separately thermal aspects such as the conditions necessary for the development of convective instability and vertical motions. The authors, nevertheless, were aware that it was important to link thermal and dynamic aspects of cyclones to achieve an understanding of the processes by which a storm was maintained against the continuous dissipation of kinetic energy by friction. Working toward the solution of this problem, Ferrel derived the thermal wind relationship and Guldberg and Mohn arrived at the concept of advection of alimentary and supplementary air.

Later investigators, such as Margules, showed that the most suitable way to analyze the relationship between characteristics of air motion and the associated temperature changes was to treat it as a problem of energy conversion. Peslin, it will be recalled, had taken the first steps in this direction when he attempted to develop an energy budget for a cyclone. Ferrel knew about Peslin's work by 1877 through the translation of one of Peslin's papers by Cl. Abbe and references to Peslin in Guldberg and Mohn's memoir.[124] Guldberg and Mohn studied Peslin's memoir and greatly appreciated his contributions to meteorology, but they chose not to follow his lead in this direction. In fact, their view that the energy sources maintaining the cyclonic circulation were, in the last analysis, located largely outside the cyclonic system, would have greatly complicated the formulation of an energy budget. It will be seen that the first quantitative estimates of the energy budget of a cyclone by Margules in 1906 still involved the assumption that, to a first approximation, a cyclone could be regarded as an energetically closed system.

[124] *Ibid.*, p. 13. W. M. Davis' remarks on Ferrel's working habits are revealing: ". . . he studied the best records and results that he could obtain, always keeping well informed on new discoveries, and showing excellent discrimination in the selection of new material . . . he was not particularly interested in making references to every author that he read . . . any of the references he gives . . . will lead us to material of value" ("Ferrel's contributions to meteorology," *Am. Met. Journ.*, **8** (1891), p. 350.

Chapter

5 The Thermal Theory Put to Observational Test

5.1 INTRODUCTION

The thermal or convective theory, we have seen, was formulated by a number of scientists during the 1860's and 1870's. These formulations differed in more or less important details, but common to all was the assertion that the formation and maintenance of large-scale cyclones depended on the thermodynamic processes associated with the ascent of warm air and the condensation of water vapor. During the 1870's the thermal theory was accepted by the majority of meteorologists as a simple and most natural explanation of the origin and maintenance of cyclones. It appeared to be superior to earlier theories in potential usefulness as a tool for practical weather forecasting because it suggested a physical relationship between the pressure field, most prominent on synoptic charts, and temperature and precipitation patterns, rather than solely statistical correlations. This was important because most meteorologists, at that time as throughout the remainder of the Nineteenth Century, were associated with governmental institutions whose primary concern was weather forecasting and storm warning.

The thermal theory could be tested directly in many of its features by examination of observations and synoptic charts. Pertinent statistical investigations, which will be discussed in this chapter, were carried out during the 1870's and 1880's. These investigations touch primarily upon the relationship between surface temperature and precipitation patterns and cyclones (Sections 5.2 and 5.3) and the flow patterns in upper levels above surface cyclones and anticyclones, as portrayed by the movement of cirrus clouds (Section 5.4). The basic assumption of the convective or thermal theory, as stated above, appeared to be confirmed in these studies.

Around 1890, the first serious objections to the thermal theory were raised. Temperature observations at mountain stations appeared to leave no doubt that, at least in Europe, anticyclones on the average were warmer than cyclones up to the height of mountain tops, except for a shallow surface layer (Section 5.5). This result contradicted the assumption, fundamental to the thermal theory and based solely on surface observations, that cyclones were warm and anticyclones cold bodies of air. It also contradicted the assumption underlying Ferrel's cyclone model that cyclones and anticyclones were linked through a thermally driven closed vertical circulation. Controversy about these unexpected data widened when American observations did not confirm European data (Section 5.6). These events sparked interest in processes at upper levels and greatly stimulated the investigation of the vertical temperature structure of the atmosphere.

In addition to these empirical findings, physical arguments put forward by Hann conflicted with the assumption of a closed vertical circulation: saturation-adiabatic cooling taking place in the ascending branch in the central part of the cyclone and dry-adiabatic warming in the descending branch in the anticyclone would necessarily result in higher temperatures in the anticyclone than in the cyclone at the same level. This argument, seemingly supported by upper level temperature observations in Europe, was considered by a number of scientists to show that the thermal theory of cyclones could not be correct. Consequently, they began to search for a dynamic explanation for the formation of cyclones, regarding the cyclone's temperature distribution as a result of the wind and pressure distribution, rather than the cause (Section 5.7).

5.2 SYNOPTIC-STATISTICAL STUDIES—FAVORABLE EVIDENCE

a. Ley (1872)

A genuine search for a physical explanation of the phenomena exhibited by large systems of low pressure was revealed in the work of the majority of scientists discussed in the previous chapter. One approach to the cyclone problem, most evident in the writings of Ferrel, and Guldberg and Mohn, was to deduce the flow patterns of air in barometric depressions from an analysis of the forces and physical processes assumed to be active in storm formation, and then to compare the results with the known facts. Others adhered to an inductive approach, believing that the detailed study of observations of atmospheric phenomena themselves would eventually uncover the processes and forces by which they are governed. Buchan especially insisted that this was the proper method of scientific inquiry. Loomis had enthusiastically expressed the same opinion at the end of his classical 1846 paper:

> If we could be furnished with two meteorological charts of the United States, daily, for one year, . . . it would settle forever the laws of storms.[1]

Actually, both of these approaches—the deductive and the inductive—proved to be indispensible in attacking the cyclone problem. The analysis of forces and

[1] Loomis (1846), p. 183.

processes helped guide the meteorologist in his observations. It helped him select for observation those variables and factors which might be of importance for a deeper understanding of the atmospheric processes. In turn, observations furnished the tool for testing the theories. This direct way of testing was extremely important and fertile for Nineteenth Century meteorology. The mutual give and take between theory and observation is clearly reflected in the investigations discussed here.

Among the most valuable synoptic-statistical investigations carried out during the 1870's was the work of the Reverend Clement Ley, which he summarized in his widely read book on *The Laws of the Winds Prevailing in Western Europe*.[2] Ley was an amateur scientist of the gifted and respected type that British science seems to bring forth rather more frequently than other countries. During the 1870's he probably knew more about clouds than anyone else. His scientific treatment of the data he collected several times daily for more than a decade was classification at its best. His often novel ways of grouping observations revealed a keen insight into meteorological processes and led to startling results, which became points of departure for numerous investigations by other workers in subsequent years. In his book, Ley concluded from his long series of storm observations that it was imperative to study atmospheric conditions not only near the earth's surface but in the upper strata of the atmosphere as well. At the time, few of his contemporaries shared his conviction on the urgency of such observations. His own systematic studies of the three-dimensional structure of cyclones produced some highly relevant and far-reaching results (and will be discussed later in Section 5.4). Ley also investigated in detail the surface conditions of cyclones. His generalizations based on a careful statistical evaluation of a large number of cyclones appeared to be derived inductively and confirmed the synoptic investigations of a comparatively small number of storms by Buchan and Mohn. In the course of his studies Ley became a stout supporter of the thermal theory. His results were regarded as unbiased and carried much weight during the 1870's and 1880's.

Ley summarized his investigation of 388 cyclones, studied over a period of four years, in 11 propositions. Proposition 7, agreeing with the basic assumption of the thermal theory, stated:

> Depression areas are dependent both for their original development and subsequent expansion on precipitation. . . . Heavy precipitation invariably precedes their first formation, and accompanies their expansion, and its cessation immediately precedes their collapse and dissipation.[3]

This rule was augmented by Proposition 8:

> The influence of precipitation, as a disturbing or motive power in the lower regions of the atmosphere, commonly varies inversely as the general temperature of the atmosphere.[4]

---

[2] Clement Ley, *The Laws of the Winds Prevailing in Western Europe*, Part I (London, E. Stanford, 1872), 164 pp. See biographical note on Ley in Appendix.

[3] Ley (1872), p. 16.

[4] *Ibid*.

Ley viewed a barometric depression basically as a thermal phenomenon. Examining the antecedents of the formation of cyclones, however, Ley could not establish any direct relation between the genesis of a barometric depression and the pre-existing temperature field, a relationship that proponents of the thermal theory had often postulated and that had been demonstrated in fully developed cyclones. Subsequently, he attempted to provide evidence that the heat source sufficient to sustain the development of a cyclone was found in the latent heat released during condensation of water vapor. Certain observations, however, did not seem to fit this view. It had not escaped Ley's attention that precipitation occurred sometimes without the subsequent development of a cyclone. Also, his studies had revealed that certain pressure conditions appeared to favor the formation of cyclones, e.g., according to his statistics 70% of the storms formed in western Europe were produced in the southwest or south-southwest portion of an old, widely-expanded cyclonic system.[5] He concluded "the abstraction of aqueous vapour must cooperate to some extent with other circumstances in order to beget the effect ascribed to it."[6] It was the investigation of these "other circumstances" that acquired great significance for the future development of the thermal theory.

Ley's statistical evaluation of storm data showed that rather extensive areas of precipitation were associated with cyclonic development while thunderstorms and showers appeared to "have almost no effect" on the pressure field. Confronted with the same observation, Reye had pointed out that the deflecting force of the earth's rotation was negligible on such small scales; hence any existing pressure differences were equalized within a short time. And, as V. Bjerknes later added, the cause producing the low pressure would have to be active for a considerable length of time, on the order of days rather than hours, to make possible the formation of an extensive storm.

As Mohn and Loomis had concluded from their synoptic studies on the movement of cyclones, Ley inferred that the amount and distribution of precipitation were decisive for the propagation of a storm. Cyclones appeared to have a "self-developed motion, independent to a certain extent of the motion of the adjacent portion of atmosphere."[7] Like Mohn, he envisioned a process of propagation analogous to that of a wave where constantly new portions of air are drawn into circulation:

> The loss of aqueous vapour on the east begins in its turn to attract fresh currents which, in accordance with the universal conditions of the earth's rotation, tend to circulate in the same retrograde direction as the former, and in the course of a few hours from the original development of the circulation the whole system occupies a position considerably to the east of the locality in which it was developed.[8]

As in the work of Mohn, it was here implied that cyclones were to be regarded as energetically open systems, drawing constantly from energy sources lying at some

---

[5] *Ibid.*, p. 27.
[6] *Ibid.*, p. 29.
[7] *Ibid.*, pp. 36–37.
[8] *Ibid.*, p. 38. Ley used the term retrograde for cyclonic circulation.

distance from the center of the storm. In contrast to Mohn, however, Ley did not emphasize the study of different types of air currents entering the cyclone, as related to the weather phenomena observed in a storm. Mohn utilized the observation that air currents converging in a cyclone, being largely homogeneous bodies of air, tend to conserve their original characteristics for long periods of time. Ley stressed the idea of air mass modification, suggesting, for example, that the originally cold and dry air from the north entering a cyclone over the Atlantic in the rear could be modified on its path around the cyclone center to such an extent, due to solar radiation and surface contact, that it would arrive warm and moist at the front and produce precipitation.[9]

In 1880 Ley attempted to explain "the tendency which the cyclonic systems exhibit to run in a series" in conjunction with his statistical result that 70% of the cyclones he had observed in their early stages developed in the southwest quadrant of a mature storm:

> When the atmosphere over an extensive district . . . over a portion of the North Atlantic . . . is much charged with water-vapour, the formation of a large Nimbus is sufficient to originate a cyclonic system; but a considerable portion of the atmosphere which is drawn into the circulation never reaches the front of the cyclone at all, being left behind . . . before it has parted with its aqueous vapour, and is in the condition favourable for the propagation of another system.[10]

The last quotation is taken from a small manual on weather forecasting which Ley prepared upon the request of the Meteorological Council. At that time Ley was inspector of the meteorological stations in England and well acquainted with the problems of local weather forecasters. In his manual, which became very popular among English forecasters, Ley discussed the development and propagation of cyclones on the basis of the thermal theory and he demonstrated quite successfully the usefulness of the theory as an aid in weather analysis and forecasting.

b. Loomis and Others (1870's)

Almost simultaneously with the appearance of Ley's book on storms, Loomis began to publish a series of synoptic-statistical studies on North American cyclones and anticyclones. He utilized the daily weather charts of the U.S. Weather Bureau, available since 1871. His results, mostly in the form of tables, charts and rules, appeared with almost clocklike precision at half-year intervals from 1874 to 1889. A fundamental change in Loomis' scientific outlook was revealed in these papers, when compared to his earlier publications. In the 1840's, he had predicted that only the study of individual storms would bring progress in the understanding of the mechanism of cyclones, and that a short period of data would be sufficient to achieve this goal. By the 1870's the variety and irregular occurrence of weather phenomena in cyclones had severely dampened his earlier enthusiasm and had convinced him that only statistical studies of a large number of cases would reveal

---

[9] *Ibid.*, pp. 34–57.

[10] Ley, *Aids to the Study and Forecast of Weather* (London, Her Majesty's Stationary Office, 1880), p. 28.

the common features and causes underlying all cyclones. This development in Loomis' work indicates the limitations of the Baconian method. As Loomis progressed in his series of publications, the data not only became unmanageable, but "the failure of the data to arrange itself automatically into general laws"[11] was becoming obvious. Even so, Loomis' methodology was backed by the majority of meteorologists, as seen in a widespread trend during the 1870's toward statistical studies.

Analyzing 152 storms, Loomis found in 1874, in agreement with Ley's and his own earlier investigations on the propagation of cyclones, that "one circumstance which appears to have a decided influence in modifying the course of a storm path is the fall of rain."[12] He showed in particular "that the average course of the storm paths for 24 hours coincides very closely with the position of the axis of the rain area [the direction in which it was most extended] for the preceding eight hours;" he added, "generally when a storm is advancing most rapidly, the rain extends to an unusual distance from the eastern side of the storm."[13] "The connection here discovered," he remarked, "cannot be regarded as accidental," but supported Espy's view that the "fall of rain" was the cause of the "fall of the barometer":

> When the vapor of the atmosphere is condensed, its latent heat is liberated, which raises the temperature of the surrounding air, causing it to expand and flow off laterally in all directions in the upper regions of the atmosphere, thus causing a diminished pressure over the region of precipitation, and an increased pressure on all sides beyond the area of the rain.[14]

Loomis corroborated his results in 1876 when he showed quantitatively that "the amount of rainfall is greatest when the pressure at the center of the storm is decreasing, or the storm is increasing in intensity."[15]

The asymmetry found in the distribution of precipitation with regard to the pressure field convinced Loomis that

> The progress of the storm eastward is not due wholly to a *drifting*, resulting from the influence of an upper current of the atmosphere from the west, but the storm works its own way eastward in consequence of the greater precipitation on the eastern side of the storm.[16]

Loomis here proposed essentially the same explanation for the propagation of a storm as Mohn and Ley, and in a sense reaffirmed his own observational results of the 1840's. As will be recalled, he had demonstrated with his first synoptic charts that two different currents of air were entering the cyclone: warm and moist air coming from the southern regions in the front part and cold and dry air from the northern regions of the continent in the rear, often clashing along extended squall

---

[11] Daniels, *op. cit.*, p. 106.

[12] Loomis, "Results derived from examination of the United States weather maps for 1872 and 1873," *Am. Journ. Sci.*, 3rd series, **8** (1874), p. 3.

[13] *Ibid.*, p. 5.

[14] *Ibid.*, p. 6.

[15] Loomis, "Contributions to meteorology," 5th paper, *Am. Journ. Sci.*, 3rd series, **12** (1876), p. 12.

[16] Loomis (1874), p. 6.

lines (Section 2.3a). Loomis consequently discarded the assumption put forward by Ferrel in his early papers that cyclones were closed, self-dependent systems drifting like an eddy in the river of the general upper westward current. (It was seen in the previous chapter that Ferrel's memoir of 1878 also moved closer to Ley's and Loomis' view on the propagation of cyclones.)

Studies like those of Loomis and Ley won many adherents to the thermal theory. Their methods of data acquisition and evaluation were regarded as objective and promising, and their results incited fellow workers to pursue a similar course of study. Confirmative studies were soon commenced at the weather services of other countries, e.g., by F. van Rysselberghe[17] in Belgium and N. Hoffmeyer in Denmark.[18] Hoffmeyer studied the observations of 120 Danish stations over a period of one year and found a decided influence of precipitation on the intensity and propagation of cyclones. For example, if precipitation was very strong in minor or secondary lows (Teildepressionen), "then they can become vigorous enough as to continue their path as independent minima." He added, "I completely agree with Mr. Cl. Ley that at least the minima that develop in Europe form in association with strong precipitation."[19] Hoffmeyer's opinion carried much weight because of the prestige his institute had acquired through the daily publication of the so-called Hoffmeyer synoptic charts covering the Atlantic (since 1874). In fact, Hoffmeyer had significantly enlarged the region of synoptic analysis over northwestern Europe and the Atlantic by establishing weather stations in Greenland, Iceland and the Faroe Islands.[20]

5.3 CONTROVERSIAL EVIDENCE

Although synoptic-statistical investigations had generally supported the thermal theory, certain empirical facts continued to puzzle meteorologists. For this reason, Julius Hann, who became director of the Austrian weather service in 1877, called for a more explicit and precise definition of the role of precipitation in storms in his 1873 review of Reye's book; in this way he greatly stimulated meteorological research. Hann questioned in particular the notion that the precipitation process was the main cause for pressure fall in midlatitude cyclones. For example, he argued, the heavy tropical rains during the wet season appeared to have no effect at all on the normal daily pressure curve observed in these regions.[21] In a paper of 1874, Hann underlined this point by demonstrating, using rainfall data of Batavia, that pressure actually increased slightly during rainfall.[22] Reye readily conceded

[17] van Rysselberghe, "Les tempêtes d'Europe." *L'Annuaire de Observatoire Royal de Bruxelles*, **45** (1878), 184–247.

[18] Hoffmeyer, "Luftdruck und Regen, Wirbelstürme," *Wien, Met. Zeits.*, **10** (1875), 6–13; also "Weitere Bemerkungen über die Luftdruckvertheilung im Winter," *Ibid.*, **14** (1879), 73–82.

[19] Hoffmeyer (1875), p. 7.

[20] See biographical note on Hoffmeyer in Appendix.

[21] Hann, "Bemerkungen über die Barometerminima in den Sturmcentren und die Luftcirculation in den Gewitterwolken," *Wien, Met. Zeits.*, **8** (1973), 102–106.

[22] Hann, "Ueber den Einfluss des Regens auf den Barometerstand und über die Entstehung der Niederschläge im Allgemeinen," *Wien, Met. Zeits.*, **9** (1874), 289–296. Hann correctly explained the pressure rise as a result of the displacement of warm rising air by cold downdrafts of outflowing air in the

that "some widespread precipitation may not result in a barometric minimum,"[23] but that "there are such cases that . . . prevent the formation of a minimum at the place of the precipitation."[24] This was to be expected, he remarked, but it did not deny the rarefaction of air during cloud formation, a fact ascertained by physical laws, and thus a sound basis for the convective theory. Reye illustrated this point by constructing several possible cases in which advected air currents of different temperature in upper and lower layers over a certain locality might offset density and pressure changes resulting from the condensation of water vapor.[25] Moreover, in the tropics from where Hann had quoted observations, differences in air density due to the condensation of water vapor should be readily equalized, because of the minimal influence of the deflecting force of the earth's rotation in these regions, so that no appreciable effect on the pressure distribution should be observed.[26] The experienced synoptician Hoffmeyer strongly supported Reye's position.[27]

Loomis in the United States was also led to the conclusion, as he progressed with his investigations of storms, that heavy precipitation did not necessarily produce a cyclone. He wrote in 1877 that "there seems to be no room for doubt that barometric minima sometimes form with little or no rain,"[28] and, almost negating his earlier positive statements on the thermal theory,

> It seems safe to conclude that rain-fall is not essential to the formation of areas of low barometer, and is not the principal cause of their formation or of their progressive motion.[29]

However, perhaps for want of a more plausible explanation, Loomis continued to support the thermal theory in principle. He emphasized, "I have found no storm of *great violence* which was not accompanied by a considerable fall of rain."[30]

Despite his reservations Hann conceded that certain circumstances appeared to make the thermal theory extremely likely. Referring to the direct vertical circulation of a rain cloud, as pictured by Mohn in his *Storm-Atlas*, Hann noted in 1873 that such a circulation could be observed in thunderstorms whose cloud distribution in most cases reflected, in shape, the inflowing and outflowing motions.

> It is interesting to watch how fast the cloud cover often spreads far away from the

---

area of rain. However, the area of high pressure in this case is associated with the mesoscale phenomena of showers and thunderstorms which are not directly comparable to the macro-synoptic scale midlatitude cyclones associated with extensive, organized areas of precipitation.

[23] Reye, "Ueber die Abnahme des Luftdruckes bei der Wolkenbildung," *Wien, Met. Zeits.*, **8** (1873), p. 178.

[24] *Ibid.*

[25] *Ibid.*

[26] Reye (1872), 138–139.

[27] He informed Hann in a note to the *Meteorologische Zeitschrift* (1875, *op. cit.*, p. 6) that "barometric maxima give dry weather; however, the more the minima are approaching us, the more rain we receive . . ." Hoffmeyer then essentially reiterated Mohn's findings. Hann conceded, but only up to a point, noting that Hoffmeyer's conclusions were not fully justified because they had been established only for places "north of the Alps." See Sprung's account of the controversy in his book *Lehrbuch der Meteorologie* (Hamburg, Hoffmann & Campe, 1885), 236–237.

[28] Loomis, "Contributions to meteorology," 7th paper, *Am. Journ. Sci.*, **14** (1877), p. 16.

[29] *Ibid.*

[30] Loomis, "Contributions to meteorology," 8th paper, *Am. Journ. Sci.*, **15** (1878), p. 7.

> original core of the thunderstorm and occupies the greatest part of the sky with its streaky opaque-whitish veil.[31]

The anvil-shaped upper part of these clouds, he remarked, reminded him of "Reye's cloud carpet over the cyclones."[32] Undoubtedly, he continued, thunderstorms must be considered as processes that reinstituted the equilibrium of "atmospheric layers lying spread out one above another." They must be seen as

> product of ascending and descending currents, [and as product] of the heat exchange between the upper and lower layers. The whirlstorms [Wirbelstürme] constitute this process even to a greater extent.[33]

In his widely read paper of 1874, Hann concluded with a strong statement in favor of the thermal theory, here quoting from Abbe's English translation of the German original:

> The causal relationship between the precipitations and the origin and the progress of storms can therefore only consist in this, that the condensation of aqueous vapor gives the air a more or less decided upward impulse, and thereby produces and continually maintains a flow of air from all sides toward the rain-cloud. But so long as no whirl is produced thereby, this process causes no notable change in atmospheric pressure in the horizontal strata of air. . . . I therefore believe the diminution of pressure in the center of a storm-area to be a mechanical effect of the whirling movement of the air. This whirl, however, continually receives new force, and is controlled by the process of precipitation. I therefore agree with Reye when he says that in the whirlstorms [i.e., cyclones, Wirbelstürme] the moving force is the latent heat of the condensed aqueous vapor.[34]

Thus in 1874 Hann readily conceded that the thermal energy associated with the release of latent heat must be regarded as the driving force of a cyclone, once it had been formed. At that time he objected only to the view that thermal energy was also the primary cause for the initial diminution of barometric pressure.

In his review of Reye's book, Hann focussed attention on still another observation that could not be fitted into the scheme of the early convective theory. His argument had been known for some time, namely, that cyclones are generally of greater intensity in winter than in summer:

> The more intensive precipitation during summer should produce stronger minima than the weaker ones during winter; to the contrary, however, the barometric minima become less and less significant toward summer.[35]

Reye met this argument by referring to the observation made by Mohn in 1870, namely, that in conjunction with precipitation, horizontal temperature contrasts

---

[31] Hann (1873), "Bemerkungen . . . ," p. 105.
[32] *Ibid.* See also Reye (1872), p. 132.
[33] *Ibid.*, p. 106.
[34] Hann, "The laws of the variation of temperatures in ascending currents of air, and some of the most important consequences deducible therefrom," translated in Abbe's first collection, (1877), *op. cit.*, p. 414, from Hann (1874), *op. cit.*
[35] Hann (1873), "Bemerkungen . . . ," p. 103.

play a decisive role in the formation and propagation of cyclones. Mohn had then proposed that the greater intensity of North American cyclones, as compared with European storms, might be explained by the greater temperature differences between the front and rear of these storms.[36] Similarly, Reye pointed out, temperature contrasts in barometric depressions show marked differences between winter and summer:

> . . . the circumstance that the temperature difference between the polar and equatorial stream in our [latitudes] is larger in winter than in summer may contribute to the fact that in our latitudes the barometer-minima are more vigorous in winter than in summer despite weaker precipitation.[37]

Thus, at this stage in the development of the thermal theory, namely, in the early 1870's, horizontal temperature contrasts and latent heat release were regarded as *complementary* in the development of cyclones. The role and importance of thermal contrasts in cyclone development was further explored and substantiated by Guldberg and Mohn in the late 1870's (Section 4.6a) and moved into the center of investigations in cyclone theory during the 1880's.

The synoptic-statistical studies discussed so far represented an extremely important contribution to the development of the theory of cyclones. They made it clear that atmospheric processes are too complex to be encompassed by overly simplifying assumptions about the physical processes involved. It had been shown that other processes, in addition to convection, were responsible for the initial pressure fall and the establishment of cyclonic motion. Nevertheless, during this encounter of theory with observations, the thermal theory had stood its ground surprisingly well. In order to clarify the influence of other causes besides convection and precipitation on the formation of cyclones, studies concerning other observable aspects of the thermal theory were intensified during the 1870's and 1880's. In particular, attempts were made to extend the range of observations above the surface of the earth. It will be seen that the analysis of cloud observations and temperature records of mountain stations was highly significant for the further development of the theory of cyclones.

5.4 CLOUD OBSERVATIONS

a. Ley (1872–1877)

If a cyclone's low surface pressure is to be maintained in conjunction with convergence and ascending motion, then a field of divergent motion is required at some altitude above the surface depression so that the inflow of air below is balanced by the outflow above. In 1876, Guldberg and Mohn (and earlier Galton and

[36] Mohn, *Storm-Atlas*, p. 24. The differences in temperature contrasts, Mohn explained, were enhanced by the differences in the position of land and sea with regard to a storm and its path. In America, the winds entering the front parts of many storms come at first from the Gulf of Mexico and later, on their way eastward, from the Atlantic and Gulf Stream, while winds from arctic America are entering in the rear. In contrast, winds from the ocean are entering the rear part of most European storms.

[37] Reye (1873), "Ueber die Abnahme . . . ," p. 178.

others) had recognized the need for such an upper divergence in support of a continuous convective current. The first statistical studies demonstrating the existence of such upper currents associated with cyclones were furnished by Ley and H. H. Hildebrandsson during the 1870's.

When Clement Ley commenced his upper air studies he was especially interested in this particular point, namely "whether any general relation exists between the motions of this stratum of air and the conditions and distribution of atmospheric pressures at the surface of the earth."[38] Such investigation, based on "the collection and analysis of a very extensive series of observations of the highest clouds,"[39] he hoped, would bring an end to the role of "deus ex machina" so often assigned by meteorologists to the upper currents in order "to explain the obscurities of the science."[40] During the 1870's, his comprehensive knowledge of clouds and their relationship to storms made him particularly qualified for this investigation.[41] Ley's first contribution to the clarification of problems associated with the three-dimensional structure of the atmosphere were based on the results of ten years of cloud observations made several times daily, as far as was possible, and reported in his book of 1872.

The point of departure for Ley's studies was the attempt to ascertain whether upper currents, as portrayed by the movement of cirrus clouds, in fact followed Buys Ballot's law—that is, whether they were subject to the same pressure field as the surface currents. Examining over 600 observations Ley concluded that upper winds generally deviated from surface winds and sometimes even opposed them, i.e., that the upper level pressure distribution generally differed from the surface pressure distribution. In particular, Ley noted a class of cyclones with "direct upper-current circulation above a retrograde circulation of the surface winds"[42] (i.e., anticyclonic circulation above cyclonic circulation). This observation appeared to suggest "that a great rarefaction near the surface of the earth may even coincide with a slight accumulation in the higher districts."[43] This feature accorded perfectly with the vertical circulation scheme assumed in the convective theory, namely that an area of high pressure associated with anticyclonic circulation and outflowing currents was located above the surface cyclone.

In most storms, however, cloud movement indicated a cyclonic circulation at the level of outflowing currents. This observation was somewhat surprising but not incompatible with the convective theory. It could be assumed that in the case of a storm, with cyclonic outflow at the level of cirrus clouds, the anticyclonic circulation set in at still higher levels. Perhaps Ley viewed such an assumption as

---

[38] Ley (1872), *op. cit.*, p. 151.

[39] *Ibid.*, p. 150.

[40] *Ibid.*, p. 149.

[41] See obituary of Rev. William Clement Ley, *Quart. Journ. Roy. Met. Soc.*, **23** (1897). On p. 104 he is quoted as saying in one of his lectures: "My own earliest recollections are those of looking at the clouds, and forming infantine speculations as to the cause of their forms and movements, and for being reprehended for exposing myself to all states of weather for this purpose. The tendency was inveterate, and to this day I have spent nearly a twelfth part of my waking existence in that occupation."

[42] *Ibid.*, p. 159.

[43] *Ibid.*, pp. 159–160.

too reminiscent of the concept of "deus ex machina." Instead he thought cross-isobaric outflow at cirrus level sufficient to maintain the cyclonic circulation system:

> When the resulting rarefaction [from extensive precipitation] has become considerable, the attenuated atmosphere tends to rise, and ascending columns of dry, warm, and light air are established above the focus of the depression. These currents continue during their ascent to gyrate in accordance with the motion originally imparted to them when near the earth's surface, and that frequently with great velocity, being freed from the obstruction of the surface. Having attained their appropriate level they incline to flow off in all directions from the axis of the depression, having their place constantly filled by fresh ascending columns from below, and themselves settling down towards the regions from which the new surface-currents have to be drawn.[44]

Detailed results such as the existence of cyclonic outflow in upper levels above the surface cyclone could only be achieved by means of careful evaluation of the cirrus cloud observations (assuming that the path of clouds represented air trajectories). The classification of the observations with regard to upper level and surface pressure distribution therefore was an important aspect of Ley's work. He ordered his data graphically, according to different segments or quadrants of the surface cyclones, oriented with respect to the path of the cyclone. He summarized his results in the form of charts that illustrated the flow patterns of a cyclone near the surface and at cirrus level (Figure 24).[45] These charts showed a pronounced upper outflow toward the east, i.e., in the direction of the path taken by the surface cyclone. This feature indicated that outflow took place most easily and unimpeded in the direction of the general westerly upper current. The cirrus flow over the rear of the cyclone coincided more closely with low-level winds.

The flow patterns indicated that in the case of a traveling cyclone southwesterly winds occurred at a later time in the upper levels over a certain locality than in lower levels. Observations like this were extremely difficult to make because the low-level clouds increasingly obstructed the view of the cirrus clouds as the center of the storm was approaching. Ley took particular care to ascertain and retest this result because it implied a very unexpected feature: that the barometric depression in upper levels was delayed with respect to the low-level cyclone (Figures 24, 25). The data appeared to be absolutely trustworthy, so Ley was forced to conclude that "the axis of a progressive retrograde circulation commonly inclines backwards."[46] Meteorologists could not easily accept this bold statement for it contradicted the wide-spread opinion that the axis of a cyclone must incline forward because the lower section of the cyclone was retarded by surface friction in its normally eastward propagation. The latter view tacitly postulated that the propagation of a cyclone was largely governed by the generally eastward flowing upper current, and it was supported by the common observation that the shield of cirrus, indicating an approaching storm, was far ahead of the cyclone

---

[44] *Ibid.*, p. 160.

[45] Ley, "Relation between upper and under currents of the atmosphere around areas of barometric depression," *Quart. Journ. Roy. Met. Soc.*, **3** (1877), 437–445.

[46] Ley (1872), p. 157.

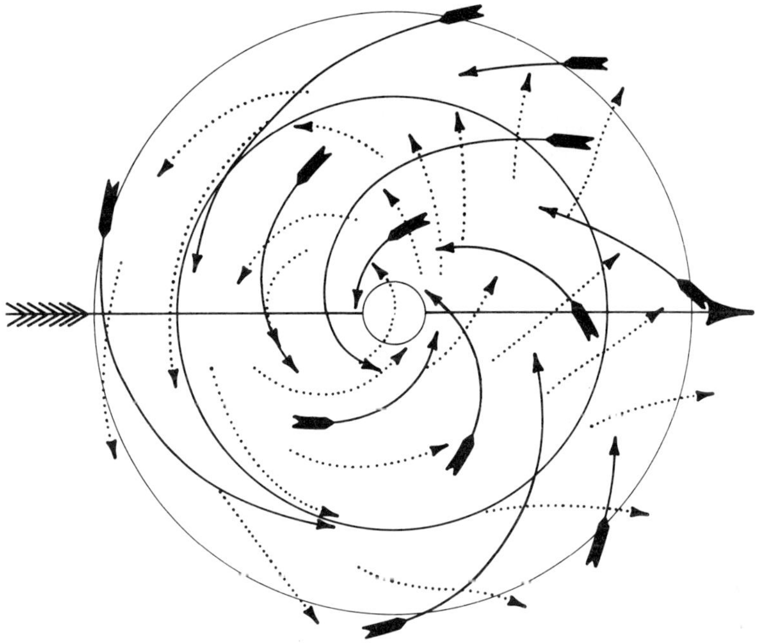

FIGURE 24. Relation between upper winds and surface winds in cyclones according to Ley reconstructed from "Relation between upper and under currents of the atmosphere around areas of barometric depression," *Quart. Journ. Roy. Met. Soc.*, **3** (1877). Thin inner and outer circles delineate area of cloud observations, with the lowest pressure in the center. Thick middle circle represents outermost of closed surface isobars. Solid arrows indicate pattern of surface currents; dashed arrows, pattern of upper currents as portrayed by movement of cirrus clouds; long heavy arrow shows direction of propagation.

center at the surface.[47] Ley attempted to explain the backward inclination of the cyclone axis, as revealed by his more exacting observations, by placing the driving force of propagation near the surface:

> When the depression is progressive, as is commonly the case, the precipitation of aqueous vapor in the lower regions of the atmosphere being rapidly propagated in one direction or another over the earth's surface, the summit of the ascending air column is left considerably behind the base.[48]

And further,

> It was this phenomenon . . . which led me to the conclusion . . . that the depression perpetually reproduces itself to the eastward side of its former position, such reproduction being due to changes of tension taking place primarily in the lower strata.[49]

[47] For example, Redfield stated convincingly as early as 1831 in "On the prevailing storms of the Atlantic coast" (*Am. Journ. Sci.*, **20**), p. 44: "The gyral axis of a storm in most cases, is probably inclined in the direction of its progress, for, being retarded by the increased resistance of the surface, the more elevated parts of the storm must necessarily be inclined forward and overrun to a very considerable distance the more quiet atmosphere, which lies near the surface. This will account for the first hazy appearance, i.e., cirrus of the storm . . . often, some hours previous to any change of wind at the surface."

[48] Ley (1872), p. 161.

[49] Ley, "On the inclination of the axes of cyclones," *Quart. Journ. Roy. Met. Soc.*, **5** (1879), p. 168. Tension refers here to barometric pressure.

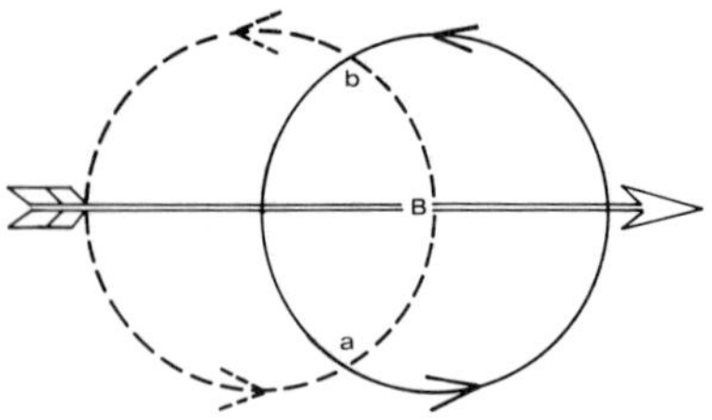

FIGURE 25. Inclination of cyclone axis with altitude; reconstructed from Ley, *The Laws of the Winds in Western Europe* (1872). Solid circle indicates position of surface cyclone, and dashed circle indicates position of upper cyclone with respect to path of cyclone. Note that the backward inclination of the circulation axis with height is also apparent in Figure 24.

Ley proposed here that the cyclonic circulation represented a wave rather than a vortex. This statement was in agreement with Mohn's experience that the particular distribution of the inflowing air masses determined the direction of cyclone progress. In 1880 Wladimir Köppen brought this argument to its ultimate and simple conclusion. He showed that the pressure field must change with height in such a way that the center of lowest pressure gradually shifted toward the coldest side of the cyclone, normally toward the rear of the storm, and that the path taken by a cyclone was therefore determined by conditions in lower as well as upper levels (see Section 6.2b).

Ley's results made it abundantly clear how accurate and useful cloud observations could be. In the absence of other regular aerological data, the evaluation of cloud observations became one of the most important empirical tools in the analysis of the three-dimensional structure of the atmosphere during the remainder of the Nineteenth Century.

b. Hildebrandsson (1870's)

In the early 1870's, the Swedish meteorologist H. H. Hildebrandsson (then lecturer in meteorology at the University of Upsala) commenced his influential cloud studies, following the example set by Ley's investigations. Subsequently, Hildebrandsson became director of the Meteorological Observatory in Upsala and professor of meteorology at the university (1878–1906). The combination of a professorship with a research institute (the Swedish weather service was located in Stockholm) was unique in Nineteenth Century meteorology. Utilizing effectively the opportunities offered by his position, Hildebrandsson established himself as a leader in international meteorology and expert in upper air research during the last decades of the century. Having at his disposal far greater means and professional help than Ley could have hoped for, Hildebrandsson organized, from 1873 onward, a 21-station network for cirrus observations which extended across Europe. It was his goal to decide by means of these observations between the convective theory and the mechanical cyclone theories put forward by the French meteorologists, E. H. Marié-Davy and H. Faye. Ley also provided Hildebrandsson with data. Hildebrandsson plotted these cloud observations directly onto synoptic charts

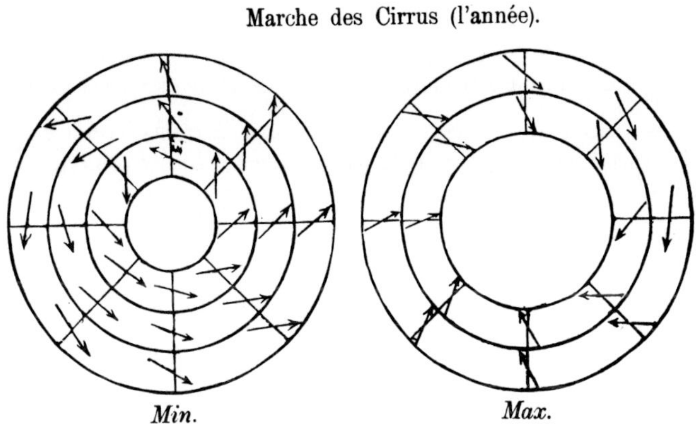

FIGURE 26. Movement of cirrus clouds above cyclones and anticyclones (Hildebrandsson, 1881), from Hildebrandsson, "Sur la distribution des éléments météorologiques autour des minima et des maxima barométriques," *Soc. R. des Sciènces d'Upsal* (1881). Arrows indicate direction of movement of cirrus clouds. Left: cyclone, inner isobar 740 mm Hg, outer isobar 760 mm Hg. Right: anticyclone, inner isobar 770 mm Hg, outer isobar 760 mm Hg.

(covering most of Europe) which were provided by N. Hoffmeyer, director of the Danish weather service.[50]

Hildebrandsson published his first results in 1875 and 1877; they clearly confirmed most of Ley's findings.[51] One of the first conclusions was that "the air flows away from centers of minima and converges toward centers of maxima in the highest regions of the atmosphere" (Figure 26).[52] Since this flow pattern was just the opposite of that found near the surface, it followed that there existed a vertical circulation between lower and upper layers. "The principal agent of that circulation," Hildebrandsson then suggested along the lines of the thermal theory,

> . . . must well be the difference in temperature and humidity at the earth surface . . . and in the highest regions of the atmosphere.[53]

There was one important point of disagreement between Hildebrandsson's and Ley's results, for Hildebrandsson found it impossible to confirm that the axis of cyclones inclined backward, except in a very few cases. This inconsistency was conveniently "overlooked" for some time. No doubt, Hildebrandsson's international reputation as compared with Ley's relatively isolated position contributed to the initial neglect of Ley's results.[54] In the course of his career Hildebrandsson collaborated with Mohn in Norway, Ralph Abercromby and Ley in England,

---

[50] H. Hildebrand Hildebrandsson, "Ueber die Richtung der Bewegung der Cirruswolken," *Wien, Met. Zeits.*, **9** (1874), 312–313. See biographical note on Hildebrandsson in Appendix.

[51] Hildebrandsson, *Essai sur les Courants Supérieurs de l'Atmosphère dans leurs Relation aux Lignes Isobarométriques* (Upsala, Berling, 1875), 14 pp., and *Atlas des Mouvements Supérieurs de l'Atmosphère* (Stockholm, 1877), 20 pp.

[52] Hildebrandsson, *Essai* . . . , 10–11.

[53] *Ibid.*, p. 11.

[54] Hildebrandsson was inclined to attribute the discrepancy to differences in cyclone structure over England and Sweden. But this was not a strong argument, and he did not stress the point elsewhere.

Teisserenc de Bort in France, Gustav Hellmann and Wladimir Köppen in Germany, and he was consequently called the "pathbreaker" of international meteorology.

Hildebrandsson stressed that the regions of cyclones and anticyclones

> . . . must be regarded as the seats of vertical currents, whereas the horizontal circulation, considered for a long time as the sole or at least principal [circulation], is, using a mathematical expression, a quantity of higher order.[55]

Hildebrandsson regarded cyclones and anticyclones as salient features of the atmospheric circulation in middle latitudes. Prior to the 1870's, no serious attempts were made to detect any influence of cyclones on the general circulation, nor, with a few exceptions, does it appear that such an influence was thought feasible. This attitude is best seen in the work of Ferrel who regarded cyclones as closed independent systems. On the other hand, the idea that cyclones and anticyclones form a significant part of the general circulation was discernible in the work of Mohn and Ley.

In summary, it may be said that the thermal theory, which had been developed on the basis of surface observations, had stood well the first test by observations from the upper air. The outflowing motion at the level of cirrus clouds above cyclones, and the observed upper current convergence toward areas of high surface pressure, could be regarded as another proof of ascending motion in cyclones. However, upper air observations had also revealed some unexpected results, such as the asymmetrical outflow above cyclones and, in the case of Ley's investigations, backward inclination of the cyclone axis with height. All these features were still awaiting their full physical explanation, let alone their mathematical description. Progress in this direction rested on the investigation of the vertical temperature structure of cyclones. Results of the first temperature records from mountain stations, which will be discussed in the following sections, underlined the complexity of the three-dimensional cyclone structure. Creating, at first, more questions than they solved, these observations greatly stimulated the search for the underlying physical processes and theoretical explanations.

5.5 UPPER LEVEL TEMPERATURE OBSERVATIONS (1880's)

A tacit assumption of the thermal theory was that the warm inner core of a cyclone reached at least as high as the cirrus level. This conjecture was an extension of the long established "rule" that cyclones were warmer at the earth's surface than anticyclones, and it found support in considerations of the release of latent heat during cloud formation. While the mainstream of meteorological research was focused upon the interpretation of synoptic charts and surface observations, there were a few scientists who saw a definite need to ascertain the validity of this assumption by detailed, quantitative studies of the vertical temperature structure of cyclones and anticyclones. The tools available in the 1870's for such an endeavor were not too promising, as the following brief review of efforts in the exploration of the upper air during the Nineteenth Century will indicate.

---

[55] Hildebrandsson, *Essai* . . . , p. 11.

Since Charles' historic balloon ascent in 1783, reaching a height of 3 km, manned balloon ascents were the principal means for observing upper atmospheric conditions. Some well-known Nineteenth Century ascents were Gay-Lussac's flight in 1804 to 7 km, Glaisher's series of ascents during the 1860's, reaching 9 km, and the series of ascents by Berson at Lindenberg (Berlin) around the turn of the century. These flights were expensive, isolated and sporadic and therefore had only limited use in the systematic observation of the upper atmosphere. Successful experiments with unmanned balloons carrying recording apparatus (sounding balloons) were not started until the 1890's. In 1893, Hermite and Besançon launched balloons to heights of 15 km. Teisserenc de Bort started regular balloon launches from his observatory at Trappes, near Paris, in 1898. In order to obtain useful data from sounding balloons (other than optical sightings) it was necessary to recover the recording instruments which descended to earth via parachute after bursting of the balloon. Recovery often took days, weeks or longer.[56] Somewhat earlier than the introduction of unmanned balloons was the systematic use of kites with instrument packages attached, reaching levels of 3–4 km. Lawrence Rotch's private observatory at Blue Hill near Boston was the site of the first regular kite launchings in 1894. Impressed by the first results, the Weather Bureau opened 16 kite stations in the United States in 1898. Important European kite stations around the turn of the century were at Trappes, Hamburg, Lindenberg, and Kew Observatory near London.

Unmanned balloon flights and kite launchings, it must be emphasized, were developments of the 1890's and later. During the 1870's, however, when questions about the atmospheric conditions in upper levels became important, the only alternative to manned balloon flights was to collect observations on high mountains. It was argued that data from solitary, steeply rising summits closely approximated conditions of the free atmosphere. Mountain observations had the advantage over balloon recordings that they could be taken at the same locality and for any length of time, while balloon observations could sample the upper atmosphere for short periods of time only.

During the mid-seventies, a small number of mountain observatories were in operation, the most important being those of Puy de Dôme (1463 m) in France and Pikes Peak (4300 m) in the United States. Unfortunately, as Hann reported on the state of mountain observatories at the second International Meteorological Congress in Rome in 1879, the publications of both these observatories were extremely unsatisfactory.[57] During the 1880's, Hann, who always had taken a special interest in mountain weather phenomena, took the initiative in establishing

---

[56] A breakthrough in the acquisition of meteorological data from the upper atmosphere was the development of the radiosonde transmitting data to the ground while the balloon was still in flight. Successful radiosondes were developed during the late 1920's and 1930's by the Bureau de France, Moltchanoff in Russia, Vaisälä in Finland and others. For more detailed reviews of the early exploration of the upper air see Assmann, *Wissenschaftliche Luftfahrten*, Vol. 1, Geschichte und Beobachtungsmaterial (Braunschweig, Vieweg & Sohn, 1899), 3–138, and Khrgian, *op. cit.*, pp. 254–299.

[57] Hann, *Bericht erstattet dem zweiten internationalen Meteorologischen Congress über die Beobachtungen auf hohen Bergen und im Luftballon* (Wien, k.k. Hof- und Staatsdruckerei, 1879), 23 pp.

mountain observatories in Austria. His subsequent pioneering studies encouraged similar steps in other countries.

In part, Hann pursued the establishment of high mountain observatories so energetically because he had obtained some highly interesting results from a study of Austrian mountain observations for the winter of 1876. By means of daily observations taken simultaneously on mountain peaks and at their bases, he showed that an area of high pressure prevailing for a period of about 10 days was characterized by abnormally high temperatures on the summits and very low temperatures in the valleys. The lower cold layer was very shallow and was separated by a strong temperature "inversion" from the body of warm air.[58] His observations directly contradicted the generally accepted explanation of areas of high surface pressure being a consequence of relatively low temperatures in the higher air columns. Examining Hoffmeyer's synoptic charts, he found that the temperature increase with height was characteristic of winter anticyclones in general and that

> . . . the reversal of the normal temperature decrease upward is not to be regarded only as effect of an abnormal cooling of the lowest strata, whereas normal temperatures prevail in upper strata; at such times the air in higher altitudes is altogether abnormally warm and, therefore, a specific heat source must be assumed for this fact. However, one hardly can look for it in southerly winds, for the phenomenon occurs only during calm.[59]

Thus, ruling out advection of warm air as the cause of the high temperature in winter anticyclones, Hann concluded that the temporary, traveling anticyclones, as they occur on synoptic charts, appeared to represent "dynamic phenomena."[60] They differed fundamentally from "the thermal[ly-produced] pressure increases in winter over the large continents"[61] which consisted of comparatively shallow stationary cold bodies of air. The high temperature and the extreme dryness observed at mountain peaks during the periods of high pressure, he felt, were most naturally explained in analogy to the foehn process, "by the descent of air from upper strata."[62] The cold air found in the lower layers, he noted, resulted from the effect of outgoing radiation. When Hann published these results in 1876 his observations did not receive much attention. At any rate, the fact that certain anticyclones had been found to be "warm core" was not accepted as decisive evidence against the thermal theory. Reflecting on the temperature structure that was assumed to exist in cyclones according to the thermal theory, Hann himself admitted in 1891, "I must confess that formerly I myself hardly doubted it because the physical train of thought, which leads to this assumption, is so obvious."[63]

---

[58] Hann, "Ueber das Luftdruckmaximum vom 23 Jänner bis 3 Februar 1876, nebst Bemerkungen über die Luftdruck-Maxima im Allgemeinen," *Wien, Met. Zeits.*, **11** (1876), 129–135. For example, stations not far apart reported the following temperatures during the middle of the high pressure period: Ischl (456 m) −9.5°C, Klagenfurt (440 m) −17.1°C, Schafberg (1756 m) 1.8°C and Fleiss (2740 m) −3.6°C. The characteristics of temperature inversions began to be studied systematically toward the end of the century.

[59] *Ibid.*, p. 133.

[60] *Ibid.*, p. 135.

[61] *Ibid.*

[62] *Ibid.*

[63] Hann, "Studien über die Luftdruck- und Temperaturverhältnisse auf dem Sonnblickgipfel, nebst

The first statistically reliable data on the vertical temperature structure of cyclones were published in 1886 by the Frenchman Marc Dechevrens, director of the meteorological observatory of Zi-ka-wei (China) from 1877 to 1887.[64] Far from centers of meteorological research and discussions, Dechevrens had developed his own theory of cyclones. Reminiscent of Marié-Davy's theory, he proposed the existence of a "whirl-generator" in elevated regions of the atmosphere which attracted "to its center the masses of air above and below its own level" (here quoting from the English translation of the French original).[65] This mechanism, he argued, resulted in relatively low temperatures around the "whirl axis" in the middle regions of the atmosphere, while high temperatures prevailed near the base of the ascending current. Dechevrens proposed to test this theory by an examination of upper level pressure and temperature observations at the Puy de Dôme, the Pic du Midi and Pikes Peak. It is these data that interest us here. Temperatures collected for intervals of 2 mm Hg of pressure from these stations over a period of five years, winter and summer, were averaged by Dechevrens. His results showed that low pressure at mountain peaks was accompanied on the average by low temperatures (i.e. while pressure between 518 and 520 mm at Pic du Midi was associated with −14.9°C in winter on the average, temperatures around −2.2°C occurred at pressures between 546 and 548 mm). Observations made simultaneously at the summit of the Puy de Dôme and at its base 1100 m below, at Clermont-Ferrand, showed that during periods of low barometric pressure (at the base and at the summit) the temperature was appreciably above normal at the base while below normal at the summit; i.e., for a period of low barometric pressure (at the base and at the summit) during December 1879, the base temperature was 2.9°C warmer and the summit temperature 6.1°C colder than the average monthly temperature at the respective levels.[66] Dechevrens' results, aside from the theory he associated with them, were quite sensational because they clearly conflicted with the thermal theory. He was able to reaffirm them in a subsequent publication of 1887.[67] In a discussion of Dechevrens' 1886 paper, the American meteorologist H. W. Harrington pointed out in defense of the thermal theory that the grouping of data according to pressure intervals rather than with respect to centers of

Bemerkungen über die Bedeutung derselben für die Theorie der Cyklonen und Anticyklonen," *Sitzber., Ak. Wien,* **100** (1891), p. 433.

[64] Dechevrens was director of the St. Louis Observatory, Jersey, from 1894. He died in 1923.

[65] Dechevrens, "On vertical currents in cyclones," *Am. Met. Journ.*, **3** (1886), translated from the French, p. 170.

[66] *Ibid.*, 178–179. This pair of summit and base stations had been a site of meteorological observations ever since 1648, when Blaise Pascal asked his brother-in-law to ascend the Puy de Dôme and measure the barometric pressure on the summit in order to compare it with the pressure at the base. He used these observations to demonstrate that barometric pressure diminishes with altitude. Using data from this station pair, Hildebrandsson also analyzed the vertical temperature structure in cyclones and anticyclones. He computed the temperature decrease between Clemont Ferrand (338 m) and the Puy de Dôme (1467 m) in winter for different pressure areas and pressure gradients and found that the vertical temperature decrease was larger in cyclones than anticyclones. See "Sur la distribution des éléments météorologiques autour des minima et des maxima barométriques," *Soc. R. des Sciènces* (Nova Acta), 1883, Upsala, 18 pp.

[67] Dechevrens, *Sur les Variations de Température Observées dans les Cyclones*, 2nd note (Zi-ka-wei, Typographie de la Catholique, 1887), 17 pp.

cyclones might have led to misleading results.[68] Low pressure on mountain tops was not always accompanied by a cyclonic circulation but could result from low temperatures in the air column below the summit.

In the meantime, in 1887, the Austrian weather service had established a first-order observatory on the summit of the Sonnblick (3090 m). Hann evaluated the observations as they became available and compared them with those of low-level stations.[69] Grouping the data according to barometric pressure at the summit, in a similar fashion as Dechevrens had done, Hann also found that the temperatures at the mountain peak are lowest with low summit pressures. Hann was able to furnish further proof of this observation during the following years.[70] Since his results were so consistent he considered it absolutely necessary

> . . . that the question for the cause of cyclonic and anticyclonic motion of air masses must take into account the fact that up to altitudes of at least 4 to 5 kilometers the average temperature of the air mass in the center of an anticyclone can be higher (perhaps even is always higher) than that in the center of the cyclone. Thus, the opinions fall which have sought the cause of these motions in the difference of specific weight of the air masses in a cyclone as compared with an anticyclone, in the "buoyancy," to which the air in a cyclone is said to be subjected. . . . And we must conclude that in traveling cyclones and anticyclones the heat conditions are conditioned themselves and do not set the conditions, that they are the result of the field of motion of the air masses, of the ascending and descending motion in the vertical circulation of the atmosphere. . . . The cyclones and anticyclones are only partial phenomena in the general circulation of the atmosphere.[71]

We see that Hann viewed the temperature distribution in cyclones as a consequence of the field of motion. In other words, he considered cyclones and anticyclones dynamic rather than thermal in origin and proposed that they constituted an integral part of the general circulation.

Since Hann's investigation had shown that temperature and pressure extremes did not always coincide in space and time, he refined his analysis by grouping four years of daily temperature and humidity observations of the Sonnblick and nearby summit and valley stations according to their position relative to low and high pressure centers.[72] He found that during all seasons, temperature and pressure changes were correlated in time, but that temperature maxima occurred mostly one day after pressure maxima, and temperature minima one day after pressure minima. Temperature minima were observed without exception when the Sonnblick was located at the eastern, or more seldom, southern edge of an anticyclone, and when a cyclone was located to the south or southeast of the summit. Although these results

---

[68] Comments on Dechevrens' "On vertical currents . . . ," *Am. Met. Journ.*, **3** (1886), 184–186.

[69] Hann, "Resultate der meteorologischen Beobachtungen auf dem Sonnblick (3090 m), Januar und Februar 1887, *Met. Zeits.*, **4** (1887), 124–129.

[70] Hann, "Das Luftdruck-Maximum von Nov. 1889 in Mittel-Europa nebst Bemerkungen über die Barometer-Maxima im Allgemeinen," *Denks. Ak. Wien*, **57** (1890), 401–425 and "Studien über die Luftdruck- und Temperaturverhältnisse auf dem Sonnblickgipfel, nebst Bemerkungen über deren Bedeutung für die Theorie der Cyklonen und Anticyklonen," *ibid.*, **100** (1891), 367–452.

[71] Hann (1890), *op. cit.*, p. 420.

[72] Hann (1891), *op. cit.*

indicated a certain asymmetry between pressure and temperature observations, there appeared to be no room for doubt that on the average barometric maxima were warmer than barometric minima. Results from balloon ascents of recent and earlier date abundantly confirmed this conclusion.

Concurrent with these empirical studies, Hann began to question the validity of the thermal theory. He realized that thermodynamic theory—always regarded as the cornerstone of the thermal theory of storms—implied a serious physical objection against it:

> . . . then my attention was drawn to the fact that this could have been concluded beforehand deductively from the temperature changes in ascending and descending air masses which proceed according to known physical laws. If, as is done in the pure convection theory of cyclones, one places the forces which keep [the cyclone] in action entirely within the cyclone, then one encounters even theoretically or strictly deductively the difficulty that the vertical circulation initiated by [these forces] results in temperature conditions which annul the prerequisites of its existence.[73]

In other words, a closed vertical circulation between cyclones and anticyclones with warm air rising and cool air sinking could not be maintained. Hann therefore regarded Ferrel's view of a "causal connection" between cyclones and anticyclones as untenable:

> In this case he [Ferrel] has overlooked the theoretical difficulty that ensues from the theory of heat for the convection theory. The ascending moist air is cooling more slowly than the air sinking alongside is warming so that theoretically the descending branch of the vertical air circulation must be warmer than the ascending branch.[74]

Hann here implied that an indirect thermal circulation was taking place between cyclones and anticyclones, requiring an outside source of kinetic energy. For this reason, he noted, cyclones and anticyclones could no longer be regarded as energetically closed systems. Ferrel, it will be recalled, in his memoir of 1881 had indeed recognized the need for a continuous source of heat and moisture in his cyclone model; Ferrel then suggested that this primary heat source was located inside the cyclonic system, but he could not provide a mechanism that would permit the replenishment of the heat source once it was depleted. In effect, his considerations on heat and moisture sources located outside the cyclonic system remained qualitative and were of little consequence for his scheme of cyclonic circulation.

5.6 THE AMERICAN REACTION (1890's)

Hann's observations and conclusions were not adopted without the exchange of heated arguments and disputes among friends. In fact, the reactions against Hann's expositions were almost violent on the other side of the Atlantic, where American meteorologists had adhered unanimously to the thermal theory under the leadership of its most eminent exponent Ferrel. It was the officially accepted theory

[73] Hann (1891), 433–434.
[74] Hann (1891), p. 434.

at the Weather Bureau and was used as the working hypothesis in the preparation of storm predictions.[75] The controversy began when W. M. Davis published an extensive summary of Hann's paper in *Science* in 1890. Davis, a well-known physical geographer, had taken up the study of meteorology during the 1880's and had become quickly an admirer of Ferrel. Noting that he himself had "frequently advocated the sufficiency of the convectional theory of cyclones," Davis nevertheless seriously questioned its validity in the *Science* article.[76] He considered it of utmost importance to introduce American readers to Hann's results which "clearly" called for a revision of current cyclone theory:

> The reason why Dr. Hann's objection to the convectional theory of cyclones appears to me so cogent and convincing is that it is presented, not as a contradiction, but as a corollary to the principles of modern physical meteorology, with which this eminent meteorologist is so thoroughly familiar, and to which he has himself contributed so much of value.[77]

In view of Hann's new evidence, Davis suggested that despite the apparently convective circulation in storms, "the cyclonic machine does not drive itself by its own store of energy: it is driven by an external motor, the general circulation of the winds."[78] That Davis so readily accepted Hann's conclusions was severely criticized by many of his countrymen. In 1890 Davis held a lonely position, indeed, and, perhaps because he was somewhat of an outsider to meteorology, it was relatively easy to dismiss his call for reconsideration and revision of the accepted storm theory. H. H. Clayton, who was at the time observer in charge at the privately operated Blue Hill Meteorological Observatory, remarked in retrospect that most meteorologists evidently regarded it as their duty "to look with special favor upon views promulgated by our own countrymen, and with corresponding disfavor upon views of foreigners."[79] The famous and respected Ferrel was the first to speak up against Hann's view and the "new convert" Davis, because "it aims a blow, not only at all recent advancement in cyclonology, but even at its very foundation in Espy's condensation theory."[80] Ferrel made it clear in subsequent communications on this subject in the pages of *Science* that he never regarded Hann's expositions as the foundation of a theory but rather as mere hypothesis, "without any attempt to form a theory from it."[81] Until a completely new theory

---

[75] See the standard text used in the training of weather forecasters, by Cl. Abbe: "Preparatory studies for deductive methods in storm and weather predictions," *Annual Report of the Chief Signal Officer for 1889*, Appendix 15 (Washington, 1890), 131 ff.

[76] W. M. Davis, "Dr. Hann's studies on cyclones and anticyclones," *Science*, **15** (1890), p. 332, and H. H. Clayton, "Various researches on the temperature in cyclones and anticyclones in temperate latitudes," *Beitr. Phys. f. Atm.*, **1** (1905), 98–99.

[77] Davis (1890), p. 333.

[78] *Ibid.*

[79] Clayton, "Cyclones and areas of high pressure," *Science*, **17** (1891), p. 66.

[80] W. Ferrel, "Dr. Hann's studies on cyclones and anticyclones," *Science*, **16** (1890), p. 345. Davis repeatedly discussed Ferrel's contributions to meteorology in appreciative articles: "Ferrel's convectional theory of tornadoes," *Am. Met. Journ.*, **6** (1890), 337–349, 418–463; "American contributions to meteorology," *Journ. Franklin Inst.*, **127** (1889); "Ferrel's contributions to meteorology," *Am. Met. Journ.*, **8** (1891–92), 348–359.

[81] *Ibid.*

had been formulated on the basis of the new facts, which would explain more than the old theory, Ferrel saw no reason to give up the old one.

Aside from these general objections, Ferrel in particular doubted the accuracy of Hann's data. He claimed that Hann's mountain-top temperatures were mere surface temperatures, which in the presence of precipitation are generally below the normal temperatures in cyclones, especially in summer and

> . . . cannot, therefore, be assumed to be the same as open-air temperatures, even at a little distance on the same levels, and, much less, can they represent the general average of the great mass of air in the interior of the cyclone, of perhaps five or six hundred miles in diameter and up to a considerable altitude.[82]

In addition Ferrel saw no reason to infer that the conditions observed in cyclones and anticyclones over the Alps should apply in America.

As Davis foresaw, Hann was the first to supplement his results with supporting observations from other regions in response to Ferrel's rather speculative objections. In final defense of his observations, Hann could cite balloon ascents near Berlin and München that indicated relatively high temperatures in the higher strata of anticyclones. Renewed inspection of the records of much earlier balloon ascents revealed that

> . . . the results of the well-known balloon voyage of Barral and Bixio on 27 July 1850 are also in agreement with the low temperature in the inner part of barometer-minima, as derived from observations on mountain summits.[83]

Although it became recognized by scientists other than Hann that the body of anticyclonic air may be warm in comparison with its environment, Ferrel continued to regard anticyclones as basically cold, simply, as he said, because he saw no other adequate explanation besides high density of cold air for the development of high pressure.[84] He continued to insist on the thermal origin of cyclones, an assumption which "only requires that there shall be a predominance of higher temperatures in the interior."[85] This, he noted in his own defense, did not mean "that there are no places within the cyclone, especially on the earth's surface, with lower temperatures than those of many places outside." Only "in the theoretical treatment of a cyclone we have necessarily to assume certain regular conditions of uniform temperature at the same distance in all directions."[86]

At this point, perhaps, a clear distinction between tropical and midlatitude cyclones would have been helpful. With such a division, tropical cyclones could have been viewed as comparatively pure examples of the convective theory, while midlatitude cyclones could have been regarded as the product of the simultaneous action of thermal and dynamic causes. Like Reye earlier, Ferrel continued to avoid

---

[82] *Ibid.*, p. 346.
[83] Hann (1891), p. 63.
[84] Ferrel, "Cyclones and areas of high pressure," *Science*, **17** (1891), 38–40.
[85] *Ibid.*, p. 38.
[86] *Ibid.*

making this division in type, perhaps because it would have impaired the principle of unity that he envisioned to exist in atmospheric processes.

5.7 THE EUROPEAN RESPONSE (1890's)

American meteorologists during the 1890's generally relied on qualitative and descriptive arguments in their response to Hann's criticism of the thermal theory. At about the same time, a number of European meteorologists attempted to treat quantitatively the problem of vertical circulation in cyclones and the source of energy for this circulation. A valuable contribution to the solution of this problem was made by Wilhelm von Bezold in Germany. Bezold was trained as a physicist, but had always shown a special interest in meteorology. In 1885, at the age of 48, he became professor of meteorology at the University of Berlin—the first chair in this field in Germany—and director of the Meteorologische Institut. In 1881, conducting an extensive series of definitive theoretical investigations on the thermodynamics of the atmosphere, Bezold illustrated clearly and effectively Hann's objections to the thermal theory with the aid of thermodynamic diagrams.[87]

Adapting Clapeyron's graphical representation of the Carnot cycle to meteorology, and on the basis of Heinrich Hertz' investigation on adiabatic changes of moist air, Bezold developed a method that allowed him to consider graphically not only adiabatic changes of dry and moist air, as Peslin had done, but also the effect of nonadiabatic processes. Thus, during the 1880's, the value of thermodynamic diagrams for the treatment of certain meteorological processes was finally appreciated, indicating a gradual shift in meteorological research from two-dimensional investigations dictated by the synoptic chart to three-dimensional analyses made feasible with the beginning exploration of the upper levels of the atmosphere. Significantly, all three, Peslin, Hertz and Bezold, had strong ties to applied physics and engineering and were particularly familiar with the usefulness of thermodynamic diagrams.

Bezold was motivated to study the exchange of air between cyclones and anticyclones by Hann's publications of the 1880's on the results of the Sonnblick observations. Bezold illustrated specific cases in a thermodynamic diagram (Figure 27) with pressure and volume as coordinates. He assumed, according to the convective theory, an ascending current associated with precipitation in the cyclone and a dry descending current in the anticyclone. It was further assumed, also according to the convective theory, that no diabatic heating or cooling took place during the horizontal exchange of air between cyclone and anticyclone; however, Bezold allowed for some diabatic heating to occur during vertical exchange of air. On the thermodynamic diagram (Figure 27), the starting point a, at the foot of the ascending column in the cyclone, indicated lower temperature and

[87] W. v. Bezold, "Zur Thermodynamik der Atmosphäre, erste Mitteilung," *Sitzber. Ak. Berlin*, (1888), 485–522. Translated in Abbe's second collection (1891), *op. cit.*, 212–242. Used here is the reprint found in Bezold, *Gesammelte Abhandlungen aus den Gebieten der Meteorologie und des Erdmagnetismus* (Braunschweig, Vieweg und Sohn, 1906). See biographical note on Bezold in the Appendix.

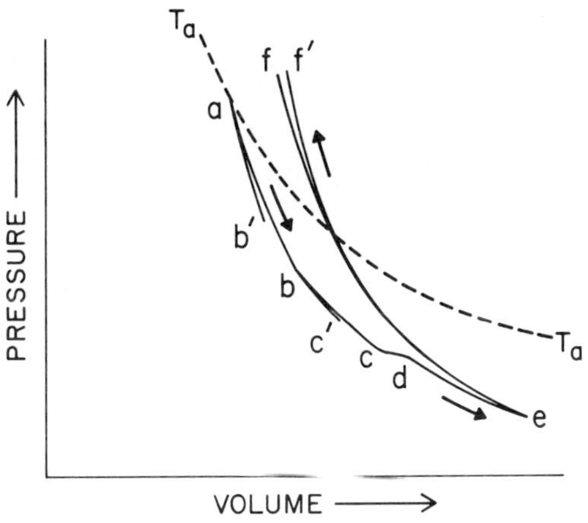

FIGURE 27. Thermodynamic diagram representing exchange of air between a cyclone and anticyclone according to the convective theory; adapted from Bezold, "Thermodynamik der Atmosphäre, erste Mitteilung," 1888 (*Gesammelte Abhandlungen*, 1906). Symbols are explained below.

T_a. isotherm of temperature at starting point a of the cycle.
Ascent: a to b, dry-adiabatic (b′ without diabatic heating)
b to c, rain stage (c′ without diabatic heating)
c to d, near dry-adiabatic
d to e, snow stage.
Descent: e to f, dry-adiabatic (f′ with diabatic heating from ground)

pressure than were found at the final point f or f′, at the foot of the descending column in the anticyclone. Thus it followed

> . . . that the air at the bottom of the anticyclone is specifically lighter than that in the cyclone despite the higher pressure, because the temperature overcompensates the influence of the pressure.[88]

Thus Bezold reached the same conclusion as Hann

In order to facilitate the discussion of this result and the analysis of similar processes, Bezold introduced a number of terms borrowed from physics into the meteorological vocabulary, the most important being "potential temperature."[89] This quantity stood for the heat content of air which in 1888 Helmholtz had defined as the temperature that the parcel of air assumes when being compressed or expanded adiabatically to a standard pressure.[90] It quickly became part of standard meteorological terminology. Using this convenient quantity, Bezold briefly and plainly described what he had expressed graphically:

---

[88] Bezold, *Gesammelte Abhandlungen*, p. 124.

[89] Also specific moisture, pseudo-adiabatic process, entropy.

[90] Helmholtz, "Ueber atmosphärische Bewegungen," *Sitzber. Ak. Berlin* (1888), 652–653, translated in Abbe's second collection (1891), 78–111. According to A. Wegener, (*Thermodynamik der Atmosphäre*, Leipzig, Barth, 1911, p. 111) early in 1888 (before publication of Bezold's paper) Köppen had already used the term potential temperature in a talk in Hamburg, entitled "Ueber die Luftmischung und potentielle Temperatur, in Anlehnung an die neueste Abhandlung von Herrn v. Helmholtz."

> In the ascending branch the potential temperature increases continuously after commencement of condensation in proportion to the condensed water, in the descending [branch] it remains constant at the maximum value reached during the entire process.[91]

In other words, "during adiabatic exchange of air from a cyclone to an anticyclone the potential temperature [is] higher in the descending branch . . . than in the ascending [branch]."[92]

This result was in conflict with the assumption of a direct thermal circulation between cyclones and anticyclones. At first, Bezold thought to resolve this contradiction by taking into account the effect of nonadiabatic processes. He suggested, for example, that radiational cooling takes place during the horizontal exchange of air between cyclones and anticyclones in upper strata because of the long distances and times involved. Examination of Hann's observations made on the summit of the Sonnblick indicated, however, that nonadiabatic processes probably were not effective enough to balance, let alone to reverse, the effect of the difference in the rate of temperature change in saturation-adiabatically ascending air and dry-adiabatically descending air. Bezold concluded in agreement with Hann

> . . . that the exchange of air between cyclone and anticyclone is by far not only a question of the specific weight of the air masses, but that above all dynamic relations come into consideration here, a point, which Hann has recently referred to in a discussion of observations from the Sonnblick.[93]

Before taking up the discussion of the consequences of these findings for the thermal theory, we note that parallel studies were carried out by Nils Ekholm at the Meteorologisk-Hydrografiska Anstalt in Stockholm. As Bezold, Ekholm was a trained physicist with an early interest in meteorology dating from his student work with Hildebrandsson in Upsala. In 1891 he applied the concept of Carnot's cycle in the analysis of the vertical circulation between cyclones and anticyclones.[94] The motivation for this investigation was, as in the case of Bezold, a paper of Hann of 1890, in which Hann had stated that the circulation between cyclones and anticyclones "does not represent a motion produced from heat, but exactly the reverse circulation, with heat produced from kinetic energy."[95] Ekholm singled out the fact that Hann's criticism could apply only to the source of energy in cyclones; that it did not affect the validity of previous analyses of the dynamics of cyclones:

> . . . the laws of the motion of air as function of the gradient force, friction and the deflecting force of the earth's rotation, as derived by Ferrel, Guldberg and Mohn and others, evidently remain unchanged, even if the air circulation is caused by the kinetic energy of moving air masses rather than the potential energy of a cyclone.[96]

---

[91] Bezold, "Zur Thermodynamik der Atmosphäre, zweite Mitteilung," *Sitzber. Ak. Berlin* (1888); see *Gesammelte Abhandlungen*, p. 134; translated in Abbe's second collection (1891), *op. cit.*, pp. 243–256.

[92] Bezold, *Gesammelte Abhandlungen*, "Zweite Mitteilung," p. 141.

[93] Bezold, *Gesammelte Abhandlungen*, "Erste Mitteilung," p. 124.

[94] Nils Ekholm, "Anwendung des Carnot' schen Satzes auf die Kreisläufe in der Atmosphäre," *Met. Zeits.*, **8** (1891), 366–372. See biographical note on Ekholm in the Appendix.

[95] *Ibid.*, p. 368.

[96] *Ibid.*

Preliminary calculation, he remarked, had shown "that such a large temperature excess of the air column of the anticyclone over that of the cyclone . . . would not be possible, if the circulation would be fed only out of its own store of energy."[97] Thus, he suggested that the circulation of cyclones and anticyclones was not as closely interrelated as previously assumed, but that both probably to a considerably degree depended for their formation and maintenance on the large store of kinetic energy associated with the upper westerlies, i.e., the general circulation. He proposed that

> . . . a part of the anticyclones in our latitudes owe their formation and maintenance not to kinetic energy produced by the cyclones surrounding them, but primarily to the kinetic energy produced by the large equatorial circulation [;] of course, this does not deny that the surrounding cyclones contribute their share of energy.[98]

Ekholm here followed closely Hann's argumentation, namely that anticyclones exist quite independently of cyclones as a link in the general circulation of the atmosphere. Ekholm himself did not follow up his considerations with the quantitative calculations he had promised. Perhaps he was too preoccupied with his official duties. Several years later, however, he succeeded in kindling Vilhelm Bjerknes' interest in the investigation of atmospheric circulation systems when he met him through their common friend in Stockholm, the physical chemist Svante Arrhenius. We will see in the following chapter that it was Bjerknes who made possible a quantitative testing of the thermal theory with the introduction of the circulation theorem.

The investigations of Bezold and Ekholm reflect the realization that the principle of conservation of energy could not easily be applied on the scale of cyclones and anticyclones, because cyclones and anticyclones could not be regarded as closed systems energetically. They proposed that it was necessary to allow for the exchange of energy across the boundaries of a cyclonic system in the formulation of a workable energy budget of a cyclone. Suggesting that the kinetic energy of storms is derived from the kinetic energy of the general circulation exhibited in the strong upper westerlies of midlatitudes, they envisioned an exchange of energy from large scale (general circulation) to cyclone scale. This view deviated somewhat from the conclusions of Mohn, Hildebrandsson and others who likewise realized that cyclones and anticyclones could not be regarded as independent systems, but suggested that a mutual interaction exists between cyclones and the general circulation, with the cyclones representing an essential part of the general circulation. All these discussions, it should be noted, were still in the form of vague suggestions. Their observational and theoretical foundations began to be established in the following decades, the period to which we now turn.

---

97 *Ibid.*, pp. 369–370.
98 *Ibid.*, p. 370.

Chapter

6 Modifications of the Thermal Theory

6.1 INTRODUCTION

The first systematic observations of conditions in the upper layers of the atmosphere had created doubts as to the exclusive validity of the thermal theory of cyclones. Following Hann's demand, a number of meteorologists began to reexamine the daily synoptic charts in the light of upper air observations. One of the points on which meteorologists began to concentrate their efforts was the long-known surface temperature asymmetry observed in traveling cyclones and its possible implications for the theory of cyclones. As will be described in this chapter, the study of this phenomenon contributed much to a deeper understanding of the structure and formation of cyclones. In particular, these investigations provided part of the background for the development of the polar front theory of cyclones.

The analysis of the three-dimensional structure of cyclones at the Deutsche Seewarte during the 1880's made it definitely clear that the scheme of cyclone circulation according to the early convective theory, with a central column of warm and moist ascending air, was no longer tenable in the case of midlatitude cyclones (Section 6.2b). W. Köppen developed a modified scheme for the vertical cyclone circulation, which featured ascending motion in the tongue of warm air in the leading portion of a traveling cyclone. He utilized the concept of the thermal wind in the explanation of the backward (westward) inclination of the cyclone axis with height as a necessary consequence of the asymmetric temperature distribution within the body of the storm. Concurrently, Köppen and his associates studied how the meteorological conditions observed at the surface were modified by processes taking place in the upper strata of the atmosphere; they found, in particular, that ascending currents of air, commonly explained by thermal convection, might be produced dynamically by horizontal divergence in upper levels of the atmosphere.

Investigations of this kind demonstrated convincingly that dynamic as well as thermal processes must be considered in the explanation of the development and maintenance of cyclones, and they underscored the need for further dynamic studies. In 1898, V. Bjerknes introduced the circulation theorem into meteorology, thereby achieving an important synthesis of the thermodynamic and dynamic aspects of atmospheric processes (Section 6.3). It will be recalled that the first efforts in this direction had been carried out by Reye and Peslin three decades earlier. The circulation theorem established baroclinicity as the basic source of energy for growth of circulation. This theorem acquired special importance with regard to the thermal theory of cyclones because it allowed quantitative evaluation, on the basis of observations, of the thermal energy available for circulation. Aerological measurements needed for the calculation of circulation changes became available around the turn of the century.

During the late 1890's Frank H. Bigelow gave new direction to cyclone research in the United States. Breaking away from Ferrel's symmetric model of the convective cyclone, he launched an ambitious program in the three-dimensional analysis of cyclones and anticyclones, along similar lines as Köppen and his associates (Section 6.4). A mutual interdependence between the general circulation and cyclones and anticyclones, Bigelow suggested, was demonstrated by air currents of tropical and polar origin which were observed to converge in cyclones and which appeared to accomplish the meridional and vertical heat exchange (by advection and convection, respectively). By rigorous theoretical analysis, Margules in 1906 affirmed Bigelow's assumption that the kinetic energy of traveling cyclones could be accounted for by the conversion into kinetic energy of the store of potential energy associated with adjacent air masses of unequal temperature (Section 6.6). Using methods developed by Helmholtz, Margules defined the conditions for dynamic stability for such a store of potential energy in his theoretical investigations on surfaces of discontinuity. A number of empirical studies during the early 1900's demonstrated the existence of surfaces of discontinuity between air currents of different meteorological properties entering the cyclone (Section 6.7).

From around 1900 onward, attempts were made to trace the life history of cyclones from an energetic point of view, relating life history to changes in cyclone thermal structure. These studies indicated that the kinetic energy budget must vary considerably during the life cycle of cyclones and led to a distinction between direct and indirect thermodynamic circulations of American and European storms.

These diverse investigations anticipated some of the essential features of the polar front theory of cyclones which was announced around 1920; and, it may be said, the thermal theory merged into the polar front theory. Thus the continuity rooted in the thermal theory, here traced from the 1860's to the turn of the century, survived into the early decades of the Twentieth Century. Of course, the thermal theory of the early 1900's was the result of significant modifications of the theory of the 1860's. According to the early versions of the thermal theory, local heating was attributable principally to the release of latent heat during condensation of water vapor in a central convective current of warm moist air. By the turn of the century it had been shown conclusively that horizontal advection of warm air, producing horizontal temperature asymmetry within the body of the storm, must be regarded as the major cause of local heating in extratropical cyclones; here the warm air was ascending in the leading portion rather than the central part of the storm, and the cold air entering the trailing portion was sinking and flowing underneath the warm air, rather than sinking in a more or less symmetrical ring outside the region of the storm. Subsequently, latent heat release received less attention in investigations of midlatitude cyclones and began to be regarded as the primary source of kinetic energy for tropical cyclones only.

6.2 ASYMMETRIC TEMPERATURE DISTRIBUTION IN CYCLONES

a. Early Investigations

The view that two distinct air currents are present in midlatitude storms is old; it clearly dates back to Dove, who in turn quoted voluminous supportive evidence from the Eighteenth Century and all the way back to Aristotle. As discussed previously, Admiral Fitzroy's colorful illustration of the confluence of polar and tropical currents in midlatitudes (Figure 20) has been immensely suggestive to the Twentieth Century viewer as an early conception of the polar front theory of cyclones. However, Fitzroy had no followers among major meteorologists, and Dove's teaching fell into discredit during the 1870's.[1] The conclusion that the thread leading to the air mass concept was lost with Dove and Fitzroy—only to be taken up again by the Bergen School of meteorologists—is therefore understandable. As has been shown earlier, however, the existence of distinct air currents in storms was noted and studied throughout the Nineteenth Century, quite apart from the work of Dove and Fitzroy. In the United States, Loomis studied the properties and interaction of different air currents in storms during the 1840's (Section 2.3), and confirmed these early results in his statistical studies of the 1870's (Section 5.3). The concept of polar and equatorial currents so closely reflected actual conditions that, once Dove had brought the idea to prominence, it could scarcely be eradicated from meteorological thought. In fact, some of the strongest critics of Dove's meteorological system, e.g. Mohn and Köppen (whose work will be discussed in this section) carried on the tradition of the analysis of air currents during the 1870's and 1880's.

During the last decades of the Nineteenth Century, the study of air currents in

[1] A. Dieckmann, in "Fitzroy. Ein Beitrag zur Geschichte der Polarfrontheorie," *Naturwissenschaften*, **19** (1893), 748–752, argued that in following Dove, Fitzroy also had to fall with Dove. Another explanation for the modest interest of professional meteorologists in Fitzroy's cyclone model (outlined in Section 4.2c) might have been that Fitzroy's book was one of the last major meteorological treatises that did not incorporate the new concepts of energy conservation and transformation. Neither Shaw nor Hildebrandsson and de Bort mentioned Fitzroy's book in their monumental historical studies. In addition, the scientific community expressed increasing impatience and opposition toward Fitzroy's weather forecasts. The Royal Society had been critical of his forecasts from the beginning; even Maury, who initially had supported Fitzroy's appointment to the Meteorological Office, turned against him, and in 1865 the patient *Times* editor of Fitzroy's forecasts called them a burlesque.

cyclones was closely linked to the investigation of the horizontal temperature asymmetry in cyclones. This asymmetry was established as an essential feature of cyclones during the 1870's, as a result of examination of synoptic charts as well as individual station records. As discussed in Chapters 4 and 5, early charts of Buchan, Mohn, Ley and others, depicting the temperature field associated with barometric depressions, indicated that normally the temperature rises with falling pressure and vice versa, with the lowest pressure along the common "edge" of warm and cold air. The close relationship between temperature and pressure was regarded a strong support of the thermal origin of cyclones. Guldberg and Mohn stressed that asymmetry was maintained because *new* air currents were constantly converging in the cyclone and that the growth of cyclones depended on the properties of these air currents.

b. Köppen and Möller (1880's)

The investigation of the role of temperature asymmetry and the associated moisture and cloud distribution as well as the dynamics of the cyclonic process became a special subject of meteorological research during the 1880's, when a group of German meteorologists made a concentrated effort to determine the causes of cyclone propagation. These studies took place at the Deutsche Seewarte in Hamburg under the leadership of Wladimir Köppen, who had been appointed director of a newly created special meteorological research division in 1879. Köppen gathered a group of able young men of different backgrounds around him: the engineer Max Möller, who became the master builder of the Hamburg harbour and professor of hydraulics at Braunschweig in 1890; Adolf Sprung who had just finished his university education in physics and chemistry and in a few years was to furnish the first German textbook on theoretical meteorology;[2] and Wilhelm Jacob van Bebber, a former teacher with a strong interest in synoptic meteorology and weather forecasting, who had replaced Köppen in his former position as director of the weather service division at the Seewarte. These scientists brought fresh points of view to meteorology and shared Köppen's enthusiasm.[3]

Köppen felt strongly that one way to advance cyclone theory was to extend the analysis of storms from the surface into the upper atmosphere and to study the connection between the upper level and lower level currents. With his associates, especially Möller, Köppen examined the results of Ley and Hildebrandsson on the nature of the upper flow patterns. They came to discard the assumption put forward by Ferrel and Hann that the upper westerlies observed in midlatitudes remain essentially undisturbed during the passage of a cyclone, and that cyclones are propagated in the upper westerlies like an eddy in a river. Three of Ley's propositions, which summarized his statistical results, appeared to make Ferrel's and Hann's view on cyclone propagation particularly untenable—namely, the

---

[2] See biographical notes on Köppen, Möller and Sprung in the Appendix.

[3] The 1880's mark the beginning of the development of *schools* of thought in meteorology. Meteorologists then began to be numerous enough and centralized in institutions so that leaders in the field could attract a group of collaborators. Meteorological schools developed in Vienna and later in Leipzig and Bergen, etc.

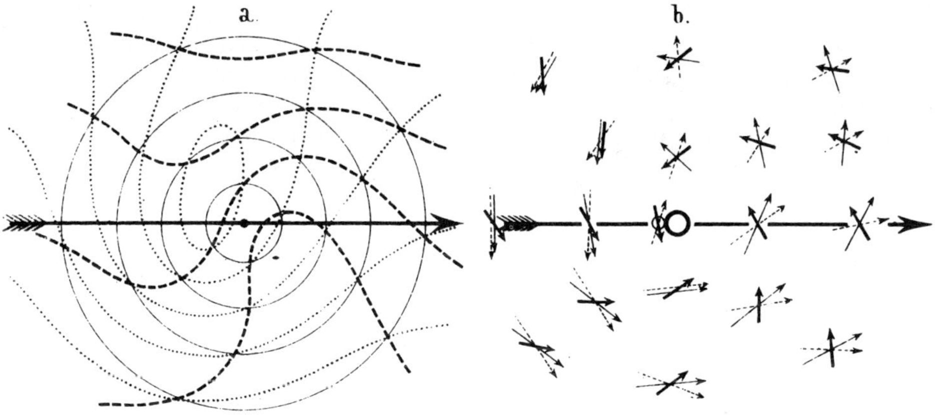

FIGURE 28. Influence of temperature distribution in cyclones on the upper level pressure field, from Köppen, "Ueber den Einfluss der Temperaturvertheilung auf die oberen Luftströmungen . . . ," *Ann. Hydr.*, **10** (1882). Left: Solid lines represent surface isobars; dotted lines are cirrus level isobars; dashed lines are isotherms. Right: Heavy arrows indicate surface winds; medium arrows indicate low cloud direction; dashed arrows show cirrus cloud direction. The circle in the center indicates calm.

backward inclination of the axis of traveling cyclones, the dependence of a storm's path on the general temperature distribution (also noted by Mohn in 1870), and the influence of areas of high pressure on the cyclone path.

Ley's findings had received little attention so far. In fact, it will be recalled that Hildebrandsson, an expert on cloud observations, plainly dismissed the general applicability of the most striking of Ley's results, namely the backward inclination of the cyclone axis. With his wide synoptic experience and physical insight, Köppen realized the true significance of this observation and demonstrated that this feature was a necessary consequence of the asymmetric temperature distribution within the body of a storm. Since pressure decreases more slowly with height in warm air than in cold air, Köppen explained, high temperatures must correspond to high pressure in upper levels and low temperatures to low pressure.[4] Thus, Ley's observation was explained in a most simple manner: ". . . the backward inclination of the vortex in the upper strata proves to be a necessary result of the cold rear."[5] This conclusion—so obvious in hindsight—had evaded Ley's searching mind probably because he viewed the rising warm and moist air, associated with cloud formation, as the center of the cyclonic vortex at all levels.

In 1882 Köppen and Möller provided a very useful graphical illustration of these results (Figure 28).[6] Köppen plotted Ley's observations of mean directions of surface winds, middle clouds and cirrus clouds relative to the center of low

---

[4] Köppen, "Ueber die mechanischen Ursachen der Ortsveränderung atmosphärischer Wirbel," *Wien, Met. Zeits.*, **15** (1880), p. 48.

[5] Köppen, "Ueber den Einfluss der Temperaturverteilung auf die oberen Luftströmungen und die Fortpflanzung der barometrischen Minima," *Ann. Hydr.*, **10** (1882), p. 660.

[6] Köppen, (1882), *op. cit.*, 657–666; Möller, "Beziehungen zwischen dem Ober- und Unterwinde einer Depression," *Ann. Hydr.*, **10** (1882), 212–226.

pressure. Adjacent to the wind diagram, he indicated the idealized surface isobars of the barometric depression and the upper level pressure distribution, as inferred from the surface wind and cloud motion observations. Köppen then obtained the mean temperature field between lower and upper levels in the traveling cyclone by graphical subtraction of the upper level isobars from the surface isobars, i.e., he connected "by lines the points of equal pressure difference between upper and lower [levels] and thus approximately equal temperature. . . . The obtained picture conforms very well to experience with regard to the horizontal temperature distribution in depressions."[7] In other words, warm air was entering in the leading portion of the cyclone, taking the form of a tongue protruding toward the center of the storm, and cold air was advancing in the trailing portion; both these features, we note, were clearly discernible on Mohn's synoptic charts of the early 1870's (Figure 17).

By reversing the procedure, i.e., by graphical addition of sea level isobars and surface isotherms, approximating mean isotherms of the air layer above, the field of isobars at a certain altitude could be constructed. In a paper of 1888, Köppen provided tables, using the barometric height formula, for the determination of the values of the isobars at the 2500 and 5000 m levels and published the first aerological weather chart of eastern North America and the bordering Atlantic for the 2500 m level.[8] This simple method of graphical addition and subtraction was fully developed by V. Bjerknes in 1911; it remains the basic means for the construction of charts depicting the thickness of the layer between two isobaric surfaces or, equivalently, the mean temperature of the layer.[9]

In the discussion of the influence of the temperature distribution on the upper pressure distribution Köppen had deliberately applied the concept of the "thermal wind," representing the variations of the geostrophic wind field with height.[10] The

---

[7] This method of graphical addition and subtraction was described extensively, including diagrams, in Sprung's widely read textbook *Lehrbuch der Meteorologie*, *op. cit.*, 218–221. It was also employed by Möller. However, using Hildebrandsson's cirrus cloud data, which in contrast to Ley's data showed no inclination of the cyclone axis, Möller's analysis of the mean isotherms indicated the warmest air directly to the south of the cyclone center rather than in the southeast quadrant as in Köppen's analysis.

[8] Köppen, "Ueber die Gestalt der Isobaren in ihrer Abhängigkeit von Seehöhe und Temperatur-Verteilung," *Met. Zeits.*, **5** (1888), 470–481. Köppen introduced the term aerology in 1906 at the 5th conference of the International Commission on Scientific Aeronautics. During the 1880's aerology remained essentially indirect.

[9] V. Bjerknes *et al.*, *Dynamic Meteorology and Hydrography*, Part II (Washington, Carnegie Institution, 1911), 69–98. Bjerknes showed that it was more convenient to construct "topographies" of isobaric surfaces rather than charts of isobars at constant height levels.

[10] The term thermal wind was first used by E. Gold in 1917 in connection with the prediction of upper winds from surface charts for determining the course of Zeppelins during World War I. See Gold, "The Meteorological Office and the First World War," *Met. Mag.*, **84** (1955), p. 173. The term geostrophic was introduced by Sir Napier Shaw in 1916 in the first *Meteorological Glossary* under the heading "gradient wind," naming its two components geostrophic and cyclostrophic, and during the same year in a lecture to the Royal Institution, "Illusions of the upper air," *Nature*, **97** (1916), p. 211. For details see E. Gold, "The origin of the word "geostrophic"," *Bull. Am. Met. Soc.*, **44** (1963), p. 249, and related articles on pages 646 and 778 of the same volume. The concept of the geostrophic wind was used or implied consistently during the second half of the Nineteenth Century. Neglecting inertial, frictional and centrifugal terms, Ferrel delineated the horizontal wind field by analyzing the pressure field. In his derivation of the thermal wind the validity of the geostrophic wind relationship is presupposed. Buys Ballot's law, also known as Ferrel's law or baric wind law, describes the approximate agreement

vertical shear of the geostrophic wind lies parallel to the mean isotherms of a layer with the cold air on the left (Northern Hemisphere) and its magnitude is determined by the horizontal temperature gradient. Köppen noted that both Ferrel and Hann had used this principle much earlier to explain the fact that the westerly winds in middle latitudes normally increase in strength with height as a result of the normal decrease of temperature toward the poles.[11] Ferrel also had applied it in his mathematical treatment of the cold polar cyclone model with descending motion and the warm local cyclone model with ascending motion and wind reversal with height (Section 4.6b). Köppen, in turn, applied Ferrel's arguments to the thermally asymmetric cyclone (Figure 28). As for surface thermal and barometric gradients, Köppen noted, following Ferrel,

> where the temperature gradient is opposite to the pressure gradient, there the pressure gradient must decrease with altitude; where both coincide, there it must continually increase upward.[12]

The latter case, which corresponded to Ferrel's cold core cyclone with descending motion, Köppen noted, "occurs in the outer region of the . . . [southwest] quadrant of our typical [thermally asymmetric] depressions, and is associated with predominantly descending motion of air . . . in an intermediate layer."[13] On the other hand, he continued, "In the major portion of our typical depressions . . . the barometric gradient is decreasing with height and ascending motion of air predominates; consequently, there must be a certain layer with outflowing motion which, however, is fed from below."[14]

Returning to the problem of cyclone propagation, Köppen also offered a new explanation for Ley's two other propositions which stated that in higher levels traveling cyclones tend to have higher pressure as well as higher temperatures toward the right of their path:

> Since the conditions of motion differ at different altitudes of the vortex, it is not the state of motion of the lowest strata that is decisive for the propagation of the vortex, but that of the entirety of layers; since the changes with altitude are continuous, one can generally use for the latter the state of motion of a certain intermediate strata whose altitude has yet to be determined.[15]

This view, although expressed rather vaguely, implies the concept of a "steering current," a notion which achieved prominence in the forecasting of cyclone movement several decades later.

---

between geostrophic wind and actual wind. In 1922 H. Jeffreys established a classification of the air currents on the basis of the equations of motion which was generally accepted: he distinguished Eulerian (no acceleration), geostrophic (pressure gradient balanced by Coriolis force) and antitriptic (pressure gradient balanced by friction) winds ("On the dynamics of wind," *Quart. Journn. Roy. Met. Soc.*, **48** (1922), 29–47).

[11] Hann, "Einige Bemerkungen zur Lehre von den allgemeinen atmosphärischen Strömungen," *Wien., Met. Zeits.*, **14** (1879), 35–38.

[12] Köppen (1882), p. 660.

[13] *Ibid.*

[14] *Ibid.*, p. 661.

[15] *Ibid.*, p. 659.

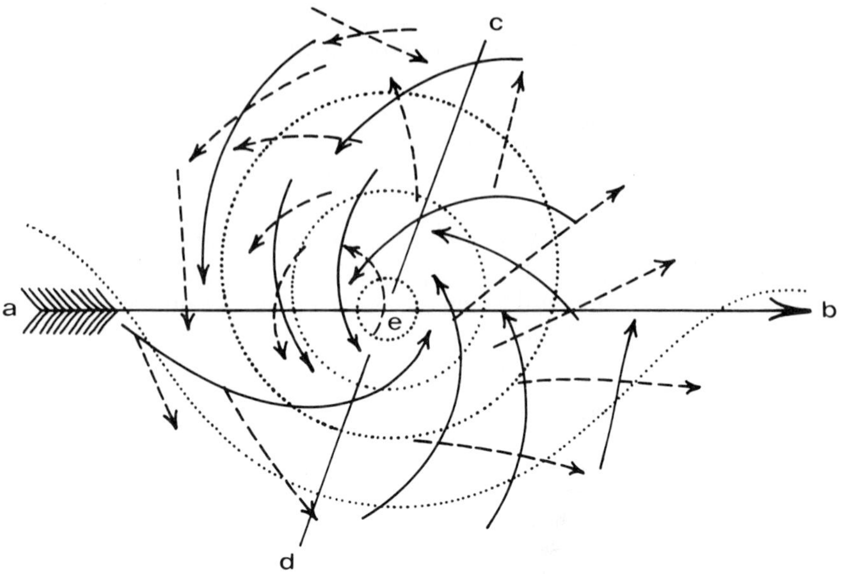

FIGURE 29. Distribution of pressure gradients in upper and surface layers of a cyclone; from Köppen, "Ueber die mechanischen Ursachen der Ortsveränderung atmosphärischer Wirbel," *Wien, Met. Zeits.*, **15** (1880). The center of the depression is denoted by e; ab indicates direction of propagation; de and ec show position and direction of greatest and smallest pressure gradient; dotted lines are surface isobars (according to Ley); solid arrows, wind at surface (according to Ley); dashed arrows, wind in cirrus level (according to Ley).

Köppen's daily occupation with weather forecasting helped him to penetrate still further into the problem of storm propagation. He and his associates became convinced that in addition to the thermal causes of propagation, as outlined by Guldberg and Mohn, dynamic causes would have to be considered. Since the influx and ascent of warm, moist air in the leading portion of a cyclone, associated with latent heat release and overcompensating outflow in upper levels, was considered the major factor leading to pressure fall and advancement of the center of low pressure, they thought it imperative to investigate all circumstances that favored pressure fall. Pursuing this idea, Köppen examined a storm with asymmetric surface pressure field. For such a cyclone, Ferrel's equations of motion, derived for steady-state conditions, applied only approximately. Modifying the equations to take these accelerations into account, Köppen demonstrated a direct connection "between the direction of the strongest gradient and the propagation of the depression."[16] Using the average distribution of pressure gradients in cyclones according to Ley (Figure 29) and considering the motions of the air with respect to the pressure distribution, he showed that the increasing pressure gradient along air trajectories in the trailing portion of the cyclone would lead to increased

[16] Köppen (1880), p. 42. Data used to obtain the average pressure gradients in cyclones were obtained from Ley (1872).

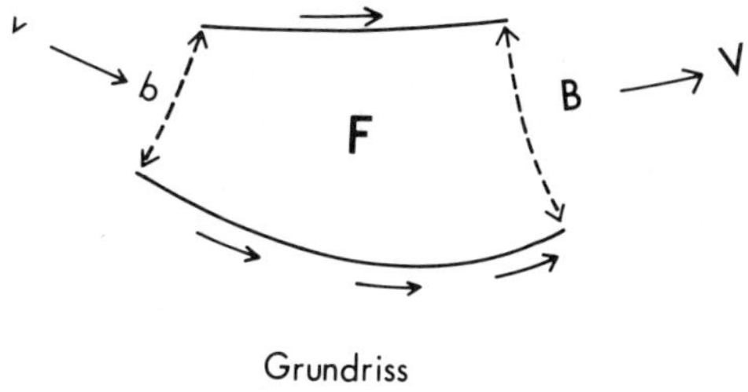

FIGURE 30. Divergence of upper air flow in a cyclone; horizontal view. Reconstructed from Möller, "Beziehungen zwischen dem Ober- und Unterwinde einer Depression und den aus diesen resultierenden Wolkenformen," *Ann. Hydr.*, **10** (1882). Arrows indicate direction of wind. Solid lines bordering area F indicate streamlines. v is speed of inflow along edge b, V is speed of outflow along edge B. Ascending motion occurs under area F "when $VB > vb$, descending motion when $VB < vb$."

convergence and filling while the decreasing pressure gradients along air trajectories in the leading portion of the cyclone would tend to minimize convergence.[17] If, in accordance with these results, the upper current in the leading portion

> . . . balances by continual outflow of air the continual filling of the depression through inflow in the lower strata, and [if the outflow], together with the atmospheric layers lying above, even predominates over the [inflow][18]

then it becomes clear that the

> depression center must propagate from left to right, that is, more or less in direction from a to b [Figure 29] which is the empirically determined direction of propagation.[19]

In close collaboration with Köppen, Max Möller extended these investigations in 1882. He emphasized that the upper pressure field actively modifies the conditions observed at the surface, in contrast to the rather passive role normally assigned to the upper levels in the thermal theory of cyclones. Möller stressed that there was a certain feedback mechanism operating between lower and upper levels. Thus, he argued,

> In the case of a deep depression we have to assume temperature contrasts that extend up to higher altitudes because of vigorously ascending air currents.[20]

The upper pressure field, which was determined indirectly by the temperature distribution below, as Köppen had demonstrated, exerted a decisive influence on the field of vertical motions. Illustrating the air flow and pressure distribution at upper levels in the front part of a cyclone (Figure 30), Möller noted that "when more air is carried out than in, then an ascending current is maintained under the area

[17] *Ibid.*, pp. 43–44.
[18] *Ibid.*, p. 47.
[19] *Ibid.*, p. 46.
[20] Max Möller, "Beziehungen zwischen dem Ober- und Unterwind einer Depression und den aus diesen resultierenden Wolkenformen," *Ann. Hydr.*, **10** (1882), p. 221.

F.''[21] Thus, he noted, upper divergence and acceleration of air motion in the leading portion of a cyclone must favor the formation of precipitation, while upper convergence and decreasing wind speed in the rear of a storm supported descending motion and clear skies. These conclusions in combination with Köppen's results revealed a definite relationship between the propagation of cyclones and precipitation that encompassed dynamic as well as thermal aspects:

> The forward spreading of air, warmed through condensation, has to be regarded as the first cause of the propagating movement of the depression. The warmer air takes the place of cooler layers and thus causes barometer [pressure] fall at the earth surface. The strong outflowing movement in the leading portion of the depression is to be seen as the second cause. The outflow is much favored in the front, while from behind little air is following across the clearing line [Aufklarungslinie]. A diminution of mass results which produces pressure fall at the surface.[22]

Since horizontal temperature asymmetry was a common feature associated with cyclones, Möller felt that perhaps it was no longer necessary to distinguish between warm and cold cyclones, so that the controversy among American and European meteorologists would become meaningless. While according to Ferrel air was ascending in cyclones with warm centers (system a) and descending in depressions with cold centers (system b), Möller suspected in 1887 ''that the leading portion of most depressions belongs to the system a, the rear portion to the system b.''[23] It is recalled that Köppen had expressed a similar view in 1882.

Köppen incorporated this idea in a treatise of 1898, in which he presented schematic illustrations of the vertical circulation in cyclones and anticyclones (Figure 31). These circulation schemes, he remarked, ''were constructed in the conviction that temperature differences between center and outer region play an essential role in the development and maintenance of cyclones and anticyclones.''[24] In his estimates of the effects of the temperature distribution on the field of motion, Köppen distinguished two groups: stationary systems with symmetric temperature and pressure distribution (left side of Figure 31) and traveling systems with asymmetric temperature distribution (right side of Figure 31). Views a to c show the vertical circulation resulting in stationary systems (a) with warm center (early convective model, horizontal pressure gradient decreasing with height, inflow impeded), (b) with cold center (polar cyclone, horizontal pressure gradient increasing with height), and (c) with warm center in lower levels and cold center in upper levels (weakest horizontal pressure gradient in intermediate layer). Köppen regarded (c) as typical of stationary cyclones in midlatitudes. Turning to traveling systems, view e shows a cyclone propagating from left to right, with ascending motion in the warm leading portion and descending motion in the cold rear. The lines of flow, indicating the component of motion relative to the moving system,

---

[21] Möller (1882), p. 220.

[22] *Ibid.*, p. 222.

[23] Max Möller, ''Ueber Verluste an äussere Energie bei der Bewegung der Luft,'' *Met. Zeits.*, **4** (1887), p. 321.

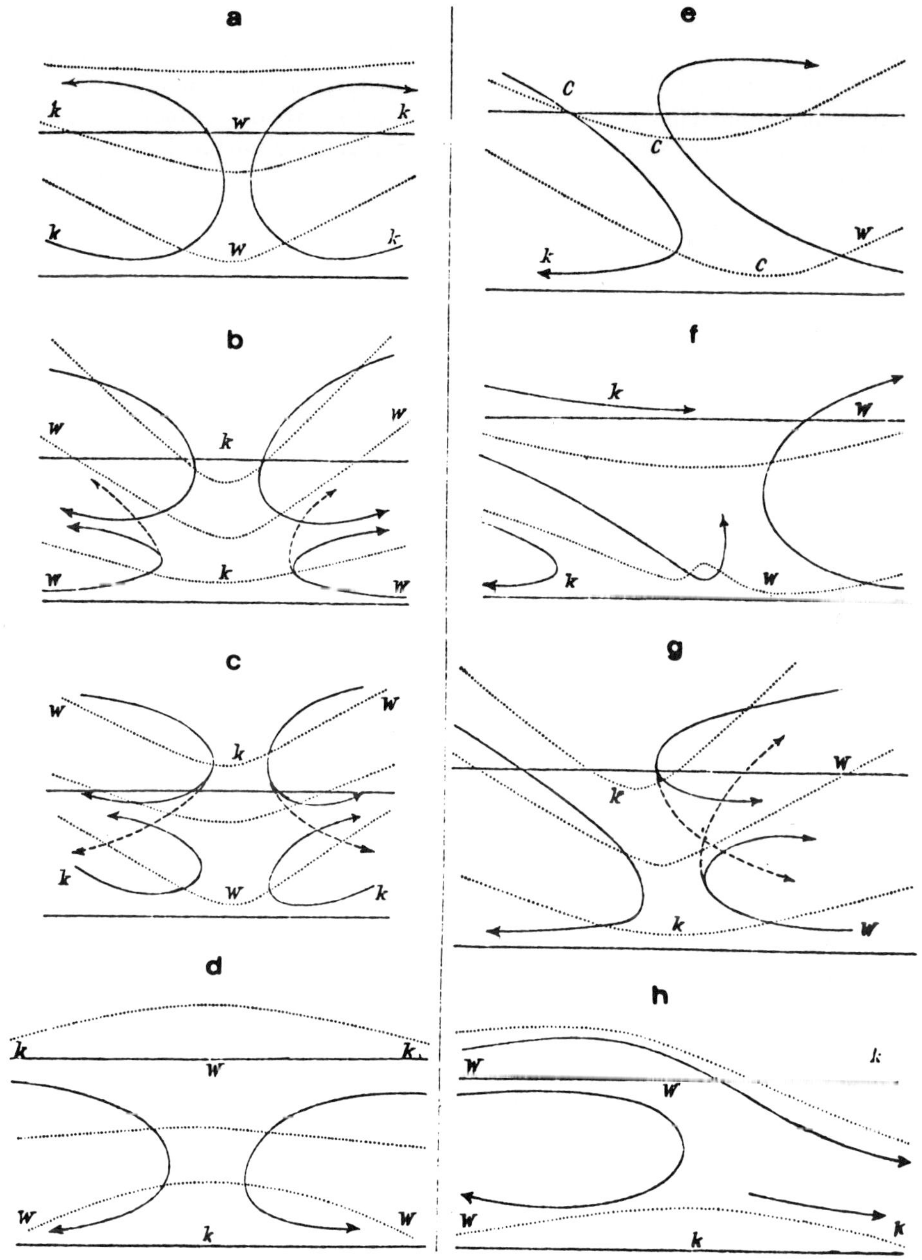

FIGURE 31. Cross sections through stationary [(a)–(c)] and traveling [(e)–(g)] cyclones and stationary (d) and traveling (h) anticyclones. From Köppen, "Ueber den Zufluss und Abfluss der Luft in Cyklonen und Anticyklonen," *Met. Zeits.*, **15** (1898). Dotted lines indicate isobaric surfaces; horizontal straight lines refer to height zero and about 10,000 m; solid lines indicate lines of flow in views (a)–(d) and component of motion relative to the moving system in views (e)–(h); dashed lines are lines of flow suggested by Möller; w, warm; k, cold; C, center of cyclone.

represented, according to Köppen, a good approximation of the circulation in cyclones arriving from the Atlantic Ocean in Western Europe. View f shows an asymmetric cyclone with warm center. The resulting vertical circulation, Köppen noted, approximated that of "secondary depressions along the southeastern edge of large depressions" associated with thunderstorms and line squalls. The asymmetric cyclone with cold center featured in view g, Köppen suggested, corresponded to secondary depressions along the southwestern edge of a large cyclone and represented the initial stage in the development of most large-scale midlatitude cyclones, in part because of favorable conditions for outflow of air at intermediate levels (level of weakest horizontal pressure gradient). Views d and h depict the circulation in stationary and traveling midlatitude anticyclones with cold center in low levels and warm center in upper levels. Köppen's circulation schemes, which emphasized the role of thermal causes in the formation and maintenance of cyclones and anticyclones, became widely known. In 1918, A. Defant still regarded Köppen's schemes as valid principles in the investigation of cyclones and anticyclones.[25]

The results of Köppen's and Möller's investigations at the Seewarte made it clear that the effects of temperature contrasts on the surface pressure field had previously been underestimated, and showed that horizontal advection of air was at least as important as vertical convection in the cyclone. Köppen and Möller further demonstrated that the physical processes taking place in a cyclone were definitely more complex than proposed in the simple convective theory of Reye or, for that matter, of Ferrel, and that dynamic causes could no longer be neglected in cyclone theory.

The investigations carried out at the Seewarte found excellent exposure in Sprung's *Lehrbuch der Meteorologie* of 1885—the first textbook which presented in a systematic fashion the results of atmospheric thermodynamics and dynamics.[26] The book was commissioned by Neumayer, director of the Seewarte, who earlier had initiated the German edition of Mohn's popular book. Sprung's principal consultant was his close friend Köppen. However, it was certainly a drawback that the Deutsche Seewarte was not associated with a university. There was little opportunity to teach the new methods. In addition, only a limited number of research positions was available. Partly for these reasons, the fruitful collaboration of Köppen, Sprung and Möller was of only short duration. In 1886 Sprung accepted a call to Berlin to the Meteorologische Institut, which was being reorganized under

---

[24] Köppen, "Ueber den Zufluss und Abfluss der Luft in Cyklonen und Anticyklonen," *Met. Zeits.*, **15** (1898), p. 168.

[25] A. Defant, *Wetter und Wettervorhersage* (Leipzig und Wien, Deuticke, 1918), 66–67.

[26] Sprung's book (*op. cit.*) provided detailed discussions and comparisons of the theoretical investigations of Guldberg and Mohn, Ferrel, Oberbeck and Marchi, as well as of the more general works of Reye, Hann, Ley, Hildebrandsson, Köppen and others. However, Sprung's book did not yet present a comprehensive system of equations for the theory of atmospheric motions. Thermodynamic and dynamic effects were still treated separately. Sprung's book was the principal textbook on theoretical meteorology in Europe for three decades (Ferrel's *Recent Advances in Meteorology*, 1886, was widely used only in the United States). It was finally superseded with the publication of V. Bjerknes' *Dynamic Meteorology and Hydrography* (1910/11) and F. M. Exner's *Dynamische Meteorologie* (1917).

Bezold, and he began to work with meteorological instruments. In 1889 Möller joined the Bureau for Hydraulics and Meteorology at the Polytechnic at Karlsruhe, and in 1890 went to Braunschweig.

A few scientists like Anton Oberbeck in Germany and Luigi Marchi in Italy continued the dynamic investigations of cyclones that Ferrel, Guldberg and Mohn had begun.[27] But, as V. Bjerknes remarked in 1898, theories applying the classical hydrodynamical equations to atmospheric motions, like those by Ferrel, Guldberg and Mohn and Oberbeck, were relatively useless for practical meteorology and weather forecasting as long as hydrodynamic aspects were separated from the thermodynamic aspects of the atmosphere. The contributions of Bjerknes toward linking these two fields of inquiry will now be discussed.

6.3 V. BJERKNES' CIRCULATION THEOREM (1898)

In 1898, V. Bjerknes, at that time professor of mathematical physics at the University of Stockholm, was persuaded by his friend Nils Ekholm, then assistant at the Swedish weather service and lecturer in meteorology at the university, to apply his profound knowledge of hydrodynamics to the analysis of atmospheric processes. Thus Bjerknes' gradual transition to the geophysical sciences began. Like Ferrel, Peslin and others several decades earlier, he became convinced that the atmosphere constitutes a system in which neither thermodynamic nor dynamic forces can be neglected without grossly oversimplifying and distorting the actual processes. He believed that it was of paramount importance for the progress of meteorology to find ways of linking these previously separate fields.

Bjerknes was an outstanding theoretician who possessed a deep physical insight for the processes he described mathematically. His awareness that the combination of these two approaches—theoretical and empirical—was the key to success in modern physical science has been attributed by his student Tor Bergeron to the influence of Bjerknes' early and admired teacher Heinrich Hertz.[28] The great theoretician and experimentalist Hertz, we might add, in turn was following his own teacher Helmholtz, who had called it an "Ikarus flight of metaphysical speculation"

---

[27] Oberbeck, "Ueber die Bewegung der Luft an der Erdoberfläche," *op. cit.*, and "Ueber die Bewegungserscheinungen der Atmosphäre," *Sitzber. Ak. Berlin* (1888), 383–395, 1129–1138; translated in Abbe's second collection, (1891), 177–197; and L. de Marchi, "Ricerche sulla teoria matematica dei venti," *Annali dell' Ufficio Centrale di Meteorologia Italiana*, **4**, part I (1882), 78–97, and "Sulla teoria dei cicloni," *Memoire del Reale Institutio Lombardo di Scienze a Lettre*, Cl. di Sci. Matematiche e Naturali, **25** (1892), 320–334, and **26** (1893), 624–637. Marchi applied to meteorology the concept of vorticity, which had been introduced by Helmholtz (Rotationsgeschwindigkeit), and he considered variations in density (using the continuity equation and the equation of state) in relation to changes in vorticity.

[28] Tor Begeron, "In memory of Vilhelm Bjerknes," *Geofysiske Publikasjoner*, **24** (1963), p. 20. Bjerknes would possibly have stayed with Hertz and electrodynamics had Hertz lived longer. The greatest and most direct influence on Bjerknes was his father, the mathematician C. A. Bjerknes. V. Bjerknes considered as perhaps his most important work the mathematical formulation of his father's theory on a hydrodynamic analogy of the alleged action at a distance of Newtonian forces [Godske, *Geofysiske Publikasjoner*, **24** (1963), p. 24]. See biographical note on V. Bjerknes in the Appendix.

when the thinking process was divorced from its natural foundation, i.e., observation and perception.[29]

Bjerknes commenced his meteorological inquiries with the study of Ekholm's synoptic charts of the distribution of air density along the earth's surface. Ekholm had begun analyzing density charts in the hope that they would be useful for the purpose of weather forecasting. These charts, he noted, showed clearly that pressure and density fields were not identical as was commonly assumed: there appeared to be a strong relationship between cyclone formation and propagation, and air density; e.g., cyclones appeared to gain in intensity and develop when a tongue of rarified air was present, and vice versa (Figure 32). Furthermore, Ekholm remarked,

> a cyclone . . . tends to form wherever air is rarified and the isodenses are very close together, and, above all, where a tongue of rarified air extends alongside a tongue of dense air, or, in brief, where the isodenses indicate a very unstable equilibrium in the lower layers of the atmosphere.[30]

Ekholm's findings also convinced Bjerknes that variations in density had to be taken into account in the theoretical treatment of atmospheric motions. The practice of treating density merely as a function of pressure in dynamic treatises, Bjerknes felt, had resulted from the assumption commonly made in classical hydrodynamics that a fluid could be regarded as homogeneous and incompressible, and thus had encouraged the separation of atmospheric thermodynamics and dynamics.[31]

For the examination of atmospheric motions resulting from varying pressure and density distributions, Bjerknes consequently applied the circulation theorem that he had developed in 1897 in the course of his studies in hydrodynamics and electromagnetism. Bjerknes' circulation theorem was a modification of the well-known theorem of Helmholtz (1858) for conservation of vortex motion (in which vorticity is introduced as a point measure of the rotation of a fluid) and the theorem of William Thomson (1867) for velocity of circulation (in which circulation is an areal measure of rotation). The Helmholtz and Thomson theorems, derived for an incompressible, frictionless fluid enclosed by fixed boundaries, Bjerknes noted,

> allow us indeed to predict certain peculiarities of the atmospheric vortices and circulations, but the fundamental question of the first formation of such movements, as is well known, is not at all touched by this theory.[32]

---

[29] Hermann Ebert, *Hermann von Helmholtz*, in *Grosse Naturforscher*, Vol. 5, (Stuttgart, Wissenschaftliche Verlagsbuchhandl., 1949), p. 101. Bjerknes' attraction to the work of Helmholtz makes one think of the affinity in their scientific ideals.

[30] Ekholm, "Étude des conditions météorologiques a l'aide des cartes synoptiques représentants la densité de l'air," *Bih. Kongl. Svenska Vet.-Akad. Handl.*, **16** (1891), Afd., **1**, No. 5, 14–15. Before using the term "isodense" Ekholm had employed "isopycne," but found it too cumbersome. He pointed out that A. von Müller-Hauenfels had introduced the term isosteres for lines of equal density, i.e., lines of equal specific volume (in a textbook entitled *Theoretische Meteorologie*, Vienna, 1883, 129 pp.). Ekholm stressed that, contrary to his own findings, Müller-Hauenfels had attributed to air density the same role as to atmospheric pressure in his analyses of density fields.

[31] An exception was the work of Marchí who had considered variations in density in relation to changes in vorticity during the 1880's (see Footnote 21).

[32] V. Bjerknes, "Ueber einen hydrodynamischen Fundamentalsatz und seine Anwendung besonders auf die Mechanik der Atmosphäre und des Weltmeeres," *Kongl. Svenska Vet.-Akad. Handl.*,

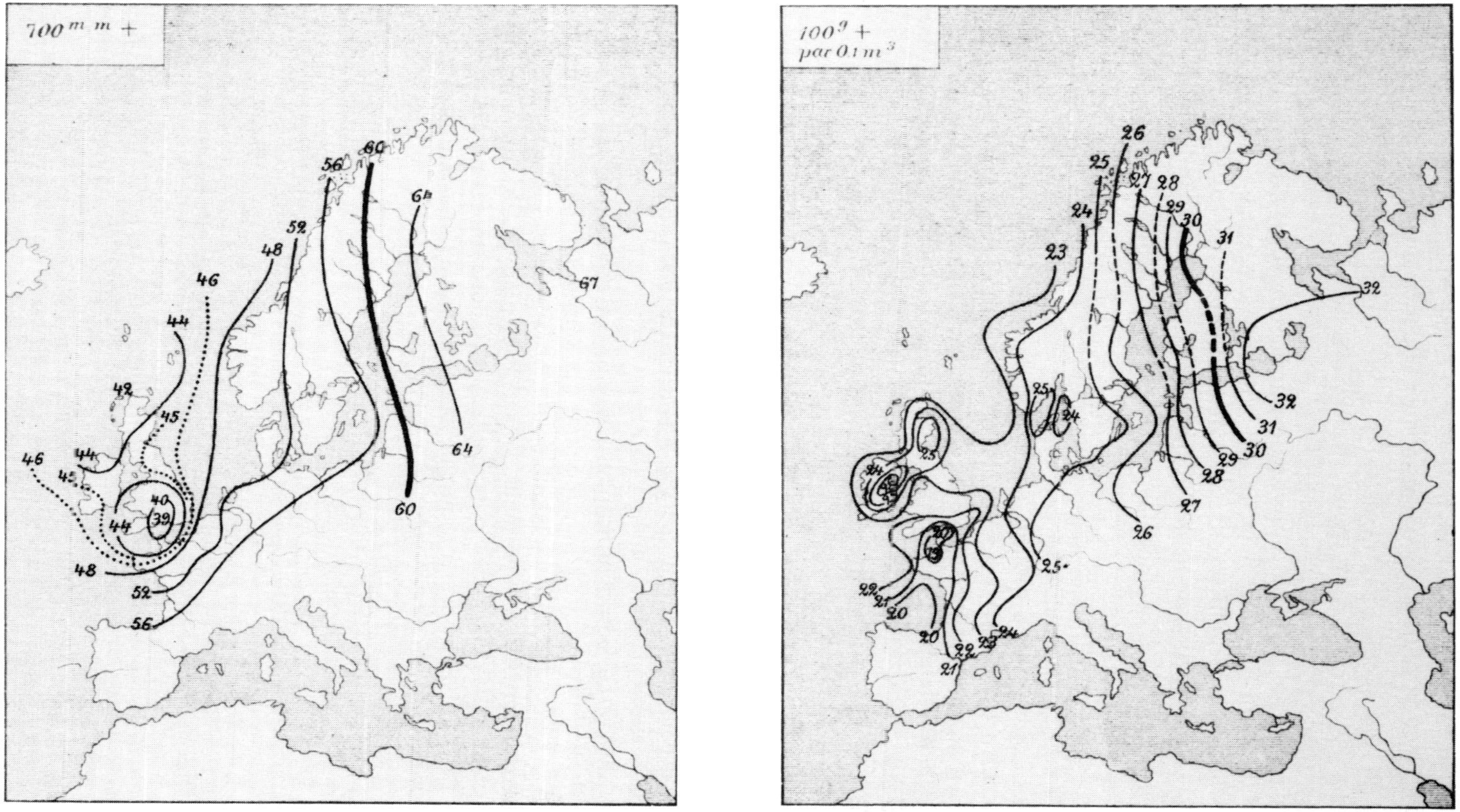

FIGURE 32. Charts illustrating pressure (left) and density (right) distributions for 24 October 1882; from Ekholm, "Étude des conditions météorologiques a l'aide de cartes synoptiques représentant la densité de l'air." *Bih. Kongl. Svenska Vet.-Akad. Handl.*, **16** (1891), Afd. 1, No. 5. Note tongues of rarified and dense air in developing storm over England.

Following Thomson, Bjerknes in 1898 defined the circulation C as the integral along a closed curve of the components of the velocity field tangential to the curve:

$$C = \oint \mathbf{v} \cdot d\mathbf{s} = \oint v_s ds,$$

where $\mathbf{v}$ denotes the velocity vector and $d\mathbf{s}$ an increment of distance along the curve and the "dot" product is indicated; v_s denotes tangential velocity. An important factor in the prediction of future states of circulatory systems was the time rate of change of circulation or the acceleration of circulation:

$$\frac{dC}{dt} = \oint \frac{d\mathbf{v}}{dt} \cdot d\mathbf{s}.$$

In 1901 Bjerknes proceeded to combine this kinematical statement with the equations of motion on a rotating earth and obtained a powerful theorem that became known as the Bjerknes circulation theorem. Noting that the absolute circulation C_a around a closed curve is composed of the circulation with respect to earth coordinates (relative circulation), C, and the circulation of the earth in space, C_e, Bjerknes wrote (using his terminology) for the acceleration of relative circulation $C = C_a - C_e$:

$$\frac{dC}{dt} = -\oint \alpha dp - 2\omega \frac{dS_e}{dt} - R,$$

where α denotes the specific volume, p the pressure, ω the earth's angular velocity, S_e the magnitude of the equatorial projection of the area S about which the relative circulation is computed ($S_e = S \sin \varphi$, φ = latitude), and R is the acceleration due to frictional forces.[33]

In his 1898 discussion of atmospheric motions on the basis of the circulation theorem, Bjerknes considered the circulation acceleration resulting from pressure forces only. This term could be computed with the knowledge of the pressure field and density (or specific volume) field, as had been analyzed by Ekholm. If the density is completely determined by pressure at each point, the term $\oint \alpha dp$ becomes zero and the circulation acceleration vanishes. This condition manifests itself by parallel surfaces of pressure, specific volume or density and temperature or

31 (1898), p. 3; "Das dynamische Princip der Cirkulationsbewegung in der Atmosphäre," *Met. Zeits.*, **17** (1900), 99–101; "Ueber die Bildung von Cirkulationsbewegungen und Wirbeln in reibungslosen Flüssigkeiten," *Videnskabsselskabets Skrifter* (Christiania, 1898); "Cirkulation relativ zur Erde," *Oversigt, Kongl. Vet.-Akad. Förhandl.*, **58** (1901), 739–757, reprinted in *Met. Zeits.*, **19** (1902), 97–108. L. Silberstein also developed the circulation theorem (the solenoid term), as Bjerknes himself pointed out, but he did not follow up his results; see Silberstein, "Ueber die Entstehung von Wirbelbewegungen in einer reibungslosen Flüssigkeit," *Bull. International de l'Academie des Sciences de Cracovie* (1896). See further, Helmholtz, "Ueber Integrale der hydrodynamischen Gleichungen, welche den Wirbelbewegungen entsprechen," *Journ. für die angewandte Mathematik*, **55** (1858), 25–55, reprinted in *Abhandlungen*, **1** (1882, Leipzig), 101–134; and Thomson, "On vortex atoms," *Proc. Roy. Soc. Edinb.*, **6** (1867), 94–105. Although minor differences exist, Thomson's assumptions are essentially the same as those of Helmholtz. Thomson developed the theory that atoms of matter were vortex rings in the ether, like smoke rings in air.

[33] V. Bjerknes, "Circulation relativ zur Erde," *op. cit.*, pp. 740–747.

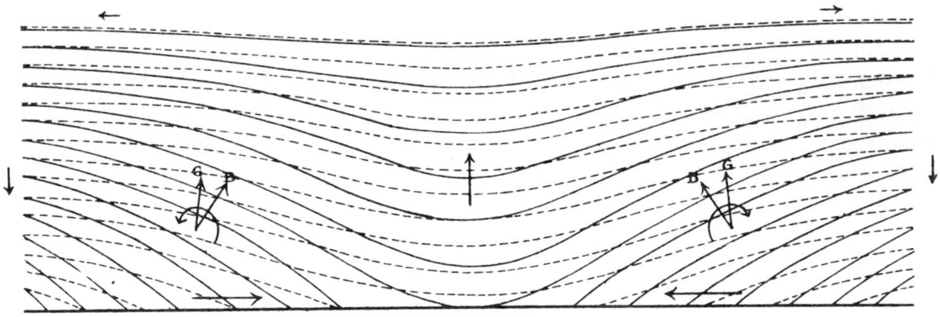

FIGURE 33. Vertical circulation in storms according to V. Bjerknes; from Bjerknes, "Ueber einen hydrodynamischen Fundamentalsatz und seine Anwendung besonders auf die Mechanik der Atmosphäre und des Weltmeeres," *Kongl. Svenska Vet.-Akad. Handl.*, **31** (1898). Dashed lines represent isobaric surfaces; solid lines are isosteric surfaces; G is pressure gradient ($-\nabla p$); B, "mobility vector" (Beweglichkeitsvektor, $\nabla\alpha$); the acceleration of circulation is directed from B to G.

potential temperature. In the real atmosphere, the isobaric and isosteric surfaces generally intersect. For the former case, Bjerknes introduced the term barotropic, and for the latter the term baroclinic. Baroclinicity, Bjerknes showed, was to be regarded as the basic source of circulation acceleration, being modified by the deflecting force of the earth's rotation and frictional forces. It depended mostly, he stated, on horizontal temperature gradients resulting from differential heating of the atmosphere (using modern terminology). In the baroclinic case, as presented in Figure 33, "the circulation acceleration which is directed from the mobility vector [Beweglichkeitsvektor, $\nabla\alpha$] to the [pressure] gradient [$-\nabla p$] will produce a circulation" with air rising over the central warm region and sinking over the colder regions at some distance; thereby potential energy of the mass distribution is converted into kinetic energy of circulation.[34] Bjerknes demonstrated that the numerical value of the term $\oint \alpha dp$ is directly proportional to the number of parallelograms delineated by the intersection of isosteres and isobars, for which he introduced the term "solenoid."

> The increase of circulation of any closed curve per unit time is equal to the number of solenoids enclosed by the curve.[35]

He saw the greatest importance of the circulation theorem not so much in the possibility "to trace numerically the atmospheric movements," but in the fact "that the theory provides a rational principle around which one can group the facts found through observations."[36]

A further advantage of the theorem, Bjerknes recognized, was its suitability for "approximate, quantitative investigations," based on a simple enumeration of the

[34] Bjerknes, *Met. Zeits.* (1900), *op. cit.*, p. 150.

[35] V. Bjerknes (1900), p. 106. According to Bjerknes the term solenoid is here used in agreement with the terminology of vector analysis, denoting vectors whose spatial distribution can be represented completely by a system of tubes. Through his work Bjerknes effectively introduced vector analysis in geophysics, choosing the terminology of Heaviside-Gibbs.

[36] *Ibid.*, p. 155.

solenoids—thus excluding difficult mathematical procedures. In particular, he thought that the circulation theorem provided the means to test the validity of the thermal and dynamic theories of cyclones because it furnished a method for determining the thermal energy available for circulation on the basis of observations. It will be recalled that quantitative testing of the thermal theory in its most rudimentary form dated back to the work of Peslin in 1868 and Reye in 1872. Peslin and Reye had developed equations for computation of the buoyancy acceleration arising from density differences by means of the parcel method. Peslin conveniently represented on a thermodynamic diagram the energy available for the accelerating motion, making use of the observed (or assumed) vertical temperature distribution at a point near the cyclone center. Bjerknes' circulation theorem made it possible to consider the large-scale motions throughout the atmospheric space.[37]

In the interpretation of the thermal theory of cyclones on the basis of the circulation theorem, Bjerknes argued that during the formation of a storm a continuous heat source over an extended area such as a warm ocean will lead to a lowering of the isosteric surfaces and eventually also of the isobaric surfaces;

> the depressions of the isosteric surfaces, however, will be the strongest, because, due to decreased pressure, these surfaces must sink as much as the isobaric [surfaces] and, because the depression due to higher temperature has still to be added to this depression. For this reason the isosteric surfaces must intersect the isobaric [surfaces] and must form a system of solenoids which surrounds the hot air masses.[38]

This formation of solenoids is illustrated in the vertical cross section of Figure 33. If the vertical circulation continues for a certain length of time, extending over large horizontal distances, then the deflecting force of the earth's rotation becomes effective and it changes "the originally radially directed inflow of air below and the corresponding outflow of air above into motions of spiral nature."[39] A rotation in the horizontal plane will be superimposed on the original vertical circulation. The intensity of the two motions will be limited by friction.

Bjerknes called the thermal theory a "physical theory of cyclones and anticyclones"[40] as opposed to what he termed the "mechanical" theory (i.e., dynamic theory as proposed by Hann and Bezold), in which the formation of cyclones was viewed "as consequence of conflicts among the great air currents of the atmosphere."[41] Thereby he indicated that he took the thermal theory to be in basic agreement with the principles of physical hydrodynamics. Concerning the "mechanical" theory he regretted that it was not possible to analyze it because

---

[37] In 1916, Sandström extended Bjerknes' theorem to include a thermodynamic cycle: Circulation will be generated, or maintained, against frictional actions, when heat is supplied at low levels (high pressure) and removed at high levels (low pressure), [see "Meteorologische Studien im schwedischen Hochgebirge," *Göteborgs K. Vetenskaps—och Vitterhetssamhälles Handl.*, Ser. 4, **22** (1916), 1–48]. However, in 1925 Jeffreys pointed out that Sandström's theorem is precise only with the additional assumption that expansion is taking place in the region of heating and contraction in the region of cooling. This has been discussed in detail by J. Dutton in *Ceaseless Wind* (McGraw-Hill, 1976), 380–381.

[38] V. Bjerknes (1900), p. 151.

[39] *Ibid.*, p. 150.

[40] *Ibid.*, p. 151.

[41] V. Bjerknes (1898), p. 32.

A more exact analysis of the mechanics of the formation of cyclones or anticyclones, based on this theory, has never been pursued, as far as I know, and thus we can not enter into a positive discussion of this theory.[42]

Penetrating further into the cyclone problem, Bjerknes examined two possible modes of cyclone propagation. In this he was following Ekholm who had divided existing theories into two types according to the principles employed in the explanation of cyclone propagation. Ekholm regarded both of these as incomplete but complementing each other: first, Ferrel's theory of cyclone propagation, extended by Köppen who had proposed that the cyclone was displaced in the direction of the current predominant in terms of "total" energy, and second, the theories of Mohn and Ley who regarded temperature asymmetry as essential for cyclone propagation.[43] Bjerknes argued that if in the first mode of propagation the vortex is only altered slowly by the forces that tend to generate or dissipate vortex motion, then the Helmholtz and Thomson theorems of conservation of vortex motion can be applied in first approximation, and under favorable conditions "the air being considered may be carried away by the large atmospheric currents, while retaining its vortex motion."[44] Thus Bjerknes considered it theoretically possible that a fully developed cyclone could propagate in the general midlatitude eastward drift in the absence of vortex generating forces, i.e., surface heating, and yet only slowly loose its identity. From this point of view, therefore, the objections voiced against Ferrel's view of cyclone propagation were substantially reduced. In the second type the cyclone propagated by displacement of the center of the vortex generating forces so that a new vortex continuously formed adjacent to the old. Consequently, Bjerknes remarked,

> the warm air present in the center is not anymore the air warmed in situ because of the given local conditions, but air having flowed in from outside; for, in general, the air flowing in from different sides will have different temperatures, and, because of this asymmetry, the place, where the air is hottest and where, therefore, the isosteric surfaces have their greatest depression, will not coincide with the momentary center of the vortex.[45]

This mode of maintenance and propagation of storms, based on the temperature asymmetry within the storm area, agreed with the views of Guldberg and Mohn. Bjerknes' description of the cyclonic process was also in accordance with the scheme of asymmetric vertical circulation suggested by Köppen, associated with rising of warm air in the front portion and descending motion in the rear. Bjerknes did not mention the names of these scientists.[46]

Having presented these two views on cyclone propagation, Bjerknes suggested

---

[42] V. Bjerknes (1900), 151–152.

[43] Ekholm, "Étude des conditions météorologiques . . . ," (1891), *op. cit.*, pp. 16–18.

[44] Bjerknes (1900), 151–152. In the case of autobarotropy, e.g., when barotropy is retained through time (adiabatic atmosphere with adiabatic motions), Bjerknes' theorem reduces to Thomson's theorem, the only difference being the assumption of compressibility.

[45] *Ibid.*, p. 150.

[46] The entire paper contains only two references. However, Bjerknes acknowledged specifically

that it was possible to test their validity conclusively by application of the circulation theorem:

> If the physical theory is correct . . . then the system of solenoids must somewhat precede the proper vortex; if, however, the cyclone is carried on by the large atmospheric currents, then the solenoid system, if present at all, will exactly follow the vortex.[47]

At the turn of the century, series of vertical cross sections through cyclones depicting the pressure and density structure at different times—required for the solution of this question—were not yet available.

However, it was possible to make valuable preliminary estimates of the thermal energy available for cyclonic circulation by calculating the number of solenoids present in individual vertical cross sections. Bjerknes suggested that

> If the physical theory is correct, then the number of existing solenoids or [solenoids] having existed must be sufficient, in order to explain the existing circulation or wind velocities.[48]

Only in the light of contrary evidence would there be reason, Bjerknes concluded, "to search for other causes of cyclone formation and to take into consideration the more distant solenoids of the large atmospheric circulation."[49]

At the Blue Hill Observatory near Harvard University, Clayton, who had already excelled in the output of cloud observations and the perfection of kite and balloon techniques, published the first data needed for a cross section of the temperature and pressure distribution in a cyclone (Figure 34).[50] Bjerknes suggested to his student J. W. Sandström, then still the "uncut diamond" whom Ekholm had recommended to him, that he construct the isobaric and isosteric surfaces of this cyclone. Sandström, a former millhand who had come to Stockholm on a stipend from the factory where he was working, soon became one of the most stimulating and important of Bjerknes' collaborators. Without Sandström's support and encouragement, Bjerknes later acknowledged, he would scarcely have continued his investigations in the field of meteorology.[51]

When working at his first assignment from Bjerknes, Sandström assumed that the cyclone passing over Blue Hill Observatory (between the 21st and 24th of September, 1898) had undergone relatively minor changes in its interior structure; consequently, kite ascents could be regarded as simultaneous observations at

---

that he had utilized Ekholm's explanations and advice, when applying the circulation theorem to atmospheric motions (*Ibid.*, p. 98).

[47] *Ibid.*, p. 153.

[48] *Ibid.*, p. 152.

[49] *Ibid.*

[50] H. H. Clayton, "Studies of cyclonic and anticyclonic phenomena with kites," *Blue Hill Meteorological Observatory*, 1 (1899), 2–19. Clayton was a pioneer in the exploration of the free atmosphere. He began his cloud studies in 1886, and organized the first use of kites lifting self-recording instruments at Blue Hill in 1894. See biographical note on Clayton in the Appendix.

[51] V. Bjerknes *et al.*, *Physikalische Hydrodynamik* (Berlin, Springer, 1933), Preface, p. vi and pp. 781–782; "In memory of V. Bjerknes," *op. cit.*, pp. 13–14. See biographical note on Sandström in the Appendix.

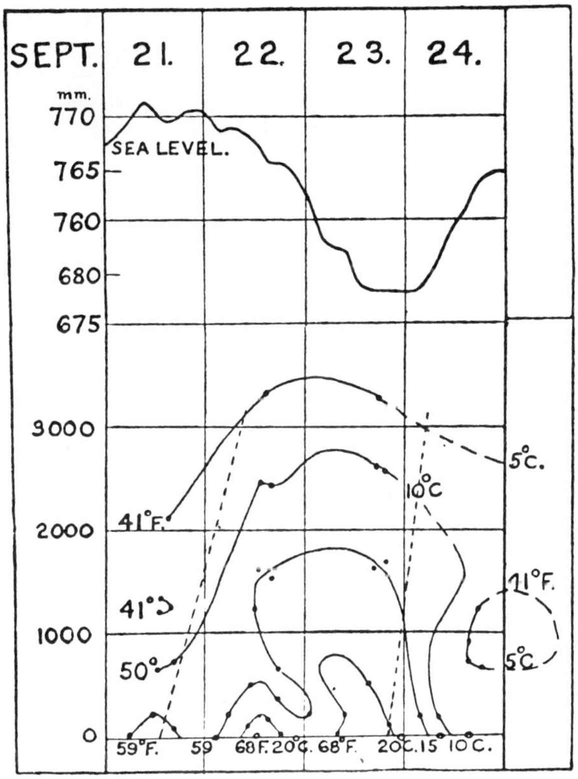

Figure 34. Vertical temperature distribution in the storm of 21–24 September 1898, by Clayton, "Various researches on the temperature in cyclones and anticyclones in temperate latitudes," *Beitr. Phys. f. Atm.*, **1** (1905); Clayton reproduced here a figure from "Studies of cyclonic and anticyclonic phenomena with kites," *Blue Hill Meteorological Observatory, Bull.*, **1** (1899). Upper part: curve of sea level barometric pressure (mm Hg). Lower part: isotherms (°F and °C), height (m); slanted, dashed lines indicate vertical axes of anticyclone and cyclone passing over Blue Hill. The diagram brings "graphically to the eye the rise of the isothermal lines with the fall of pressure" (Clayton).

different points along the cyclone path and could serve as a vertical cross section. This procedure had already been followed by Clayton when he published the results of the kite ascents (Figure 34). Sandström developed a numerical and graphical method for the determination of isosteric surfaces from the pressure, temperature and moisture data.[52] His results for the North American cyclone are presented in Figures 35–37. The synoptic charts of the eastern United States for 21–24 September, 1898 (Figure 35), portray a cyclone coming from the Gulf of Mexico and moving across the Great Lakes area toward the New England states, accompanied by extensive precipitation in the front part. The vertical cross section for the same period (Figure 36) shows the cyclone axis passing over Blue Hill between the 23rd

[52] J. W. Sandström, "Ueber die Anwendung von Professor V. Bjerknes' Theorie der Wirbelbewegungen in Gasen und Flüssigkeiten auf meteorologische Beobachtungen in den höheren Luftschichten," *Kongl. Svenska Vet.-Akad. Handl.*, **33**, No. 4 (1900), 23 pp.

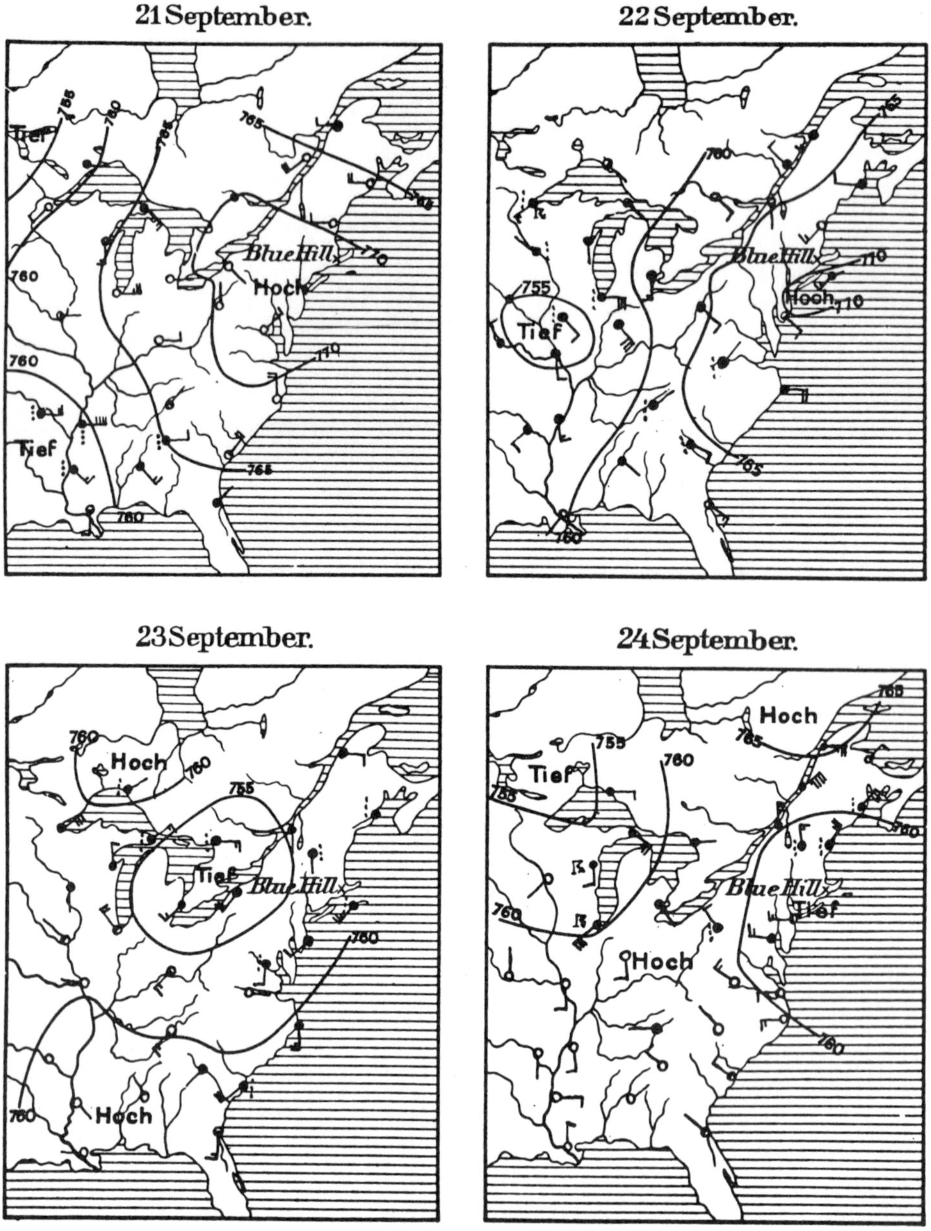

FIGURE 35. Synoptic charts corresponding to the vertical cross section of the storm in Figure 34, passing over Blue Hill on 21–24 September 1898, 8 a.m.; from Sandström, "Ueber die Anwendung von Professor Bjerknes' Theorie . . . ," *Kongl. Svenska Vet.-Akad. Handl.*, **33**, No. 4 (1900).

and 24th of September. The region of humid air in the front part of the cyclone is associated with precipitation and a dry tongue of northerly flow extends behind the cyclone axis. Sandström's vertical cross section of the pressure and density distribution (Figure 37) indicated that the region of warmest air (deepest depression

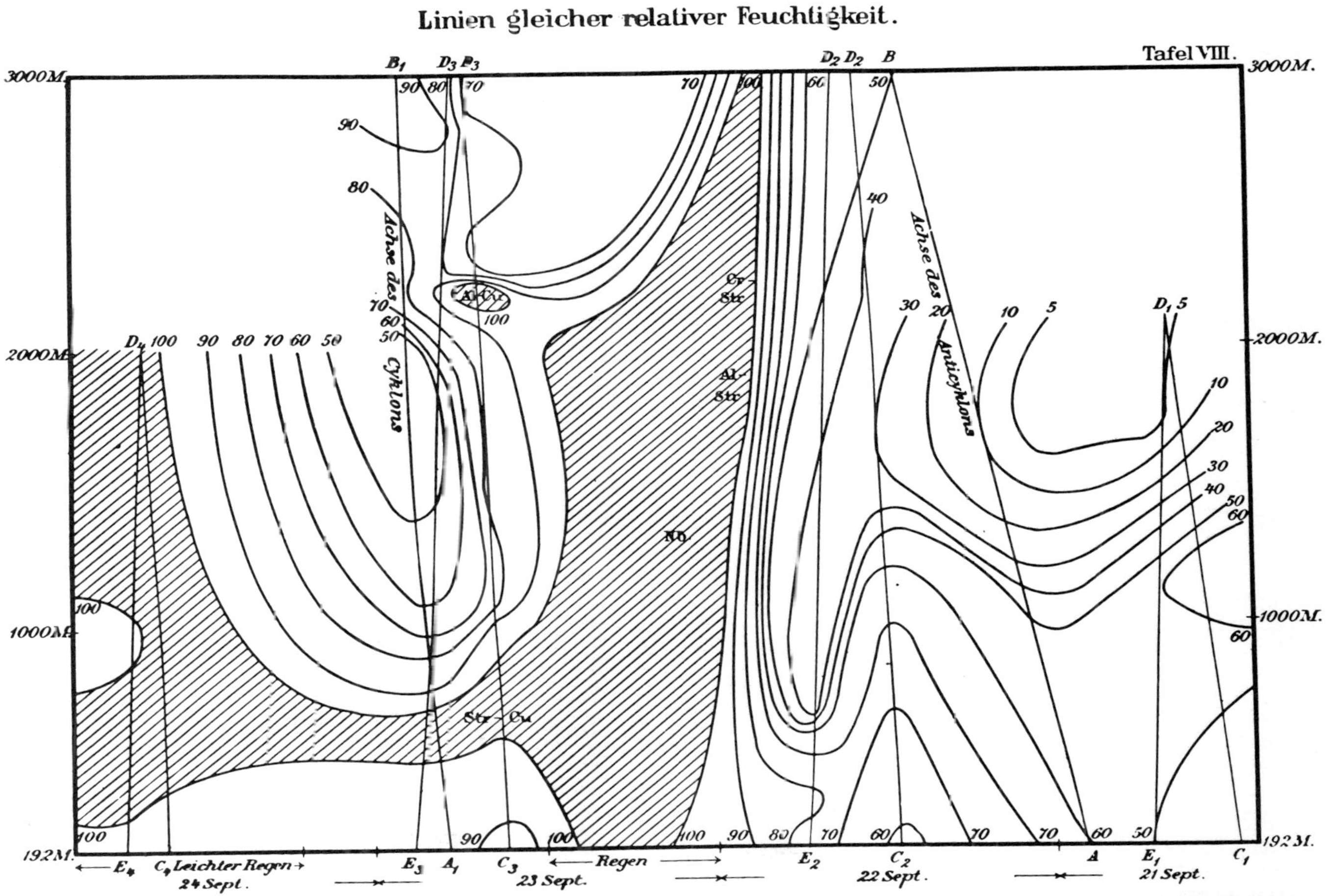

FIGURE 36. Vertical cross section of lines of equal relative humidity of the storm passing over Blue Hill on 21–24 September 1898; from Sandström, "Ueber die Anwendung von Professor Bjerknes' Theorie . . . ," *Kongl. Svenska Vet.-Akad. Handl.*, **33**, No. 4 (1900). AB indicates axis of anticyclone; A_1B_1, axis of cyclone. $C_1D_1E_1$, . . . , $C_4D_4E_4$ show paths of kites during the four days that were analyzed. Hatched area indicates clouds.

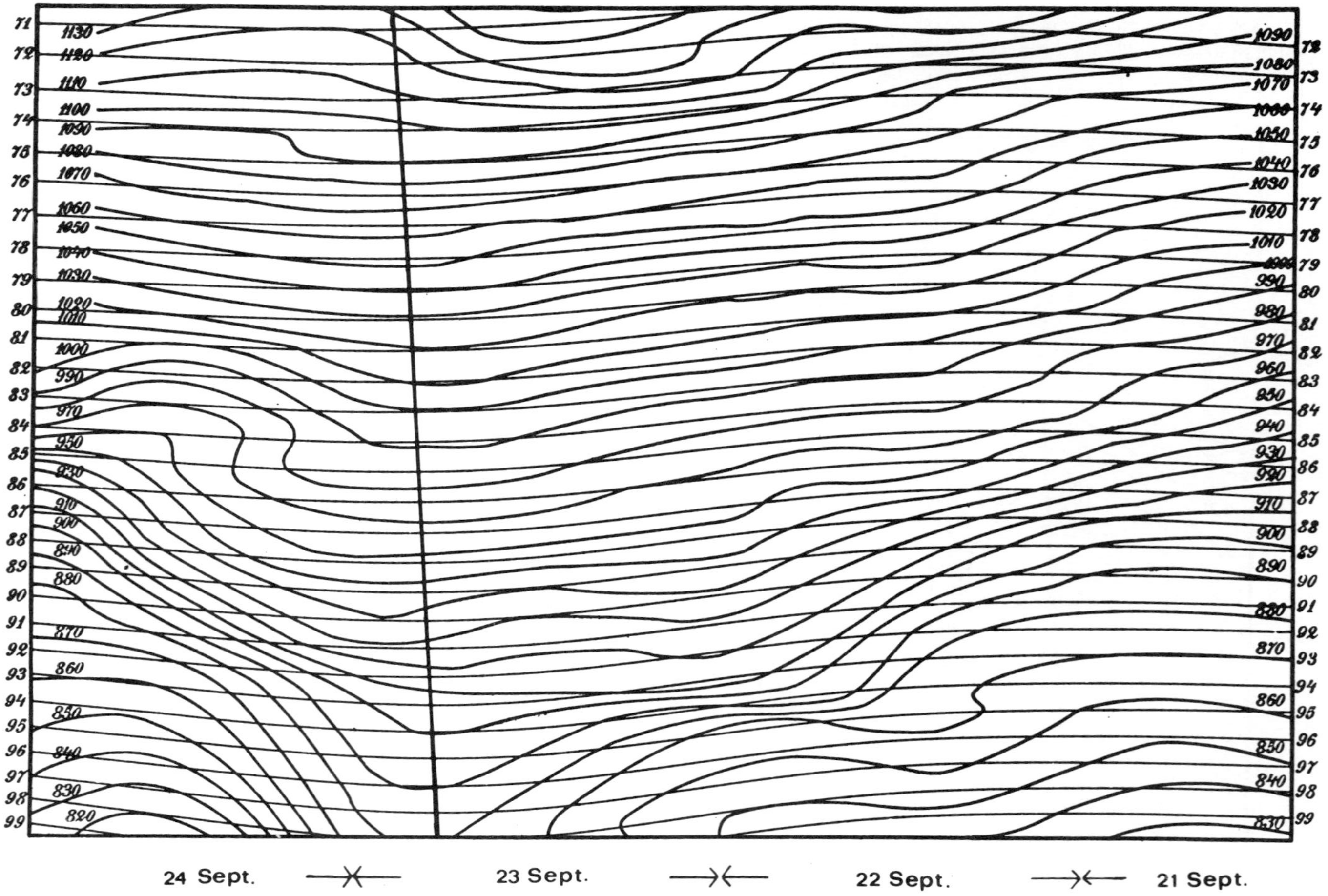

FIGURE 37. Vertical cross section of isobars and isosteres of the storm passing over Blue Hill on 21–24 September 1898; from Sandström, "Ueber die Anwendung von Professor Bjerknes' Theorie . . . ," *Kongl. Svenska Vet.-Akad. Handl.*, **33**, No. 4 (1900). Isobars are analyzed for each 10^4 g cm^{-1} s^{-2}, isosteres for each 10 cm^3 g^{-1}. Thus each parallelogram area includes 10^5 solenoids. Vertical line, indicating axis of cyclone, and dates are added by author.

of the isosteres) is along the cyclone axis. The acceleration of circulation corresponding to this pressure and density distribution results in ascending motion along the cyclone axis. Viewing the cyclone as divided in two parts by its axis, Sandström found that "the contour to the left" of the axis includes "about $9 \cdot 10^6$ and the contour to the right about $12 \cdot 10^6$ solenoids." Furthermore,

> In order to obtain the greatest observed wind velocity of 13.0 m/sec the system of solenoids to the right [sic; should read: left] consequently needs to operate for 15 hours and the system to the left [should read: right] for 8 hours.[53]

Considering the influence of the earth's rotation on the increase of circulation

> . . . the cyclone is completely developed in about 14 hours. Considering that a cyclone normally needs 1 to 3 days for its formation, then we see that a large surplus of energy is available in order to overcome retarding forces which have not been taken into account in this computation. In the case in question, therefore, it appears to be superfluous to seize at other causes for cyclone formation than the physical [causes] considered here.[54]

In the light of these calculations, it is clear that Sandström regarded the "physical" cyclone theory as perfectly plausible and credible. He concluded that since the cyclone appeared to change very little during the time period considered, it could be assumed that there was an equilibrium between accelerating forces due to solenoids and retarding forces due to other factors.

6.4 SYNOPTIC STUDIES OF HORIZONTAL TEMPERATURE CONTRASTS (EKHOLM, BIGELOW AND SHAW, THE 1900's)

A fundamental difference between European and American cyclones and anticyclones was acknowledged by investigators of the late 1890's and early 1900's. Most European workers accepted Hann's results of 1890; namely, that above a shallow surface layer anticyclones were on the average warmer than cyclones (at least in Europe). American meteorologists, however, maintained that on the average cyclones were warmer than anticyclones. By the turn of the century, with steadily improving observations of the upper strata, a few investigators were able to relate these differences in part to the life history of cyclones. It was proposed that the United States experienced predominantly young growing cyclones, while cyclones arriving at the European continent in most cases had reached a mature stage of development. Ekholm in 1906 made a significant contribution toward a deeper understanding of the life history of storms when he investigated the upper temperature field in storms in relation to the passage of isallobaric areas, i.e., areas of rising and falling pressure.[55]

Ekholm had taken the method of isallobaric analysis from its long time obscurity and had employed it successfully alongside the analysis of the pressure field for forecasting purposes at the Swedish Meteorological Service.[56] This

[53] *Ibid.*, p. 22.

[54] *Ibid.*

[55] N. Ekholm, "Die Luftdruckschwankungen und deren Beziehung zu der Temperatur der oberen Luftschichten," *Met. Zeits.*, Hannband (1906), 228 242.

[56] Isallobars define lines of equal pressure change with time. According to Khrgian, *op. cit.*, 197–198, isallobaric charts were first constructed in 1864 by Müller at the Main Physical Observatory in

method, Ekholm suggested, should make it possible to distinguish between traveling and stationary cyclones and anticyclones. He explained that traveling cyclones should be preceded by an area of falling pressure and followed by an area of rising pressure. The reverse applied in the case of anticyclones. He found indeed that "all very dangerous storms of northwestern Europe"[57] were preceded by areas of rapidly falling pressure. Traveling anticyclones, often encountered in North America, were observed relatively seldom in northwestern Europe, he suggested, because "the areas of pressure rise are mostly so shallow that only wedge-shaped isobars can develop."[58] In accordance with Mohn's view, Ekholm attributed storm propagation to the influx of warm air, associated with pressure fall, in the front portion of the cyclone and of cold air, associated with pressure rise, in the rear. Ekholm found that stationary cyclones tended to be cold, and had "the remarkable property to act as a center of action with regard to approaching areas of pressure fall."[59] That is, approaching areas of falling pressure tended to be "attracted" and "absorbed" by stationary cyclones.

Hoping that grouping cyclones and anticyclones as traveling or stationary systems would shed some light on the differences observed between American and European storms, Ekholm reinvestigated certain widely quoted temperature data on cyclones and anticyclones obtained at the Aeronautische Observatorium at Lindenberg near Berlin. These data had received contradictory interpretations by different scientists. W. v. Bezold and A. Berson (1900), in their official treatment of 65 manned balloon ascents made at Lindenberg (many of them conducted by Berson), had concluded that on the average cyclones were colder than anticyclones in central Europe.[60] Thus their results supported Hann's earlier findings. On the other hand, in 1906 Clayton interpreted the same data as showing "a tendency for the . . . inverted pressure curve [dip means rise of pressure] to rise and fall with the temperature, as is true at Blue Hill [in the United States]"[61] in all cases of traveling cyclones studied (see, for example, Figure 43). Ekholm noted that Bezold had averaged over all cyclones, regardless of whether they were traveling or near stationary, while Clayton had assumed that low pressure in the local barograph record was associated with the passage of a cyclone. With the aid of concurrent synoptic charts Ekholm could identify only a single cyclone center traveling over Berlin during the period considered by Clayton. During the passage of this one low

Leningrad. Isallobaric charts were used at the Russian, French and American weather services already during the 1870's.

[57] Ekholm (1906), p. 233.

[58] *Ibid.*

[59] *Ibid.*, p. 234.

[60] *Wissenschaftliche Luftfahrten*, Vol. 3 (1900), R. Assmann and A. Berson, Eds.; see Berson, "Die Lufttemperatur," 104–115 and Bezold, "Theoretische Schlussbetrachtungen," 311–313. A closer examination of this publication shows that Bezold indeed made this conclusion. He acknowledged that this result applied only to fully developed cyclones which were most frequent over central Europe. Berson, on the other hand, emphasized the temperature contrast between front and rear of cyclones due to the advection of warm and cold air. He showed further that above 4000 m the temperature lapse rate decreased considerably over cyclones while it increased over anticyclones, indicating that temperature compensation took place in upper levels. Berson appears to have been more cautious in drawing conclusions from the rather small number of ascents in cyclones than Bezold who somewhat unjustly viewed the data as confirmative of Hann's thesis.

[61] Clayton, *op. cit.*, p. 104.

pressure center, however, "the temperature of the upper strata then was still quite high."[62] It began to fall several hours later and reached a minimum two days after the cyclone passage. An unequivocal result was obtained by considering isallobaric areas:

> . . . considering the areas of falling and rising pressure instead of the cyclone, we find immediately that the barometer fell, when the temperature of the upper strata rose, and vice versa.[63]

Additional data on European storms generally confirmed this observation. Ekholm concluded that Bezold's and Berson's results reflected conditions in cold and nearly stationary cyclones that were most common in the data series, whereas Clayton's claim, based on a loose interpretation of the observations, was correct only for traveling cyclones that are frequently encountered in the United States. Ekholm concluded

> . . . that traveling cyclones and anticyclones . . . must behave similar to the areas of falling and rising [pressure], by which they are produced, that is, the traveling cyclones are warm and the traveling anticyclones are cold. Such traveling cyclones and anticyclones are quite rare in Europe, and generally give rise to such strong storms that no observations can be made on the temperature of their upper strata. Therefore, these are hardly taken into consideration in the computation of the average temperature of the upper air strata in cyclones and anticyclones. On the other hand, they are alledgedly every day phenomena in North America, and this fact would simply and completely explain the disparity of the results which have been found by European and American meteorologists.[64]

Thus, essential differences between American and European storms appeared to have found their natural explanation in the life history of storms. Yet, Ekholm's conclusion was based on limited data. He noted that he had not made an analogous study of American cyclones.

We will now turn to the discussion of pertinent observational studies in the United States, in particular the work of Frank H. Bigelow on the three-dimensional structure of cyclones. Bigelow was professor of meteorology at the Weather Bureau for almost 20 years, and, at the same time, he was minister at St. John's in Washington. His meteorological investigations became relatively well known in Europe, and his influence can be traced in the work of Margules, Hanzlik, V. Bjerknes and, later, J. Bjerknes.[65] Bigelow stressed that a detailed knowledge of the kinematics of the atmosphere was absolutely necessary for the advancement of

---

[62] Ekholm (1906), p. 237.

[63] *Ibid.*

[64] *Ibid.*, p. 239.

[65] American meteorologists at the Weather Bureau paid comparatively little attention to his investigations. His biographer and close associate A. J. Henry outlined some of the possible reasons as follows: "Personally, he was reserved and was not what is commonly called a 'good mixer.' Owing to the highly mathematical and often obscure character of his papers the leading officials of the Weather Bureau found it difficult to follow the force of his arguments or concur in the integrity of his conclusions. This led to a sort of isolation of the author. . . . Indeed, discouragement . . . probably was an important factor in the termination of Bigelow's connection with the bureau." Henry in "Frank Hagar Bigelow," *Mon. Wea. Rev.*, **52** (1924), p. 166. See also biographical note on Bigelow in the Appendix.

meteorology. Like V. Bjerknes, he regretted the "deficiency of modern meteorology" in studies of the dynamics of the atmosphere.[66] In contrast to his European colleagues, who worked with mountain observations and balloon ascents, Bigelow analyzed primarily cloud observations and kite ascents. For this reason, we will begin the discussion of his work with a brief sketch of the efforts of the International Cloud Year of 1896/97 which provided the data base for Bigelow's far-reaching investigations.

At the turn of the century, temperature observations of the upper levels of the atmosphere were made regularly only at a few selected localities. As previously described, the upper pressure field normally was deduced from the upper winds as inferred from the flow patterns of clouds in different height levels and also from surface pressure and temperature, assuming hydrostatic equilibrium.[67] Cloud observations were irregularly spaced and timed. A significant step toward the improvement of this situation was taken when the International Cloud Committee, appointed at the International Meteorological Conference at Munich in 1891, invited all countries "to take part in a common investigation of the upper currents of the atmosphere by means of observations of the direction, and by measurements of the altitudes and the motions of the different forms of clouds" from May 1896 to July 1897.[68] The choice of methods and instruments to be used was left open. Measurements by eye, on which Ley had exclusively relied, and with the nephoscope were made at as many stations as possible. At selected stations the altitude and velocity of clouds was determined by means of baseline measurements with two theodolites with telephone connection.[69] In addition, photogrammeters were used for the observation of clouds and their heights.[70]

The American observations were presented by Bigelow in a report of almost 800 pages. Bigelow had at his disposal more than 30,000 theodolite and nephoscope observations of clouds from 16 stations distributed quite uniformly east of the Rocky Mountains. From these data, he derived mean vectors of the motion in cyclones and anticyclones for six levels between the surface and 10,000 m. Although the charts of these mean vectors "give only a mean or average scheme of the circulation and are necessarily somewhat idealized, since they include all the

---

[66] As quoted by Bigelow in "Report on the international cloud observations," *Report to the Chief of the Weather Bureau*, Vol. II, 1889–1899. (U.S. Dept. of Agriculture, Washington, 1900), p. 19.

[67] The first comprehensive theoretical treatment of this procedure is found in Sandström, "Ueber die Beziehung zwischen Temperatur und Luftbewegung in der Atmosphäre unter stationären Verhältnissen," *Oversigt Kongl. Vet.-Akad. Förhandl.*, **58** (1901), 759–777 and "Ueber die Beziehung zwischen Luftbewegung und Druck in der Atmosphäre unter stationären Verhältnissen," *ibid.*, **59** (1902), 87–103.

[68] Bigelow, "Studies on the statics and kinematics of the atmosphere in the United States, II. Method of observing and discussing the motions of the atmosphere," *Mon. Wea. Rev.*, **30** (1902), p. 80.

[69] This method had been developed by Ekholm and Hagström in "Mesures de hauteurs et des mouvements des nuages," *Acta Soc. Reg. Scient.*, Upsala, 1885. The method was subsequently adopted at the Blue Hill Observatory by Clayton and Fergusson; see their paper "Measurements of cloud heights and velocities," *Annals of the Astronomical Observatory*, Cambridge, Mass., 1892.

[70] For a comprehensive contemporary report of the results of international observations of clouds see Hildebrandsson, "The international observations of clouds," *Quart. Journ. Roy. Met. Soc.*, **30** (1904), 317–343.

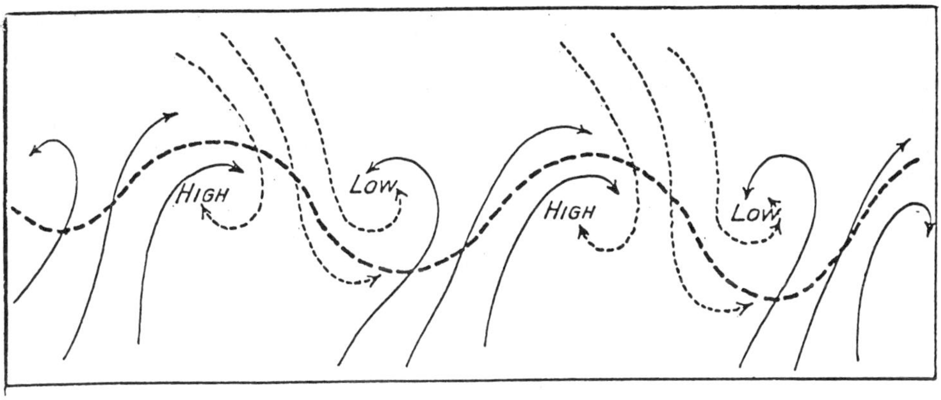

FIGURE 38. Bigelow's model of currents in cyclones and anticyclones; from Bigelow, "Studies on the statics and kinematics of the atmosphere in the United States," III., *Mon. Wea. Rev.*, **30** (1902). Warm currents are shown by solid lines with arrows, cold currents by dashed lines with arrows; heavy dashed line indicates resulting sinuous eastward flow at 3000 m elevation.

anticyclones and cyclones of the cloud year, many of which are only imperfectly developed," Bigelow felt nevertheless that they were a good approximation of flow patterns in cyclones and anticyclones.[71] In order to obtain a clear picture of the cyclonic and anticyclonic wind components, Bigelow presented corresponding charts of the motion vectors after removal of the component of the annual mean eastward drift. He felt this was justified because—according to his charts—the low and high pressure systems produced only a relatively slight distortion of the mean flow, at least at levels of the upper clouds, i.e., above 5000 m. Nevertheless, even in the original charts cyclonic influence was discernible up to 10,000 m. The cyclonic components themselves, he found, "are very symmetrically formed throughout the entire stratum of air" except for a section shifting from NNE at the surface to WNW at 10,000 m where "the vectors are almost exactly opposed to each other in direction, those on the east side flowing outward and those on the west side flowing inward."[72] A similar discontinuity in flow was found in the southwest quadrant of the anticyclones.

According to Bigelow, these discontinuities in flow, in combination with other features observed in cyclones and anticyclones, suggested that there were two distinct streams of air, flowing northward and southward, respectively, taking part in the circulation of these systems. The entire flow pattern exhibited in cyclones and anticyclones, illustrated in Figure 38, indicated in Bigelow's mind a "conflict of two counterflowing, horizontal streams which tend to produce vertical rotation, but in fact fail to reach this ideal, except possibly in highly developed cases of severe storms."[73] Thus Bigelow substantiated and broadened the conclusions of Mohn and

[71] Bigelow, "Studies on the . . . , III. The observed circulation of the atmosphere in the high and low areas," *Mon. Wea. Rev.*, **30** (1902), p. 121.

[72] Bigelow (1902), p. 121.

[73] *Ibid.*, p. 122. Bigelow's conclusions were substantiated by Stanislav Hanzlik's investigations of

Ley that different types of air currents meet in a cyclone. Further, in Bigelow's model, which became known as the "counter current" model, renewed emphasis was placed on the boundary between air currents. Although such boundaries are often very pronounced in the United States and had been noted as early as 1841 by Loomis, their significance for the cyclone processes never had been thoroughly investigated before Bigelow.

Bigelow's findings entailed important consequences for the theory of the general circulation as well as for the theory of cyclones. Bigelow proposed that the exchange of air between low and high latitudes took place at the same horizontal level rather than different levels. The flow patterns observed in high and low pressure areas indicated a mutual interdependence between the general circulation and local anticyclones and cyclones, at variance with the assumption that midlatitude cyclones and anticyclones merely were disturbances of the general circulation. He remarked:

> It is much more natural to suppose that these two systems are mutually interdependent, and that the excess of energy of the general cyclone is transformed into the driving forces of the local circulation; also, that the acquired motion of the local cyclone reacts upon and retards the excess of motion of the general cyclone in the temperate zones.[74]

Bigelow directed his criticism primarily against Ferrel's theory in which "the general circulation and the local cyclone" are presented

> . . . as if they were in a sense *independent of one another* since separate sources of heat energy are assigned to each, and two characteristic laws of circulation are deduced therefrom.[75]

In addition, Bigelow felt, Ferrel's view of a vertical circulation cell between low and high latitudes with connecting meridional currents at different horizontal levels was no longer tenable.

In pursuit of a more accurate knowledge of the circulation in cyclones and anticyclones, Bigelow in 1903 initiated a program of extended observations in the United States that provided data not only of wind and pressure, but of temperature and vapor tension at certain levels above sea level. Observers from 174 stations began to mail daily data, interpolated to three height levels, to Washington. Bigelow published these data in map form, the first of their kind.[76] Simultaneously, he undertook a special study of the temperature conditions at various height levels in cyclones and anticyclones, using data from Blue Hill observatory, Hald in

---

European cyclones and anticyclones, based on observations from 10 European mountain observatories. See, "Die räumliche Verteilung der meteorologischen Elemente in Zyklonen," *Denks. Ak. Wien*, **88** (1913), 67–128. Hanzlik concluded, "the exchange of air between higher and lower latitudes takes place through horizontal convection currents. (Bigelow's counter current theory)." (p. 128). According to Hanzlik, these currents gave rise to the formation of a "thermal couple," the fast traveling and shallow cold anticyclone and the warm cyclone. Hanzlik pointed out that cold cyclones and warm anticyclones, being in the final phase of development, are slow traveling or stationary.

[74] Bigelow, "Studies on the . . . IV. Review of Ferrel's and Oberbeck's theories of the local and the general circulations," *Mon. Wea. Rev.*, **30** (1902), p. 171. The term general cyclone is here defined as polar vortex.

[75] *Ibid.*

[76] Bigelow, "The structure of cyclones and anticyclones on the 3500 foot and 10,000 foot planes for the United States," *Mon. Wea. Rev.*, **31** (1903), 26–29.

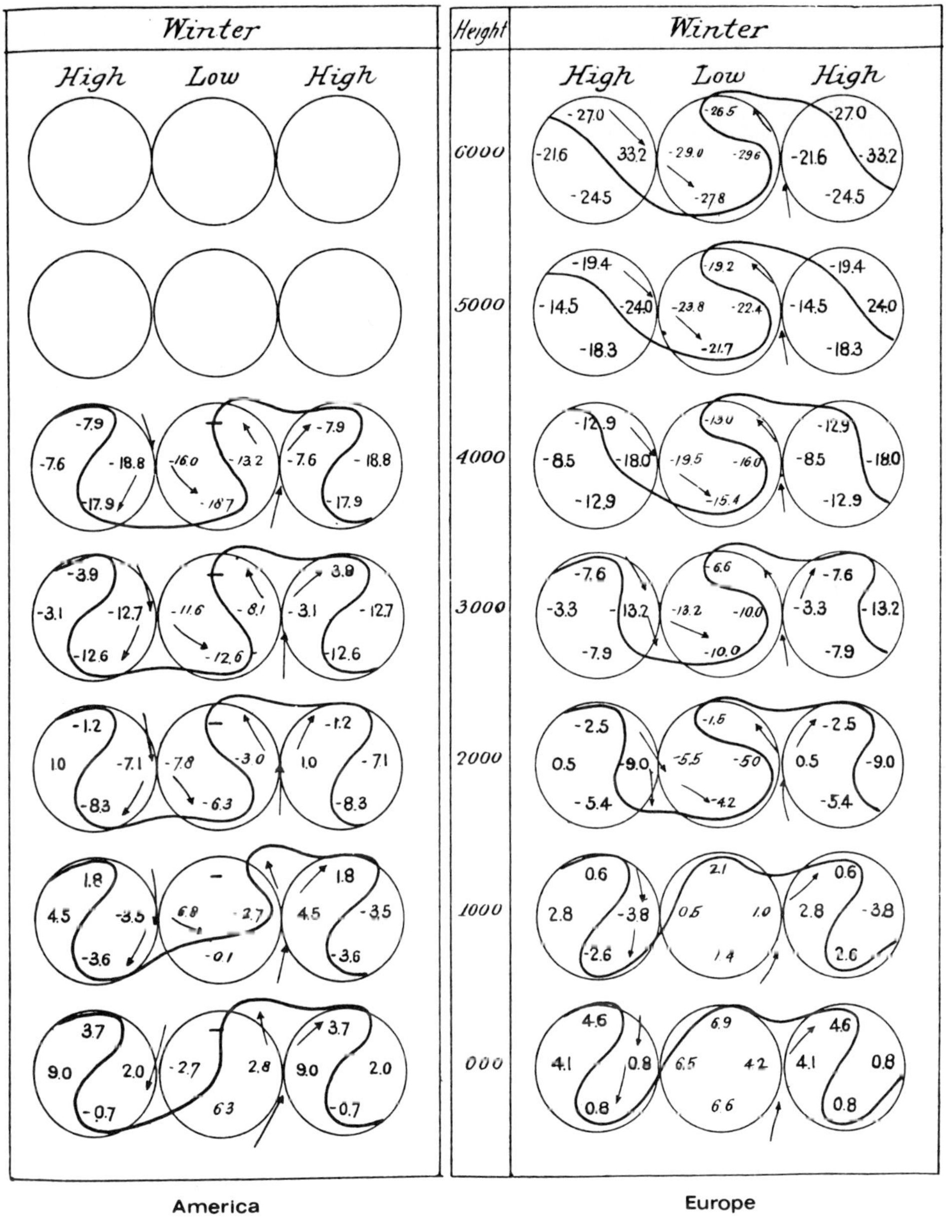

FIGURE 39. Temperature distribution in American and European cyclones and anticyclones at different height levels (Bigelow, 1906); from Bigelow, "Studies on the thermodynamics of the atmosphere," I. Asymmetric cyclones and anticyclones in Europe and America, *Mon. Wea. Rev.*, **34** (1906). Temperatures are given in degrees centigrade, heights in meters, and the lines of demarcation separate regions of warm air from regions of cold air. Arrows indicate generalized flow.

Denmark, and Berlin (Figure 39). He came to the conclusion that, despite disagreements between American and European meteorologists on this point, the temperature distribution

> . . . is fundamentally the same in the American and European circulation. There is an inflow of cold air from the northwest between the centers of barometric high and low pressure, and an inflow of warm air from the south, likewise between the centers of low and high pressure. There are no cold-center anticyclones in any level, nor any warm-center cyclones in any level.[77]

This finding confirmed Max Möller's impression of 1887 that cyclones are warm in the front and cold in the rear, and that there was no such thing as a cold or warm center cyclone. It also agreed with Ekholm's results for traveling—as opposed to stationary—cyclones: isallobaric areas of falling pressure preceding a traveling cyclone are generally warm, while the following isallobaric area of rising pressure is associated with cold temperature. On the other hand, Ekholm had assumed there was a decisive difference between American and European cyclones explainable by the fact that the majority of storms encountered in the United States were fast traveling systems, whereas stationary cyclones were more common in Europe. Bigelow did not make this distinction. He derived his results from a relatively rough division of cyclones and anticyclones into four sectors, each represented by one temperature value averaged over all stages and intensities of cyclone development (Figure 39). It could not be expected that this simple classification would reveal significant differences between American and European cyclones.

Bigelow noted pointedly that his analysis of the cloud data and temperature conditions in cyclones was incompatible with Ferrel's model of a symmetric, convective cyclone. In an area of low pressure, Bigelow stated, "the stream of warm air from the south curls around towards the west as it ascends from the surface to the upper levels."[78] But, Bigelow stressed, "there is no evidence that these motions are primarily due to the vertical convective currents developed during the local heating or cooling of restricted areas near the center of the cyclonic and anticyclonic areas, respectively."[79] Considering the energetics of storms, Bigelow emphasized that dynamic as well as thermal forces are of fundamental importance in cyclones. He therefore deviated from Hann, Bezold and Ekholm (see Ekholm's early paper of 1891), who had argued for a dynamic theory and had suggested that the kinetic energy of the relatively small-scale motion of cyclones was derived principally from the partial conversion of large-scale kinetic energy associated with the zone of strong midlatitude westerlies. Being less exclusive in his point of view, Bigelow wrote in 1903

> There is undoubtedly a certain amount of dynamic action which enters into the construction of cyclones, but there must also be a powerful mechanical force derived from the effort to restore the thermal equilibrium between currents of different temperature.[80]

---

[77] Bigelow, "Studies on the thermodynamics of the atmosphere, I. Asymmetric cyclones and anticyclones in Europe and America," *Mon. Wea. Rev.*, **34** (1906), p. 14.

[78] Bigelow (1902), p. 121.

[79] *Ibid.*, pp. 122–123.

[80] Bigelow, "The mechanism of countercurrents of different temperatures in cyclones and anticyclones," *Mon. Wea. Rev.*, **31** (1903), p. 72.

This becomes evident, he reasoned, if one considers the interaction of "three practically independent currents of air" in cyclones, namely: (1) the great overflowing eastward drift, (2) the underflowing cold current from the northwest, and (3) the underflowing warm stream from the south."[81] A persistent source of energy for the maintenance of cyclones was to be found in the

> *Thermal action due to the overflow of layers of cold air upon masses of warm air.* Abnormal stratification of air currents, where the relatively cold is above the warm, necessarily involves an upward current having an energy proportional to the difference of temperature.[82]

Bigelow modified this statement in 1906, stressing the "overflow" of warm masses upon cold masses in upper strata and "underflow" of cold masses beneath warm masses. This process, he noted, resulted in an "amount of kinetic energy corresponding to the movements of the air masses from one level surface to another:"

> In the low area, in the strata from the surface to about 4000 meters, to the southward of the center, the cold mass tends to underrun the warm mass, while to the northward of the center in the strata above 4000 meters, the warm mass tends to overflow the cold mass.[83]

Bigelow concluded

> This stratification and interpenetration of currents of different temperature is the true source of energy in storms. . . . The fact is that storms are produced by *horizontal convection* more than by *vertical convection*.[84]

In 1906 Ekholm came to the same conclusions as Bigelow with regard to the source of energy in cyclones from his study of areas of pressure fall and rise associated with cyclones. He observed that isallobaric areas appear to derive the energy for their maintenance from a process which depends on their propagation. Investigation of the temperature conditions within these areas convinced Ekholm that most probably

> . . . this energy is produced by means of two, nearly opposed, approximately horizontal air currents of which the one, that is flowing towards the area of [pressure] fall and is accumulating there and whirling about, is warm, and the other, flowing towards the area of rising [pressure] and accumulating there and whirling about, is cold. The barometer falls because of the former and rises because of the latter.[85]

Like Bigelow, Ekholm believed that the potential energy of adjacent air masses of different temperatures is partly transformed into the kinetic energy of traveling cyclones, while cold dense air is flowing underneath warm, less dense air which is ascending. When the cyclone becomes stationary, i.e., when no fresh warm air

---

[81] *Ibid.*, p. 82.

[82] *Ibid.* Italics are Bigelow's.

[83] Bigelow, "Studies on the thermodynamics of the atmosphere, V. The horizontal convection in cyclones and anticyclones," *Mon. Wea. Rev.*, **34** (1906), p. 564.

[84] Bigelow, "Studies on the thermodynamics of the atmosphere. I. Asymmetric cyclones and anticyclones in Europe and America," *Mon. Wea. Rev.*, **34** (1906), pp. 9 and 14. Italics are Bigelow's.

[85] Ekholm (1906), pp. 239 and 240.

enters the cyclone in the front producing pressure fall, the air within the cyclone cools due to ascent and outgoing radiation from the upper cloud layers, so that the body of the cyclone as a whole soon becomes colder than the environment. The cyclone gradually decays, using up its store of potential energy. It has changed, Ekholm noted, from a thermodynamic machine transforming thermal energy into kinetic energy to a machine "which produces cold at the expense of mechanical energy. As soon as the kinetic energy is used up, the machine stops."[86]

These conclusions of Ekholm and Bigelow received strong observational support from a meticulous and comprehensive analysis of the *Life History of Surface Air Currents*, by Sir Napier Shaw and R. G. K. Lempfert in 1906.[87] Shaw was trained as an experimental physicist and had studied under Maxwell and Helmholtz. He became secretary of the Meteorological Council in 1900 and director of the Meteorological Office in 1905, transforming it through the introduction of trained scientific staff and emphasis on studies of the physics of the atmosphere. Introducing the concept of an air trajectory, he developed a method that allowed one to follow "the actual path described by an isolated portion of air moving along the surface."[88] It was found that the motion of air in a circular cyclone was not "properly described as circular motion . . . transformed into spiral motion"[89] but that instead the trajectories showed convergence at certain parts of the storm area and divergence at others. In particular, most fast traveling cyclones took all their air from the south or southwest, with rain formed by ascent of air, generally not far northward from an area of convergence in the southeastern quadrant. Descent and divergence took place in the rear. In the case of slow traveling storms two source regions of air were identified

> . . . feeding the storm from the South and from the North-east, respectively . . . the air from these two sources was at decidedly different temperatures, and the courses of

[86] *Ibid.*, p. 242. Sandström had argued in a similar fashion in 1902, but for a *warm center* cyclone evolving into a cold center cyclone; see "Ueber die Beziehung zwischen Luftbewegung und Druck in der Atmosphäre unter stationären Verhältnissen," *Oversigt, Kongl. Vet.-Akad. Förhandl.*, **57** (1902), 87–103, reprinted in *Met. Zeits.*, **19** (1902), 161–171. Sandström suggested in this paper that cyclones arriving in central Europe from the Atlantic "most probably result from the accumulation of warm, moist air masses over the Gulf Stream." (p. 168) "These storms are with a warm center." However, he continued, "the more kinetic energy the vortex receives, the more it becomes independent of the Gulf Stream, and soon it is separated from it and travels eastward. Due to surface friction, the layer associated with strongest cyclonic circulation rises upward. . . . The cyclone is cold below this layer and warm above." Sandström then presented observational evidence in support of his view. He also argued that it was necessary to assume a cyclone with warm center above a cyclone with cold center, the two cyclones being separated by a layer of maximum cyclonic circulation (p. 169). See also Section 6.5, on the discovery of the tropopause.

[87] N. Shaw and R. G. K. Lempfert, *The Life History of Surface Air Currents*, M. O. Memoir, No. 174 (1906), reprinted in *Selected Meteorological Papers of Sir Napier Shaw* (London, MacDonald and Co., 1955), 15–131. This memoir was a continuation of Shaw's investigation of air trajectories in storms published in 1903: "The meteorological aspects of the storm of February 26–27," *Quart. Journ. Roy. Met. Soc.*, **29**, 233–258. See biographical notes on Shaw and Lempfert in the Appendix.

[88] *Ibid.*, reprint, p. 16. According to A. Defant, Köppen first expressed the idea to examine air trajectories in traveling cyclones in "Wissenschaftliche Ergebnisse," *Monatliche Uebersichten der Witterung*, Vols., 1 and 2 (Deutsche Seewarte, 1877). Streamlines were first constructed by Francis Galton in his *Meteorographia* of 1863 (*op. cit.*), in his analyses of the replacement of one air current by another for several cases, on the basis of very limited surface data.

[89] *Ibid.*

> these trajectories suggest that the processes going on in the depression consisted in the warm air from the South rising up over the top of the cold air from the North-east, while the latter flowed South-ward along approximately semicircular paths to take its place.[90]

The distributions of pressure and rainfall were found to be "not conspicuously dissimilar in the two cases."[91] His graphical representation of the two cases is reproduced in Figure 40. In his popular textbook, *Weather Forecasting*, Shaw summarized these investigations in a schematic illustration of surface flow patterns in a cyclone (Figure 41) which has since been regarded as an anticipation of the frontal cyclone model.[92] It was certainly a drawback that Shaw's major work of 1906 appeared in an edition of only 350 copies, and it is said to have passed relatively unnoticed by the meteorological world.[93] Nevertheless, the memoir was extensively reviewed and apparently was utilized by meteorologists in Europe.[94]

6.5 THE TROPOPAUSE (1900's)

The investigation of the three-dimensional temperature structure of the atmosphere accelerated markedly after 1890 with the advent of systematic unmanned balloon ascents and kite launchings. The most remarkable and unexpected result of the balloon ascents was the announcement in 1902, by Teisserenc de Bort, of the existence of an "isothermal layer," beginning at about 10 km.[95] In the following we will briefly discuss some of the implications of this discovery for the theory of cyclones during the early decades of the Twentieth Century.

The discovery of the upper inversion, as the tropopause was often referred to in the early 1900's, required a revision of the assumption that the state of the atmosphere approximated that of convective equilibrium. As discussed in Chapter 3, W. Thomson had introduced the concept of convective equilibrium in his explanation of the observed temperature decrease with height. The validity of this assumption for the atmosphere as a whole began to be doubted, when Helmholtz and others pointed out that for the case of perfect convective equilibrium the temperature would reach absolute zero at 28 km (assuming 10°C at the surface, 1°C

---

[90] *Ibid.*, p. 51.

[91] *Ibid.*, p. 31.

[92] Shaw, *Forecasting Weather* (London, Constable and Co., 1911).

[93] This appears to have been the main reason that Shaw requested from his trustees to publish a volume of his collected works. See R. Corless in his review of that volume (1955) in the *Meteorological Magazine*, **84**, 322–324.

[94] See, for example, F. M. Exner's review in *Met. Zeits.*, **24** (1907), 520–523, and Köppen's discussion, *Met. Zeits.*, **28** (1911), 159–167; A. Defant, in his popular book, *Wetter und Wettervorhersage* (Leipzig und Wien, Deuticke, 1918), devoted 20 pages with many illustrations to his highly appreciative discussion of Shaw's memoir.

[95] Teisserence de Bort, "Variations de la temperature de l'air libre dans la zone comprise entre 8km et 13km d'altitude," *Comp. Ren.*, **134** (1902), 987–989. Similar investigations establishing the existence of the stratosphere were carried out simultaneously by R. Assmann at Lindenberg. However, he published his results only after de Bort had taken the decisive step of declaring the upper temperature inversion as the rule rather than exception. Assmann, "Ueber die Existenz eines wärmeren Luftstromes in der Höhe von 10 bis 15km," *Sitzber. Ak. Berlin* (1902), 495–504. For a modern review of the discovery of the tropopause see G. Ohring, "A most surprising discovery," *Bull. Am. Met. Soc.*, **45** (1964), 12–14.

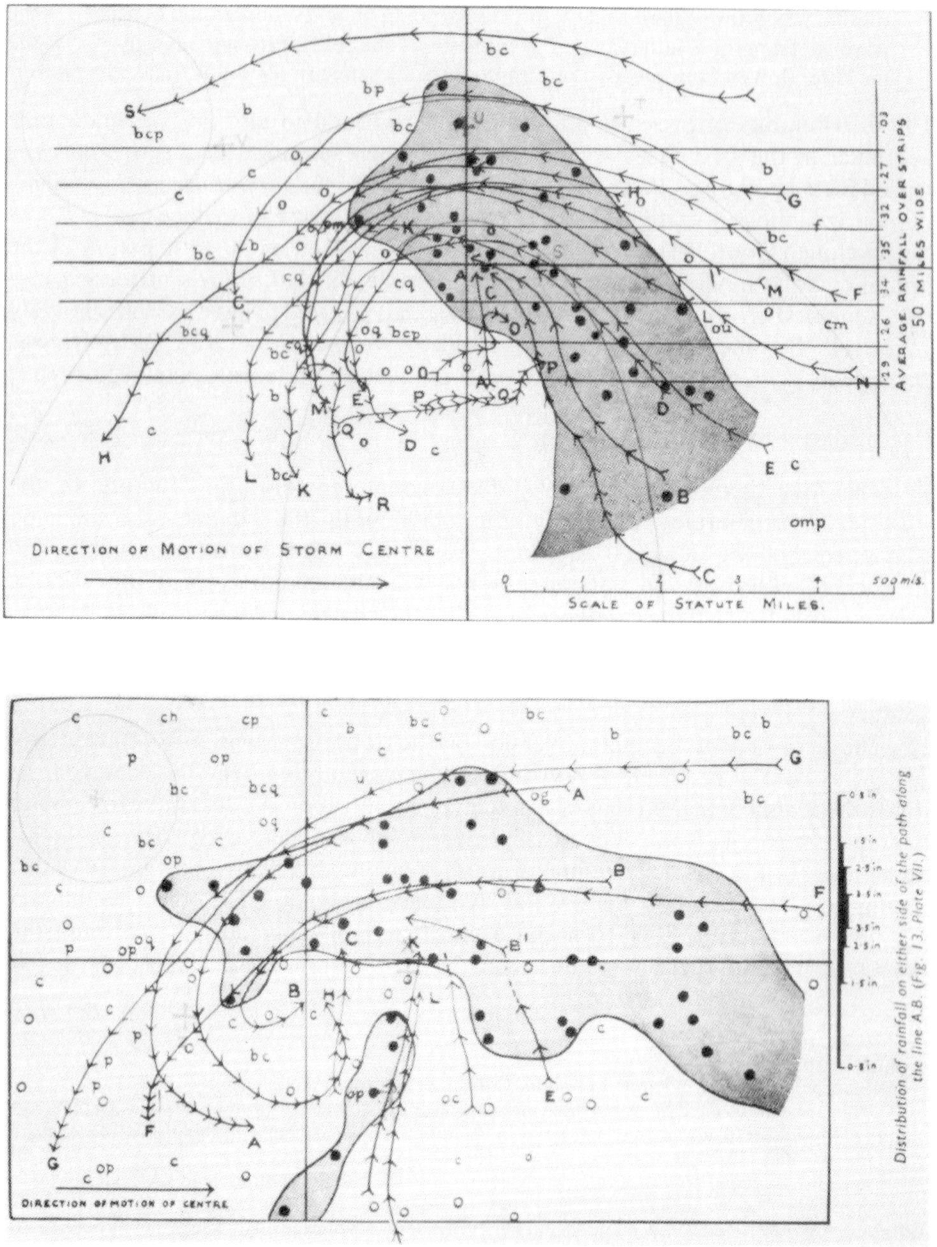

FIGURE 40. Motion of air relative to the storm center and distribution of precipitation. Top: fast traveling storm of 24–25 March 1902; bottom: slow traveling storm of 11–13 November 1901; from *Life History of Surface Air Currents*, M. O. Memoir, No. 174 (1906). Lines with arrowheads show the motion relative to the storm center for successive 2 h intervals; center of low pressure is indicated by crossing of the thick lines; shaded areas indicate regions of precipitation. Small letters indicate weather, i.e., o, overcast; bc, partly cloudy; n, no rain.

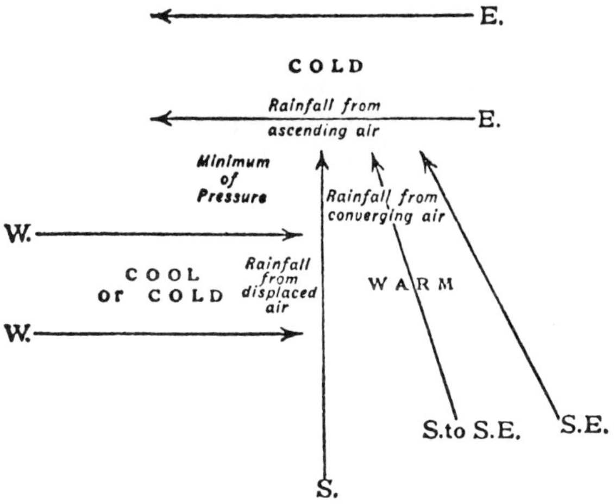

FIGURE 41. Cyclone model by Shaw, from *Forecasting Weather* (London, Constable and Co., 1911). This schematic flow pattern was based upon numerous analyses of surface air currents. See for example Figure 40.

temperature decrease per 100 m). The existence of the upper inversion made it clear that the assumption of convective equilibrium could only be valid for the layers below, for which de Bort coined the term troposphere. The temperature structure of the layer above, called stratosphere by de Bort, was thought to be controlled by radiation. Furthermore, a rethinking of the accepted schemes for the general circulation of the atmosphere was necessitated by the discovery of the tropopause, since it could no longer be assumed that the entire atmosphere was taking part in the general circulation between pole and equator.

Subsequent observational and statistical investigations yielded a number of significant relationships between the tropopause and other meteorological elements: The tropopause was found to be higher in summer than in winter and higher in the tropics than in the polar regions; in addition, the higher the tropopause, the lower was its temperature. Finally, the tropopause was found to be higher in anticyclones than in cyclones.[96] This latter remarkable result received an early interpretation by Ekholm in 1907, incorporating to some extent the idea of compensation. Distinguishing between traveling and stationary pressure systems, he demonstrated that in the case of a large stationary anticyclone centered over Paris in May 1904 tropospheric temperature increased (over two days) from −52 to −32°C at 9 km altitude.[97] Ekholm suggested that these large tropospheric

[96] This was established as early as 1902 by de Bort in "Variations de la temperature . . .", *op. cit.*, p. 989.

[97] Ekholm, "Ueber die unperiodischen Luftdruckschwankungen und einige damit zusammenhängende Erscheinungen, Teil V. Ueber die Luftströmung in den stationären und beweglichen Zyklonen und Antizyklonen, sowie den isallobarischen Gebieten, und über die Beziehung der Luftströmung zu der Temperatur der oberen atmosphärischen Schichten," *Met. Zeits.*, **24** (1907), 108–110.

temperature increases are "compensated" by corresponding temperature decreases in the stratosphere.[98]

One of the most valuable of these early Twentieth Century investigations of the vertical temperature structure of the atmosphere was the work of Arthur Wagner at the Meteorologische Zentralanstalt in Vienna.[99] Wagner's treatise was based on a relatively abundant data source, 380 international balloon ascents made during the years 1902–1907. Wagner confirmed earlier findings on the horizontal temperature asymmetry in cyclones, namely, that stationary and slow traveling cyclones generally are warm only in their front portion, up to 9 km, and cold in all other sections. Complementing Ekholm's suggestion on compensation, Wagner found that in cyclones above 9 km the opposite temperature distribution occurs: "the front section is cold, the other sections and, in particular, the rear section are warm."[100] "For fast traveling vortices," he noted, "only a few cases could be established, but the temperature conditions existing in these deviated to such an extent from the rest that a separate treatment was necessary."[101] According to Wagner's analysis, fast traveling cyclones were warm in lower and middle strata, but cold in the highest levels. Furthermore, "the greatest height and the lowest temperature of the isothermal zone." Wagner concluded, "should be found northwest of the center of the anticyclone, and the largest opposite deviation in the northwest of the cyclone."[102] In addition, corroborating earlier results of Ekholm and Hanzlik, Wagner found that fast traveling anticyclones were cold in lower layers and warm in the highest layers, above the tropopause.[103] Stationary high pressure systems were found to be warm throughout the troposphere, in agreement with earlier results going back to Hann, but cold in layers above the tropopause, as Ekholm had suggested. These results, finally, made it possible to adopt a simple hydrostatic explanation of the low pressure in cold cyclones, in view of a warm stratospheric layer. Similarly, the high pressure in warm anticyclones could now be explained hydrostatically, taking into account the cold stratospheric layer; thus the puzzle created by Hann's sensational temperature observations on mountain tops during the 1880's and 1890's had in part been solved.

The carefully assembled, detailed results of Wagner, it appears, were soon overshadowed by the widely publicized, equally thorough investigations of the English meteorologist William Henry Dines, beginning in 1911.[104] In a paper of 1911

---

[98] Lacking observations above 12km, Ekholm performed a simple calculation, using the barometric height formula. He concluded "that only an average temperature decrease from −55 to −63°C, that is 8°C, is required in the air layer between 12km and 13km height, in order to compensate the large observed, simultaneous increase of temperature. . ." (*ibid.*, p. 110).

[99] Wagner, "Die Temperaturverhältnisse in der freien Atmosphäre," *Beitr. Phys. f. Atm.*, **3** (1910), 57–167.

[100] *Ibid.*, p. 153.

[101] *Ibid.*, p. 160.

[102] *Ibid.*, p. 162. These results were confirmed by Hanzlik in "Die räumliche Verteilung der meteorologischen Elemente in den Zyklonen," *Denks. Ak. Wien*, **88** (1913), 67–128.

[103] Ekholm (1907), *op. cit.*; Hanzlik, "Die räumliche Verteilung der meteorologischen Elemente in den Antizyklonen," *Denks. Ak. Wien*, **83** (1908), 163–256.

[104] Dines, "The vertical temperature distribution in the atmosphere over England, and some remarks on the general and local circulation," *Phil. Trans.*, Ser. A, **211** (1911), 253–278, reprinted in

Dines submitted upper air observations of about 200 ascents to an extensive statistical analysis. Attempting to uncover a possible connection between processes and conditions in upper and lower levels, Dines worked out extensive correlations between pressure and temperature at the surface and various height levels. He found pronounced positive correlations between surface pressure and temperatures at levels up to 9 km, the height of the tropopause, and the mean temperature in the troposphere up to 9 km. Correlations between surface pressure and temperatures of the stratosphere were negative. To some extent, these results confirmed the findings of Wagner. In contrast to Wagner's treatment of upper air observations, however, Dines had not separated his data according to developing and mature cyclones; nor did Dines consider the number of observations sufficient to warrant statements on temperature differences in various sections of the cyclone.[105] For this reason, Dines' results were in certain respects more general than those of Wagner and, as a consequence, could be interpreted in fundamentally different ways. On the basis of his statistical data, averaging over all sections of the cyclone and all stages in its development, Dines concluded that the cyclonic circulation resulted from dynamic processes in upper tropospheric layers or the lower stratosphere rather than from thermal processes in the troposphere. He stated

> that a cyclone is a region in which the lower air is being sucked upwards, for this explains its coldness [up to the tropopause]; and the upper air above 10 kilometers is being sucked downwards, since this explains its warmth.[106]

This idea was not entirely new. In fact, Sandström had made similar statements as early as 1902.[107] However, it was Dines whose numerous publications made it widely known. Dines' statistical results and conclusions subsequently formed the point of departure for various hypotheses which attempted to explain pressure variations at the surface on account of processes in the upper troposphere and lower stratosphere.[108]

Collected Papers of W. H. Dines, (London Roy. Met. Soc., 1931), 220–243; and "Further contributions to the investigation of the upper air," Meteorological Office, *Geophysical Memoir*, No. 2 (1912), 31–50 (pp. 1–30 of that memoir include an 8-page abstract of Dines' 1911 paper and an informative preface by Shaw), reprinted in *Coll. Papers*, 245–264. See biographical note on Dines in the Appendix.

105 *Coll. Papers*, p. 239.

106 Dines, "Cyclones and anticylones," *Journ. Scott. Met. Soc.*, **16** (1914), reprinted in *Coll. Papers*, p. 295.

107 Sandström, "Ueber die Beziehung zwischen Temperatur und Luftbewegung . . . ," *op. cit.*, 169–170. Sandström then noted: "One can also think of the development of cyclones in ways different than through heating at the earth surface. Let there be, for example, a strong air stream in upper levels and along its left side another [stream], which is moving in the opposite direction. According to rule IV [clouds moving faster than surface winds results in dynamic upward sucking (dynamisches Emporsaugen) . . .], the air lying below the region between the two streams is sucked upward and the air above is sucked downward, and if this [process] is stronger localized at one place, then the conditions are present for the development of a regular cyclone. Such a cyclone, too, has a cold center below and a warm center above the layer of strongest cyclonic circulation."

108 Early in his career, Dines, as most meteorologists at that time, favored the thermal theory of cyclone formation. He stated in 1891, when comparing thermal and dynamic cyclone theories: "It appears to me that the convectional theory is the most probable . . . ;" from "On the vertical circulation of the atmosphere in relation to the formation of storms," *Quart. Journ. Roy. Met. Soc.*, **17** (1891), *Coll. Papers*, p. 207.

Shaw, a great admirer of Dines, introduced Dines' correlation studies as marking "at least the end of a long chapter in meteorological history, if not the commencement of a new era in meteorological work, . . ." establishing "that the dominant cause of the sequence of pressure changes at the surface is the sequence of pressure changes at 9 kilometers. . . . Pressure changes at the surface must be regarded as produced not by, but in spite of, differences of temperature in the air."[109] Consequently, Shaw largely abandoned his promising study of air trajectories (Section 6.4), since, in his words, "the investigation of the 'substratosphere' seems to be, for the time being, the most promising line of meteorological research."[110]

The exploration of the upper air, and in particular the discovery of the tropopause thus gave new directions to cyclone research and meteorological research at large. The further discussion of these new approaches, which sought the "seat" of pressure changes in the upper layers of the atmosphere, lies beyond the scope of this book; instead we will now turn to investigations which continued to view tropospheric processes as the cause of cyclone formation. We will discuss, in particular, the work of Max Margules whose far-reaching investigations on the energetics of storms had as their point of departure the asymmetric tropospheric temperature distribution associated with cyclones of midlatitudes.

6.6 MARGULES' INVESTIGATIONS OF THE ENERGY OF STORMS (1901–1906)

Bigelow's opinion that the kinetic energy of midlatitude storms derived from the rearrangement of air masses of unequal temperature was affirmed in the rigorous theoretical investigations of the Austrian Max Margules. In 1882, Margules, a trained theoretical physicist, accepted a position at the Zentralanstalt für Meteorologie in Vienna under the directorship of Hann.[111] He developed an interest in meteorology only gradually, and not until the early 1900's did he begin his penetrating studies of atmospheric energetics, a subject going right to the heart of the cyclone problem.

The source of energy in storms most certainly was a topic of frequent discussion at the Zentralanstalt during the 1890's. As an alternative to the thermal theory of cyclones, Hann had proposed a dynamical theory, based to a large extent on the findings of two meteorologists working in India, Henry F. Blanford and J. Elliott.[112] Their investigations demonstrated that cyclones occurring in the Bay of

[109] Shaw, Introduction to Dines', "Further contributions . . . ," (1912), *op. cit.*, pp. 13–14.

[110] *Ibid.*, p. 22.

[111] At that time he resigned from his position as privatdocent at the university and thus terminated a university career for which he was well suited. His reasons for this decisive step are not known. See also the biographical sketch of Margules in the Appendix.

[112] The studies of Blanford and Elliott on cyclones developing in the Bay of Bengal appeared to indicate that cyclones tended to develop in an area of slight barometric depression. [H. F. Blanford and J. E. Gastrell, *Report of the Calcutta Cyclone* (Calcutta, O. T. Cutter, 1866), 150 pp., Blanford, "On the Origin of a Cyclone," *Proc. Roy. Soc.*, **113** (1869), 472–482; J. Elliott, "Ueber die Entstehung der Cyclonen in der Bai von Bengalen," *Wien, Met. Zeits.*, **12** (1877), 276–284].

Bengal tended to develop in an area of slight barometric depression "between preexisting areas of higher pressure."[113] Since Hann's investigations had shown that the same conditions precede the formation of storms over the Atlantic, Hann concluded that it was no longer necessary to assume "that our cyclones should have a different kind of origin than those of the tropics."[114] He added, but this was more of a guess, that the potential energy of the preexisting pressure distribution was a sufficient source of energy for the formation of cyclones. This energy, Hann noted,

> . . . consists in that the preexisting meteorological conditions make it possible that air masses from all sides and from afar flow towards a certain place while forming a vortex. Under these conditions a very small [pressure] gradient can supply the observed kinetic energy for the inner vortex rings.[115]

According to Hann's hypothesis, temperature and moisture conditions played a secondary role in the development of storms. Otherwise it would have been impossible for Hann, in view of his earlier statements, to suggest an analogy between tropical cyclones (most frequent during warm and moist summer months) and midlatitude cyclones (most intense during the cool winter months when there is little moisture in the air). His dynamic theory of storm formation, in conjunction with his observational results of the temperature conditions in cyclones and anticyclones, received wide attention (see Section 5.7).

Perhaps familiarity with Hann's qualitative theory induced Margules in a paper of 1901 to investigate quantitatively whether the energy associated with the horizontal pressure distribution in storms, as observed on synoptic charts, was sufficient "to produce the kinetic energy of the storm, if the air masses were displaced only horizontally from their equilibrium position."[116] He proceeded by approximating conditions of the cyclonic circulation in a mathematical model. He

---

[113] Hann, "Bemerkungen über die Entstehung der Cyklonen," *Met. Zeits.*, **12** (1877), p. 309.

[114] *Ibid.* In a reply to Hann's report, *Report on the Madras Cyclone of May 1877* (Calcutta, Office of the Superintendent of Government Printing, 1879), 117 pp., Elliott strongly criticized Hann's hypothesis. Aside from the fact that the widely different weather conditions in the Atlantic and the Bay of Bengal did not appear to warrant a meaningful comparison between the cyclones occurring in these areas, Elliott felt that the slight barometric differences that do occur in the Bay were insignificant for cyclone formation. Repeated studies convinced him that at least in tropical storms "the source of the energy was the latent heat set free during the process of aqueous vapour condensation and rainfall" (p. 102). In his "Application of the doctrine of energy to the case of cyclones," Blanford, a trained physicist, firmly supported Elliott; see Blanford's *Indian Meteorologist's Vade-Mecum* (Calcutta, Thacker, Spink and Co., 1877), 281 pp. He stated that the pressure field only acts as a transmitter of energy whose "potential energy requires . . . constant renewal" (pp. 250–251). Citing the work of Loomis and Mohn, and Reye's calculation in the case of the Cuba hurricane, Blanford concluded, "No source of energy competent to supply these demands, other than the latent heat of the condensed vapour has yet been pointed out" (p. 252).

[115] As quoted by Margules, "Zur Sturmtheorie," *Met. Zeits.*, **23** (1906b), p. 492; from Hann, *Lehrbuch der Meteorologie*, 1st ed. (Leipzig, 1901), p. 578.

[116] Margules, "Die Energie der Stürme," *Jahrbücher der K.-K. Zentralanstalt für Meteorologie und Erdmagnetismus*, **40** (1903), p. 3; translated in Abbe's third collection (1910), *op. cit.*, 533–595. Shaw was asking essentially the same question concerning air currents in 1906: "Does their energy represent the exhaustion of the potential energy of the pressure difference, between anticyclones and cyclonic depressions, . . . or are surface air currents . . . moving in a circle needing only to be guided by the distribution of pressure?" (p. 33). In favor of the latter, Shaw felt, was the good geostrophic approximation observed in the atmosphere; further, that "a number of depressions may

showed that in a closed atmospheric system, i.e., in a mass of air bounded by vertical walls, the energy associated with the pressure field was identical with the work of expansion during a particular change in the pressure distribution and that the work of expansion was completely determined by the initial and final pressure distribution, assuming that the density was a function of pressure only. Using this relationship, it was possible to compute for a simple model cyclone the energy associated with the pressure field available for conversion into kinetic energy. Margules compared the results of such calculations with the kinetic energy that actually would be observed in a cyclone of the same pressure distribution. He found

> the comparison of the kinetic energy of a simple vortex with the energy [available from the horizontal pressure field] teaches that the kinetic energy is by far the greater of the two.[117]

Margules showed that in general the kinetic energy available from the horizontal pressure distribution, contrary to Hann's hypothesis, was less than 10% of the kinetic energy of the winds balancing it. He concluded in 1903 that "great velocity of air masses over extended areas can develop under the influence of the horizontal pressure gradient only when the gradient is maintained by a store of energy."[118] "The pressure gradient . . . plays only the role of distributor of kinetic energy"[119] in this process; "the horizontal pressure distribution appears as a mere cog-wheel in the storm's machinery,"[120] and not as its motor. Affirming what Peslin, Blanford and others had expressed earlier, Margules felt that the problem was to find the cause that maintained the horizontal pressure gradients.

In accordance with V. Bjerknes, he argued that proper treatment of atmospheric energetics would require the application of thermodynamic and dynamic laws. In his classic paper of 1903 Margules attacked this question on a quantitative basis. According to physical principles, he stated, "the kinetic energy of an air mass is derived from its internal energy and gravitational potential energy (Arbeit der Schwerkraft, or, potentielle Energie der Lage, in Margules' terminology)." The state in which energy available for conversion into kinetic energy is stored, he suggested, is found when "horizontal differences of entropy of specific amount exist at the level considered."[121] From his synoptic studies he was led to believe that squall lines, often marked by strong sudden temperature changes, represent such situations. He felt that similar conditions normally prevail in midlatitude storms.

---

safely be passed before air becomes involved in the rotary system" and that the flowing air current was, "on the whole, a more stable and persistent feature than the depression" and that often "cyclonic whirls appear as comparatively local phenomena on the Northern margin of a vast current, originating at a great distance in the West . . ." (p. 33, Shaw, reprint 1955).

[117] Margules, "Ueber den Arbeitswert einer Luftdruckverteilung und über die Erhaltung der Druckunterschiede," *Denks. Ak. Wien*, **73** (1901), p. 329; translated in Abbe's third collection (1910), *op. cit.*, pp. 501–530.

[118] Margules, "Die Energie der Stürme," (1903), *op. cit.*, p. 3.

[119] Margules, "Zur Sturmtheorie," (1906b), *op. cit.*, p. 483.

[120] Margules (1903), p. 26.

[121] *Ibid.*, p. 3.

The phenomena of motion in the great storm areas that are called cyclones are less intelligible than those of the squalls. In middle and higher latitudes these also consist of warm and cold air masses, lying side by side horizontally; behind the passing storm, cold air often spreads out in the lower strata. It is, therefore, not unlikely that these storms are maintained by the potential energy of a similar initial state as we have assumed above."[122]

Margules specifically cited Bigelow's synoptic studies as evidence that two air masses of contrasting temperature converge in a cyclone. Margules' own empirical results on the structure of cyclones served as a starting point for his thorough theoretical analyses and quantitative examples and calculations.

First, Margules formulated an equation of energy which could be applied to the atmosphere and whose terms could be calculated for certain simplified models of atmospheric conditions. Using Margules' notation, the energy equation may be written

$$\delta K + \delta P + \delta A + R = 0$$

and the thermodynamic equation

$$Q = \delta I - \delta A,$$

where δK represents the change in kinetic energy, δP the change in gravitational potential energy (potentielle Energie der Lage), δA and R the work done by pressure and frictional forces, Q the heat added to the system and δI the change in internal energy. Combining these equations Margules derived a relation in which the work done by the pressure forces was eliminated

$$Q = \delta(K + P + I) + R$$

In this equation, K, P and I could be expressed by measurable quantities. Margules first applied the relation to a simple two-chamber model of a closed system, in which two masses of dry air at different temperatures, in stable or neutral equilibrium, were separated by a vertical wall (Figure 42a). Margules then studied "What amount of kinetic energy becomes available, when the wall is removed and the masses move adiabatically."[123] He assumed that the pressure along the top surface of the chambers remained constant. When the final state of thermal stability and minimum potential energy was reached, the center of gravity of the entire system had been lowered and

every horizontal layer is a surface of equal pressure and equal temperature, the entropy (or the potential temperature) increases with altitude . . . the available kinetic energy of the system, including the loss by friction, is determined by

$$\delta K + R = -\delta(P + I) = (P + I)_a - (P + I)_e,$$

where subscripts a and e refer to conditions at the beginning (Anfang) and end (Ende) of the redistribution process.[124] Accordingly, the kinetic energy of the

[122] *Ibid.*, p. 4.
[123] *Ibid.*, p. 2.
[124] *Ibid.*, p. 1.

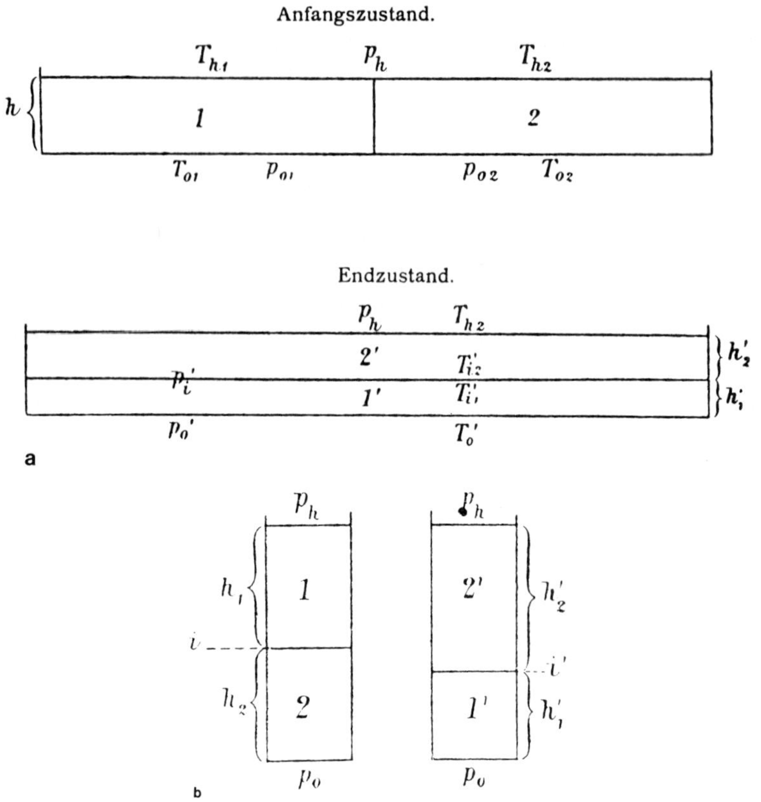

FIGURE 42. Margules' two-chamber model, from Margules, "Ueber die Energie der Stürme," *Jahrbücher der K. -K. Zentralanstalt für Meteorologie und Erdmagnetismus,* **40** (1903). Potential temperatures of chambers 2 are higher than those of chambers 1; h denotes height of chambers; T, temperature; p, pressure; subscripts o, i, h denote conditions at lower, separation and top surfaces. Primes indicate conditions after redistribution. Parts a and b are described in text.

system that could be "realized" (was "verfügbar") could be expressed as the difference between the sums of gravitational potential energy and internal energy at the beginning and end of the redistribution process. This quantity is now called "available potential energy."[125]

[125] Margules also used the two-chamber model as additional illustration of the results of his 1901 paper that, contrary to Hann's hypothesis, the kinetic energy realizable from pressure differences alone is not sufficient to explain the kinetic energy in storms. In this case it was assumed that the two masses of air, as shown in Figure 42a, were of the same entropy at the same height; thus the greater pressure was on the side of the warmer air, 10 mm Hg pressure difference at the surface implying only 1°C temperature difference. Consequently, "If the wall is removed and the volume remains unchanged then the horizontal layers that initially were at the same altitude unite to form a new layer. The vertical sequence remains the same; likewise the altitude of the center of gravity. The change of internal energy, computed for the unit mass, depends only on the initial pressure difference, not on the height of the chambers. . . . The available kinetic energy [for 10 mm Hg pressure difference] has the value that is equivalent to a velocity of 1.5 m/sec for the entire mass; the [kinetic energy] available for the unit mass is far smaller than in systems with horizontal entropy differences, while the distribution of surface pressure is the same." (1903, p. 3).

Margules applied the energy equation for the computation of the realizable kinetic energy for a number of special cases. The first of two basic types of initially unstable mass distributions occurred when cold air was lying over potentially warmer air (Figure 42b). In the second basic type, as discussed earlier (Figure 42a), a warm and cold air mass were lying side by side. Margules showed that "when the overturning of masses takes place, as assumed above, and when the volumes of both chambers are equal,"[126] the average velocity v of the wind developed in the two air masses, which could be used to compute the realizable kinetic energy in the system, $\frac{1}{2}Mv^2$ (where M is the total mass of air in the system), was approximately

$$\tfrac{1}{2}[gh(T_2 - T_1)/T_1]^{1/2},$$

where g denotes the acceleration of gravity, h the height of the two chambers, and T_1 and T_2 their initial mean temperatures. For a temperature difference of 10°C between the air masses at the same horizontal level and layers of 3000 m thickness, Margules found that the air masses would acquire an average velocity of 17.3 m s^{-1} during the isentropic redistribution. Margules' equation for average velocity is similar in form to the equations obtained by Reye and Peslin several decades earlier for the vertical velocity attained by a mass of buoyant air rising through an undisturbed environment. But, whereas Reye and Peslin had based their concepts of the energy budget of storms on the essentially local horizontal temperature inequalities produced by the release of latent heat, Margules had conceived his model from observational evidence for horizontal temperature contrasts between large-scale adjacent air masses.

Margules' computations had to be carried out with the utmost accuracy, since, as is seen in his equation, the net gain of kinetic energy (δK) is a relatively small difference between two large quantities $[(P + I)_a - (P + I)_e]$. His results had other limitations as well. Since in the real atmosphere some energy must always be lost in friction, Margules' values represented maximum values for kinetic energy production. Furthermore, in the real atmosphere cyclones were not dynamically and thermodynamically closed systems, so that energy processes taking place during development of a cyclone had to be regarded as more complicated than the corresponding processes in Margules' models. Margules was well aware of the limitations of his models. He remarked:

> our analysis gives only a general idea of the source of energy in storms; a useful model of the cyclone with asymmetric temperature distribution has not yet been constructed.[127]

His computations and models, he stated modestly, provided nothing more than general suggestions of the source of energy for atmospheric motions.

The agreement between the values of realizable kinetic energy in Margules' models and actually observed kinetic energy in storms for temperature differences of about 10°C was certainly very striking. It left no doubt in the minds of Margules and his—relatively few—contemporary readers that the development of cyclones

---

[126] *Ibid.*, p. 2.

[127] Margules (1903), p. 4.

is explained by the displacement of warm air by cold air. Examination of synoptic charts had revealed that precisely these motions take place in storms and are made evident by precipitation in the rising warm air in their front portions and clearing skies in the descending cold air in their rear. "Hence," Margules noted,

> the storm develops through descending and ascending motion [Fallgeschwindigkeit und Auftriebsgeschwindigkeit], even though these evade attention because of the large horizontal and small vertical dimensions of the [storm] area.[128]

Margules' investigations, as well as those by V. Bjerknes conducted simultaneously, contained extraordinarily fruitful suggestions and deeply influenced meteorological thought in the following decades. Both investigators had developed powerful tools of combining atmospheric dynamics and thermodynamics. While Bjerknes emphasized possible circulation tendencies associated with baroclinic regions in the atmosphere, Margules concentrated his efforts on the analysis of possible energy conversions in the atmosphere that contributed to an increase of kinetic energy. They arrived at analogous results insofar as the acceleration of circulation is associated with an increase in kinetic energy.

In his 1903 paper, Margules also investigated the role of latent heat release as a source for the kinetic energy exhibited in midlatitude cyclones. He noted that during the 1870's emphasis on patterns of surface isobars in cyclones, which were more or less circular in shape, had led to the view that ascent of warm moist air, associated with condensation and latent heat release, took place only in the inner, central part of the cyclone. Further considerations of the confluence of different air masses in storms during the 1880's and 1890's had indicated that ascending and descending motions occurred over the entire body of the cyclone. This circumstance complicated the energetics of storms. As Margules pointed out, while it was relatively easy to compute the velocity of an ascending moist air parcel in a mass of air at rest (as is recalled from the computations carried out by Peslin and Reye), for calculation of the realizable kinetic energy of a large and complex system:

> . . . where an extended mass [of air] of high water vapor content lies next to or under another, one has to carry out long computations which cannot be avoided, however, if one wants to state which part of the heat of condensation is converted into kinetic energy.[129]

He carried out a detailed analysis of the effect of latent heat on the value of realizable kinetic energy within the framework of his two-chamber model. One chamber contained warm saturated air, and the other cold dry air. Since saturated air cools less during expansion than dry air, it also contributes less to the available potential energy than dry air. The difference, Margules argued, was exactly compensated by the addition of latent heat. "It follows that the heat of

[128] *Ibid.*, p. 26.
[129] Margules (1906b), 482–483.

condensation contributes nothing to the energy of a storm. The available kinetic energy remains unchanged.''[130]

Margules modified this statement in a paper of 1906, when discussing the cyclone models of Ferrel and Helmholtz. Reconsidering the effect of latent heat, he noted that ''where air of high water vapor content breaks through dry masses while ascending, there kinetic energy develops at the expense of heat of condensation.''[131] He recognized that the liberation of latent heat during condensation of water vapor may alter the thickness of the layers which take part in the production of kinetic energy.[132] Nevertheless, Margules maintained that the release of latent heat could not be regarded as a major source of kinetic energy in midlatitude cyclones. He argued that only part of the heat liberated during condensation will be available for conversion into kinetic energy, while the other part will appear in the relatively high temperature of the rising air. Although his computations indicated substantial values for the energy production from the release of latent heat, he found that even for the mass distribution proposed in the tropical cyclone model of Helmholtz, where a large amount of latent heat was assumed to be released, ''the store of [realizable kinetic] energy of the system, based on the same area, is smaller than that of the two chamber system at 10°C temperature difference and 2000 m altitude.''[133] Thus, in the absence of accurate upper air data of tropical storms, Margules noted

> . . . that the potential energy depending on the horizontal temperature distribution which appears to be the main source of storm energy in our latitudes also does not disappear in the tropics in relation to that portion of the heat of condensation that is convertible into kinetic energy.[134]

Nevertheless, Margules insisted that these two views on the cause of storm formation—asymmetrical horizontal temperature distribution and convection of warm saturated air—were not mutually exclusive, as Bigelow appeared to imply, since both involve a diminution of total potential energy. He suggested ''that the first theory describes correctly the essential conditions for the development of storms in middle and higher latitudes, the second theory in the tropics.''[135] It will be recalled that in 1876 Guldberg and Mohn argued convincingly that these two effects can work in unison during storm formation in midlatitudes.

Margules' 1906 paper was not widely known, at least not in English-speaking countries, perhaps because it was not included in the 1910 collection of translations by Abbe which became the principal source of information on Margules' work in the United States and in England. On the other hand, Margules' 1903 paper on the energy of storms containing his preliminary result that latent heat release has no effect on the increase of kinetic energy in storms, became widely known. This may

---

[130] Margules (1903), p. 3.
[131] Margules (1906b), p. 482.
[132] *Ibid.*, pp. 491–492.
[133] Margules (1906b), p. 495; see Section 4.5 for a description of Helmholtz' model.
[134] *Ibid.*, p. 495.
[135] *Ibid.*, p. 482.

partly explain why years later, when Margules' work was regarded as authoritative, meteorologists largely neglected the role of latent heat in storms while they emphasized the importance of temperature contrasts and, in Bigelow's terms, horizontal convection, i.e., advection.

6.7 SURFACES OF DISCONTINUITY

Situations such as Margules had analyzed, where two air masses of contrasting temperatures are separated by sharp zones of transition or surfaces of discontinuity, had been the subject of meteorological investigations throughout the Nineteenth Century. An example of the ascent of warm air over cold air had been described by Dove in 1837:

> One is often puzzled, why, when SW blows after a strong cold, thaw commences practically immediately. This is so, because the SW has already penetrated the entire atmosphere, except below (at the surface). Thus I observed on 18th January 1828 that after [the passage] of the barometric maximum the warm wind with rapidly falling barometer had already acquired predominance in the upper regions of the atmosphere to such an extent that, while it was $-5°$ [R; $-6°$C] below, partly true rain, partly transparent pieces of ice were falling, which obviously were rain drops frozen while falling.[136]

Most frequently, however, meteorologists described the progression of cold air and associated phenomena during the passage of squall lines. Especially in the United States there had been a constant stream of synoptic studies of cold waves and squall lines since Loomis' pioneering studies in 1841 (Figure 7). In Europe squall lines began to be studied systematically after the sinking of the British corvette *Eurydice* near the Isle of Wight during the unexpected passage of a squall line in 1878. Ley and Köppen studied the *Eurydice* squall line in detail.[137] In an extensive analysis of a squall line passing over central Europe in 1881 Köppen suggested that the strong temperature contrasts along the squall could be traced back to the pressure distribution according to which "the lower air currents along the front and rear side of the [squall] definitely were of different origin, without transition."[138] He noted in particular the potential of such temperature contrasts for the generation of kinetic energy in the form of tornadoes and so-called secondary depressions which often

---

[136] Dove, *Meteorologische Untersuchungen, op. cit.*, p. 176. Nevertheless, neither Dove, nor later Fitzroy saw any strong reason to keep the two currents separate in their storm models. In fact, mixing appeared to be an essential element in these models, since they insisted that most precipitation associated with storms was formed through mixing of the air masses along their boundaries (see Dove, p. 193).

[137] Ley, "The *Eurydice* squall," *Meteorological Magazine*, **13** (1878), 32–39; Köppen, "Beiträge zur Kenntnis der Böen und Gewitterstürme," *Ann. Hydr.*, **7** (1879), 324–335.

[138] Köppen, "Der Gewittersturm vom 9. August 1881," *Ann. Hydr.*, **10** (1882), p. 597. Summarizing his results (p. 737), he remarked: "The western part [of the warm air] is overflowed . . . by the cool air from the west. Rain develops along the boundary between the warm and cold regions on account of the buoyancy of the warmer air; the rain produces low temperatures close to the boundary of high temperatures, a temperature step is produced which propagates towards the side of higher temperatures—following the air current and the precipitation which takes place continuously along the boundary of the warm region. A pressure step develops in the lower 600 m on account of the temperature step and also due to the field of motion. . . ."

developed in the southwest quadrant of an extended decaying cyclone. In 1892, E. Durand-Gréville made extensive investigations of thunderstorms associated with squalls; he was able to trace their advancement across Europe (Figure 43). He concluded that the thunderstorm activity was not the essential feature of the phenomenon; rather, quoting from a summary of his results in the *Meteorologische Zeitschrift*,

> . . . the variations of pressure and wind are essentially the main phenomena of a squall which develops along an area of certain depressions and which can then become associated with other phenomena.[139]

And further,

> There are all cases of transition between depressions with strong squalls and ordinary depressions. One even can assert that there is hardly a depression without an area of squalls in which weak showers can develop.[140]

When Margules embarked on the study of surfaces of discontinuity during the 1890's, he felt that a detailed knowledge of the aerological structure of such surfaces was of utmost importance. In 1892, in pursuit of this goal, he undertook his first and only balloon ascent for the collection of upper air data.[141] After 1895, he began to install a small station network around Vienna. Observations from these stations and nearby mountain stations allowed him, with the aid of small-scale synoptic charts and continuous observation records of individual stations, to study the progression of waves of cold and warm air masses and sudden variations in barometric pressure and wind during the passage of squalls and cyclones. These investigations appear to have been the first attempt at a mesoscale analysis. From 1901 onward he was able to use observations from the famous Sonnblick Observatory and two valley stations on both sides of the mountain chain, only 18 km apart, in his three-dimensional analysis of the progression of air masses.

Having studied a large number of "sudden warmings" (plötzliche Erwärmungen), Margules concluded in 1900 that

> the warm wind ascends along the boundary of the cold region. . . . The progression of the thermogram step [Stufe] depends upon the warm current penetrating into new regions along the surface. If the wind trajectory is curved upward, one cannot expect that the step below progresses with the velocity which the wind had behind the curve.[142]

These suggestions were supported by the frequent observation of a slow advance of the temperature "step" while wind velocities in the warm air were high. He found

---

139 Emile Durand-Gréville, "Les grains et les orages," *Annales Bureau Centrale Météorologique de France*, **1** (1892); reviewed in *Comp. Ren.*, **118** (1894), 829–832, and in *Met. Zeits.*, **11** (1894), p. 312.

140 Durand-Gréville, *Met. Zeits.*, **11** (1894), p. 313.

141 See Assmann, *Wissenschaftliche Luftfahrten*, Vol. 1 (Braunschweig, Vieweg & Sohn, 1899), p. 107.

142 Margules, "Temperaturstufen in Niederösterreich im Winter 1898/99," *Jahrbücher, K.-K. Zentralanstalt für Meteorologie und Geodynamik*, 1900, part 5, p. 2. Similar discussions are found in Margules, "Einige Barogramme und Thermogramme von Thal- und Bergstationen," *Met Zeits.*, **15** (1898), 1–16; "Ueber Temperaturschwankungen auf hohen Bergen," *Met. Zeits.*, **20** (1903), 193–214, and "Ueber rasche Erwärmungen," *Met. Zeits.*, **20** (1903), 183–186.

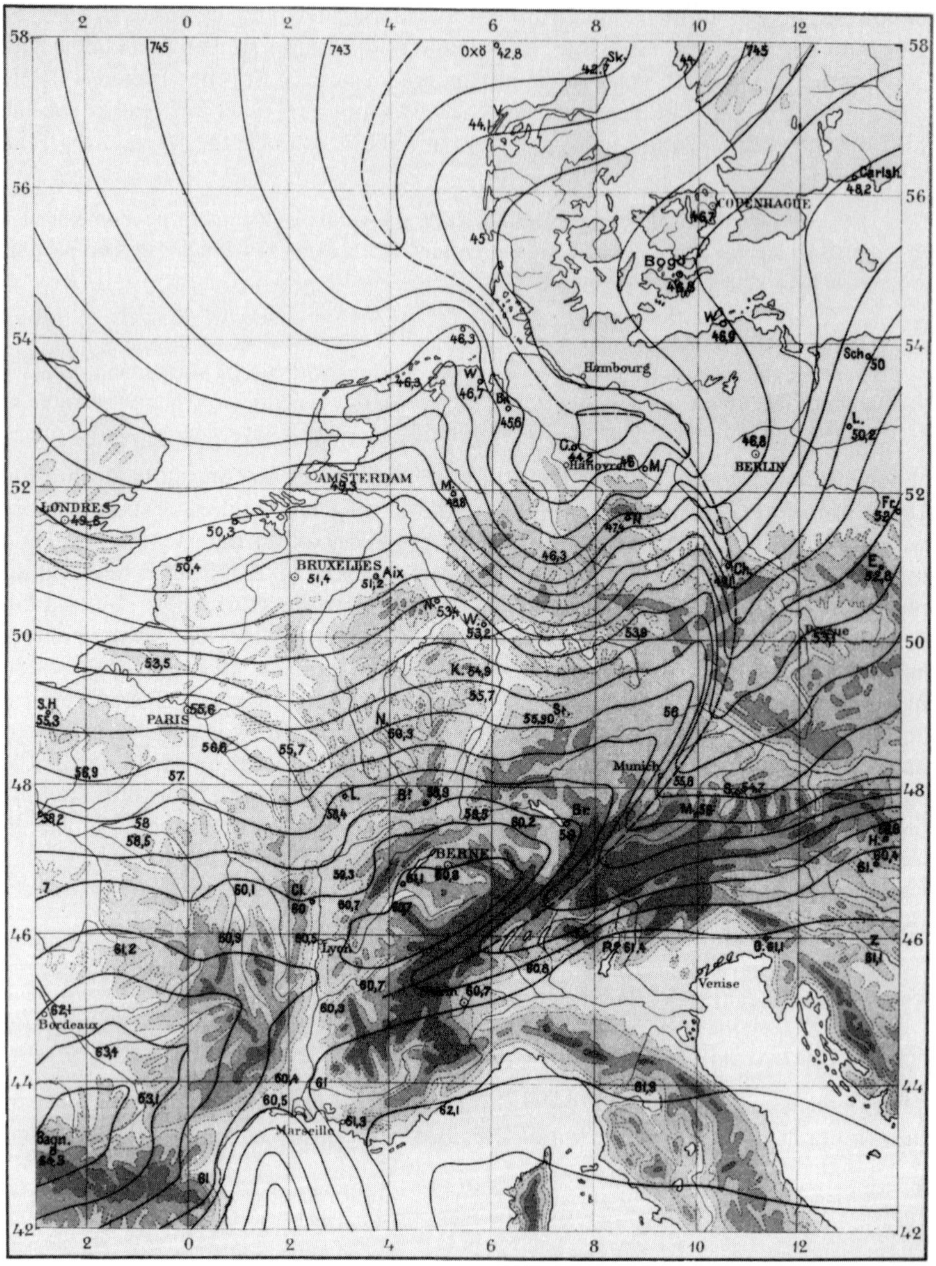

FIGURE 43. Analysis of the squall line of 27 August 1890 at 9 p.m. by Durand-Gréville; from H. H. Hildebrandsson and T. de Bort, *Les Bases de la Météorologie Dynamique* (Paris, Gauthier-Villars, 1907). The squall line passed across Europe in 32 hours. Durand-Gréville analyzed its advance for every hour. The characteristic form of the isobars along the squall line, he noted, reflects the slow decrease and sudden increase of pressure in individual barograms. Numbers indicate station pressure (mm Hg) with the initial figure 7 omitted.

that in most cases of "sudden warmings" the air temperature between 500 and 800 m above the ground was higher than near the surface for hours and even days, before the nearly stagnant air layers close to the ground were replaced by the warm air.[143] Margules found that such warmings were not unusual in winter and that the temperature "steps" were smaller in summer. "Sudden warmings" differed fundamentally from the progression of cold air, for "the cold air advances as a wall of many hectometers height and effects a rapid pressure step below (Barogramm-Stufe)."[144] His analysis of squall lines, after which his two-chamber system was modelled, indicated that

> air masses of different temperatures at the same level are separated by a sharp boundary that advances with the storm towards the warm side. The temperature difference, often 10°C at the surface, persists up to an altitude of nearly 2000 m. At greater altitudes, not far from the boundary, the pressure is equal over the warm and the cold regions, at the surface [the pressure] is greater over the cold region.[145]

Margules' numerous, precise observations of surfaces of discontinuity were little exploited at his time, partly, perhaps, because he published them in an extremely condensed, sketchy form. These notes, remarked one of his admirers, "were not easier to understand than his theoretical works despite the absence of any mathematical apparatus and because of their telegram style."[146]

Margules had carried out empirical studies of situations where two air masses of different temperature are separated by a surface of discontinuity because they represented a certain store of potential energy. However, in 1903, after having theoretically analyzed such a store of potential energy in his two-chamber models, he still had to admit: "I have as yet no definite idea as to how a state with a large store of potential energy can develop without discharge taking place through air movement beforehand."[147] Three years later, embarking on the theoretical treatment of surfaces of discontinuity, Margules found a way toward the solution of this problem in Helmholtz' work on surfaces of discontinuity. Helmholtz' results will be outlined briefly here because of their importance for meteorology.

Helmholtz had begun to investigate equilibrium conditions of surfaces of discontinuity separating two air masses of differing properties in connection with his studies on the general circulation. In 1888 he developed a dynamical theory for rings of air rotating around the earth, with rotational axes coincident with the

---

[143] As a striking example he quoted Helm Clayton's observations of "fog layers which reached only to the tree tops along the edge, [and] up to a few hundred meters further away; the movement was indicated through formation of clouds;" from "Temperaturstufen . . ." *op. cit.*, p. 3.

[144] Margules, "Ueber rasche Erwärmungen," (1903), *op. cit.*, p. 185. At this promising stage of investigation Margules hinted for the first time that he was thinking of leaving the field of meteorology (p. 186): "Although I do not consider this investigation exhaustive, I do not intend to continue it. The next step which one could expect to be profitable would be an exacting analysis of the layer in proximity of the surface of separation, or the transition zone of warm and cold air."

[145] Margules (1903), p. 2; see further, Margules, "Vergleichung der Barogramme von einigen Orten rings um Wien," *Met. Zeits.*, **14** (1897), 241–253.

[146] H. von Ficker, "Max Margules," *Das Wetter*, **37** (1920), p. 163.

[147] Margules (1903), p. 4.

earth's axis.[148] He demonstrated that two adjacent strata of rotating rings of air of different potential temperature and different angular momentum can exist in stable dynamic equilibrium if separated by an inclined surface of discontinuity whose slope depended on the temperature and angular momentum of the two air masses. On earth, with temperature and angular momentum increasing toward the equator along the surface (here quoting from Abbe's translation of the German original), "The equilibrium is stable when the strata containing the greater quantity of heat lie at higher elevations on the side towards the celestial poles," and "the angle of inclination is smaller than the latitude of the location of the discontinuity."[149]

Margules took up the ideas of Helmholtz and derived a generalized formula, analogous to Helmholtz' formula for rotating axial rings, for the slope of stationary surfaces of separation (Trennungsfläche), denoting a discontinuity in the density and wind field for air in steady horizontal motion, neglecting friction. This formula showed that the angle of inclination (α) of the surface of separation, or discontinuity, rises when the difference of velocities increases and the difference of temperatures decreases.[150] Specifically,

$$\tan \alpha = \frac{f}{g} \frac{T_2 v_1 - T_1 v_2}{T_2 - T_1},$$

where $f (= 2\omega \sin \varphi)$ denotes the Coriolis parameter, g the acceleration of gravity, T the temperature, v the velocity parallel to the surface of discontinuity, and the subscripts 1 and 2 represent conditions in air mass 1 and 2.[151] For a state of minimum potential energy the cold air would lie completely under the warm air with zero slope of discontinuity. The only factor that could prevent the cold air from spreading under the warm air in response to pressure gradients was the deflecting force of the earth's rotation. Margules calculated that for a surface with the characteristics $T_2 - T_1 = 10°\text{C}$ and $v_1 - v_2 = 10 \text{ m s}^{-1}$ "with constant α, the surface of separation would rise 1000 m over 237 km distance."[152] In other words, in this case the inclination of the surface of discontinuity, now referred to as frontal slope, was 1:237. The sparse aerological data available at the time of Margules did not yet allow a quantitative confirmation of this value which indeed is now known to be within the observed range of slopes of actual fronts. Instead, Margules presented as indirect evidence for sloping surfaces of discontinuity the results of his earlier mesoscale investigations of surface temperatures and winds during the passage of "sudden warmings." Margules also pointed out that the slopes of surfaces of discontinuity were to be contrasted with the much smaller slopes of isobaric surfaces which rarely exceeded 1:1000. Searching for "a definite conception of how

[148] H. v. Helmholtz, "Ueber atmosphärische Bewegungen," I, *Sitzber. Ak. Berlin* (1888), 647–663, and II, *ibid.*, (1889), 761–780; translated in Abbe's second collection (1891), *op. cit.*, pp. 78–111.

[149] *Ibid.*, p. 88.

[150] Margules, "Ueber Temperaturschichtung in stationär bewegter und ruhender Luft," *Met. Zeits.*, Hannband (1906a), 243–254.

[151] For air masses of unequal water vapor content, Margules noted, one should use the virtual temperatures (defined by Guldberg and Mohn) instead of the actual temperatures.

[152] Margules (1906a), p. 245.

the cold and the warm air are separated at higher elevations,"[153] Margules consequently emphasized the need for detailed three-dimensionally distributed observations, because

> Even with a slope of the surface of discontinuity, which amounts to only a fraction of a degree, the potential energy of the system can be very great; with temperature differences of 10°C, reaching up to an altitude of several kilometers, it would still be sufficient to produce storm.[154]

Margules' theoretical investigations on surfaces of discontinuity complemented and brought to fruition his extensive synoptic studies and his earlier expositions on the nature of "sudden warmings" and squall lines. His work in part anticipated and supported later investigations on frontal slopes by meteorologists in Bergen around 1920. Significantly, his work on surfaces of discontinuity also coincided with and in part stimulated a number of related studies. In the following, some of the most important results of these studies will be mentioned.

Simultaneously with Margules' 1906 paper on the inclination of surfaces of discontinuity, Shaw and Lempfert in England had published their far-reaching memoir on the *Life History of Surface Air Currents*; their work on identifying the existence of air currents of different properties and origin converging in cyclones has already been described. In the same paper, Shaw and Lempfert described in more detail the characteristics of the boundaries between these air currents. They concluded from examination of individual cases that changes in wind direction and force were not continuous but discontinuous along such boundaries and were associated with sudden changes in pressure, temperature and precipitation. An example of their results is reproduced in Figure 44. In their analysis of the advance of isochronous lines of sudden changes they suggested that in the case of

> a sufficiently large number of stations the sudden increase of pressure shown by all of the barograms would presumably have found expression in the isobars as a 'fault' running along the isochronous lines.[155]

These studies were extended by Shaw's close collaborator Lempfert in 1906 and by Lempfert and R. Corless in 1910.[156] Performing refined mesoscale analyses of line squalls associated with barometric depressions, Lempfert supported Shaw's suggestion of representing sudden pressure changes by a "fault," or discontinuity, in the isobars. He stated

> . . . in drawing the charts I have adopted this method of representation. With the large number of records at my disposal it would have been difficult to represent the facts in any other way; smooth isobars of the ordinary type would have involved the rejection of a large proportion of the observations. In all the maps I have endeavoured to make the size

[153] *Ibid.*, p. 246.
[154] *Ibid.*
[155] Shaw and Lempfert, *Life history . . .* , *op. cit.*, p. 99.
[156] R. G. K. Lempfert, "The development and progress of the line-squall of February 8, 1906," *Quart. Journ. Roy. Met. Soc.*, **32** (1906), 259–280; and Lempfert and Corless, "Line-squalls and associated phenomena," *Quart. Journ. Roy. Met. Soc.*, **36** (1910), 135–170.

No. 8. SUDDEN VEER OF WIND—FEBRUARY 24, 1903

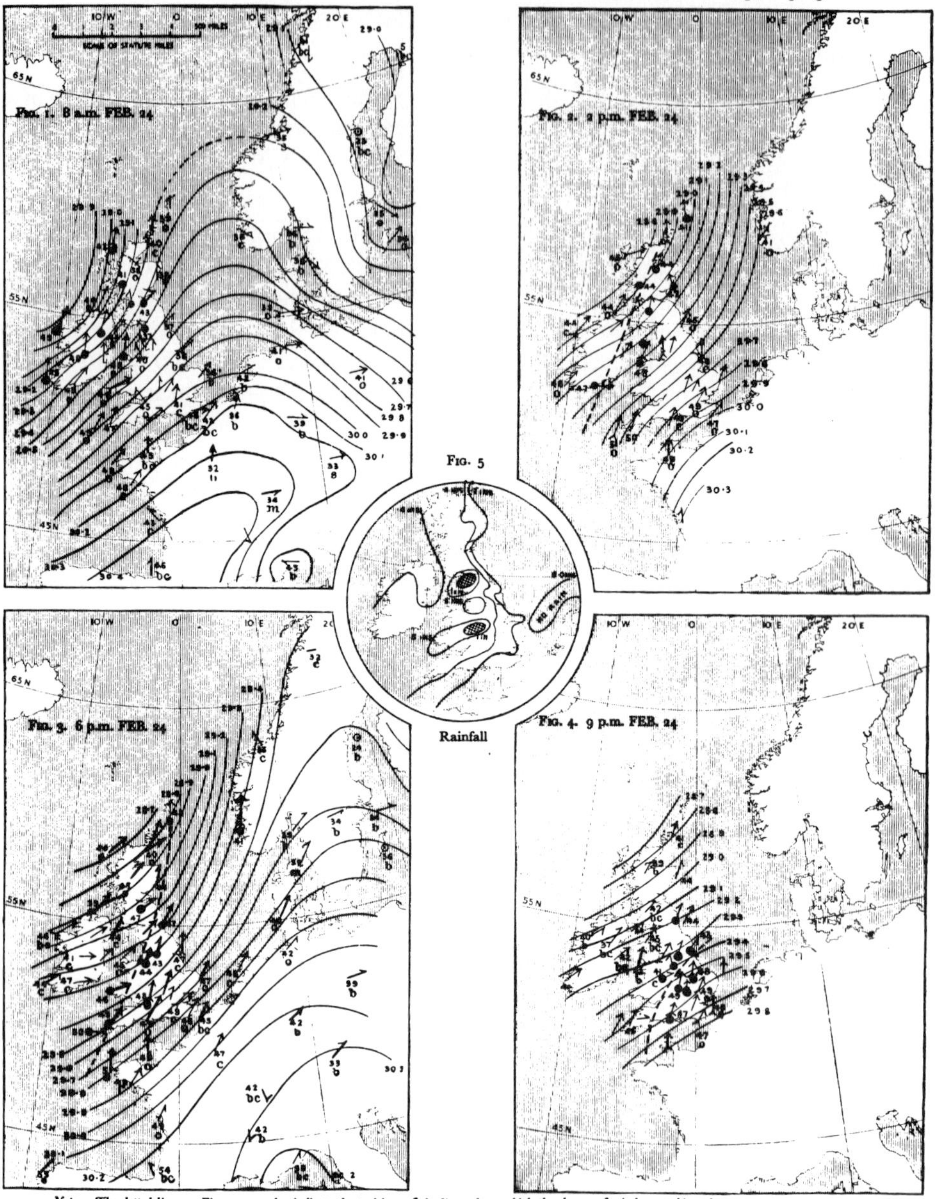

Note.—The dotted lines on Figs. 2, 3 and 4 indicate the positions of the lines along which the change of wind was taking place. The mark • shows that rain was falling at the hour of observation.

FIGURE 44. Advance of lines associated with sudden changes in wind, pressure, temperature and weather during the passage of the storm of 24 February 1903, according to Shaw; from Shaw and Lempfert, *The Life History of Surface Air Currents*, M. O. Memoir, No. 174 (1906). Dashed line indicates line of "wind shift." Numbers next to stations are temperatures (°F), the mark • shows rain and small letters indicate weather, i.e., o, overcast, c, cloudy, bc, partly cloudy.

of the 'fault' in each isobar represent the magnitude of the sudden increase of pressure.[157]

An example of Lempfert's analyses is reproduced in Figure 45. Lempfert and Corless recognized the line squall as a boundary between two different air currents:

> A current from a southerly direction in its progress from warmer latitudes is invaded by a colder current coming from more northern regions. . . . The tendency will be for the cold and, therefore, heavy current to force its way under the warm and humid and, therefore, light current, forcing the latter into upper regions.[158]

In their analysis of the vector changes of the winds (assumed to be proportional to the gradient winds) during the passage of a line squall, Lempfert and Corless introduced a component of motion in a vertical plane normal to the direction of the line squall (Figure 46). This scheme clearly indicated "upward motion in front of the line and downward motion behind it."[159] About the same time, in 1911, Shaw constructed his now well-known diagram of air currents in a cyclone which implied lines or surfaces of separation between air currents of different meteorological properties entering the cyclone (Figure 41).

Simultaneously, V. Bjerknes and his collaborators in Oslo (1908–1913) had intensified their investigation of lines of convergence and divergence in the surface wind field. These lines had previously attracted their attention when they appeared as prominent features on the first streamline charts constructed by Sandström at the beginning of the century.[160] In 1910 V. Bjerknes gave a lecture in London on a detailed analysis of lines of flow, convergence and divergence and the associated fields of vertical motion, cloud and precipitation patterns for an individual cyclone in the United States.[161] In his analysis (Figure 47), two distinct "lines of convergence" and a "point of convergence" (cyclone center) are discernible in the storm. The general pattern of lines of flow in the cyclone agreed well with Shaw's results for air trajectories. Bjerknes noted in particular the potential usefulness of lines of convergence and divergence for weather forecasting. He sought, therefore, the support of Shaw in his demand for drastically improved and increased observations (at hourly intervals) and their rational organization and publication. These, he suggested, would permit similar analyses on a regular basis, a prerequisite for "a rational method of taking up the problem of forecasting the weather."[162] This method, he explained, should be based on precalculations of "charts representing the field of horizontal motion and the field of pressure" and

---

[157] Lempfert (1906), p. 268; he also noted that it appeared that Durand-Gréville was the first to suggest analyzing isobars with a "fault" along line squalls.

[158] Lempfert sand Corless (1910), 158–159.

[159] *Ibid.*, p. 160.

[160] V. Bjerknes made this comment in "Wettervorhersage," *Met. Zeits.*, **36** (1919), p. 69.

[161] V. Bjerknes, "Synoptical representation of atmospheric motions," *Quart. Journ. Roy. Met. Soc.*, **36** (1910), 267–286. Results presented in this talk form part of the textbook V. Bjerknes *et al.*, *Dynamic Meteorology and Hydrography*, *op. cit.*

[162] *Ibid.*, p. 283.

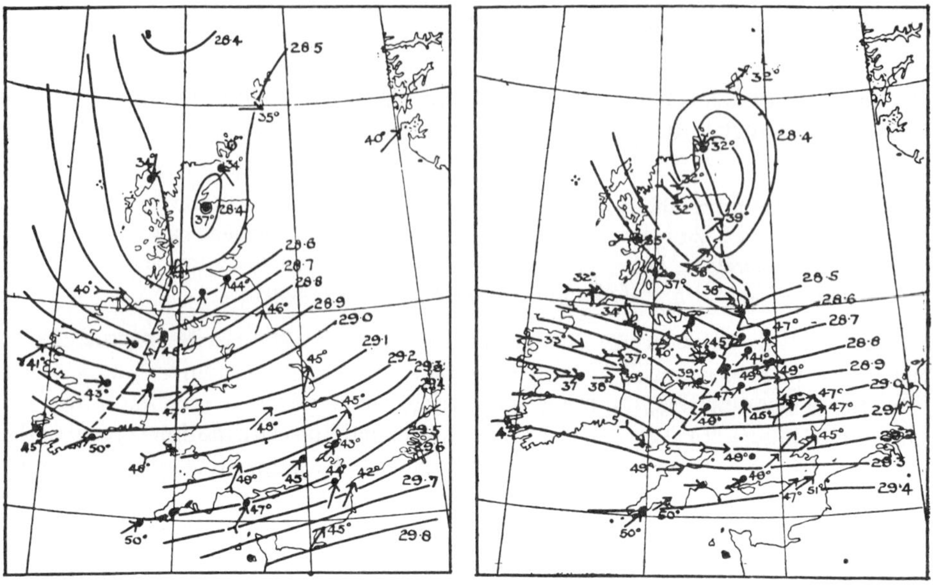

Synoptic Chart, 6 p.m., Feb. 19, 1907. Synoptic Chart, 9 p.m., Feb. 19, 1907.

FIGURE 45. Synoptic charts of February 19, 1907, showing advance of line squall (dashed line) and 'fault' in isobars (solid lines) along the line squall, by Lempfert; from Lempfert and Corless, "Line squalls and associated phenomena," *Quart. Journ. Roy. Met. Soc.*, **36** (1910). Winds, temperatures and precipitation (•) are indicated.

deriving from these "the chart of correlated vertical motion, and from this chart the further details of the kind of weather, precipitation, cloudiness, clear sky."[163] Jacob Bjerknes' (V. Bjerknes' son) first scientific paper (prepared at Leipzig) was, for the most part, an attempt in this direction. Investigating the kinematic features of lines of flow in the vicinity of lines of convergence, J. Bjerknes developed a mathematical expression for the propagation of lines of convergence.[164]

While scientists in England at the Meteorological Office and the group of V. Bjerknes and his collaborators in Oslo concentrated on the examination of the wind field and the pressure distribution associated with surfaces of discontinuity, the Austrian school of meteorologists, under the influence of Margules, approached the subject by placing emphasis on the role of temperature contrasts associated with discontinuities.[165] In 1910 and 1911, H. v. Ficker in Austria published two works on

[163] *Ibid.*

[164] Jacob Bjerknes, "Ueber die Fortbewegung der Konvergenz- und Divergenzlinien," *Met. Zeits.*, **34** (1917) 345–349. He found that the movement of lines of convergence is a function of the vorticity gradient due to the lines of flow on both sides of the line of convergence.

[165] This trend is also discernible in the meteorological textbooks available of this period: V. Bjerknes *et al.*, *Dynamic Meteorology and Hydrography, Part II, Kinematics* (Washington, Carnegie Institution, 1911) and F. M. Exner, *Dynamische Meteorologie* (Leipzig and Berlin, B. G. Teubner, 1917); see also A. Defant, *Wetter und Wettervorhersage* (Leipzig and Wien, F. Deuticke, 1918).

$$u > U > v_1;\ U = \text{or} > v_2.$$

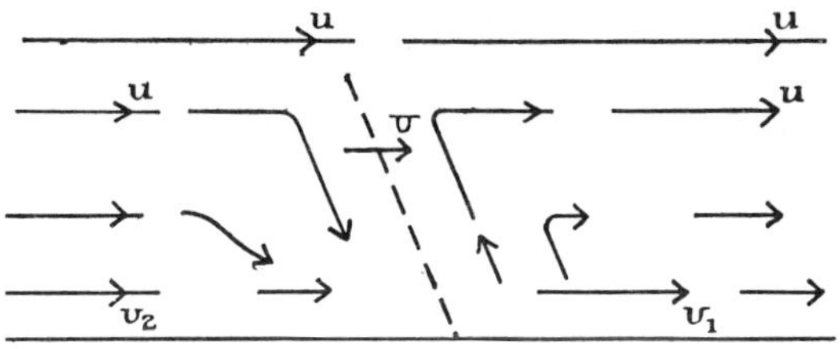

Absolute Component Motion in a Vertical Plane normal to the direction of the Linear Front.

FIGURE 46. Vertical cross section of absolute component of motion normal to the direction of a line squall by Lempfert and Corless; from Lempfert and Corless, "Line squalls and associated phenomena," *Quart. Journ. Roy. Met. Soc.*, **36** (1910). *U* denotes velocity of propagation of the squall (dashed line); *u* denotes component of gradient wind velocity at right angles to the line-squall; v_1, v_2 are components of the surface winds in front and behind the squall.

the advance of waves of cold and warm air in Europe and North Asia, in which he showed that a cyclone consists of two air currents of different temperature.[166] Ficker developed a scheme (Figure 48) similar to Bigelow's (Figure 38), which showed the wave-like boundary between warm and cold tongues of air and the associated wind field. The warm air and the cold air located to the west (regions IV and V in Figure 48) form a cyclonic system with the center of low pressure located at the tip of the tongue of warm air:

> The depression, therefore, consists of two air currents of different temperature flowing side by side, a warm wave in the front portion, a cold wave in the rear.[167]

Ficker also considered the associated field of vertical motion. He noted that along the boundary between warm air and cold air in the rear of the cyclone (between regions IV and V in Figure 48) "cold air pushes under the warm air whereby the warm air is lifted."[168] The southwest winds (in region IV), representing advection of warm moist air, Ficker noted, ascend over the cold air in the front part of the cyclone (region III) and give rise to cloud formation.[169] He further considered the warm and cold waves as important links in the general circulation of the atmosphere, performing an essential role in the mass and heat transport between lower and higher latitudes. The results of Ficker and Bigelow were confirmed by the Austrian Stanislav Hanzlik's investigations of cyclones and anticyclones. In 1911 Hanzlik concluded on the basis of European mountain observations that a warm, southern current, initiating a cold counter current from the north, is of primary importance for the formation of a warm cyclone. He demonstrated that the "surface

---

[166] v. Ficker, "Die Ausbreitung kalter Luft in Russland und Nordasien," *Sitzber. Ak. Wien, Abt. IIa*, **119** (1910), 1769–1837, and "Das Fortschreiten der Erwärmungen (der 'Wärmewellen') in Russland und Nordasien," Ibid., **120** (1911), 745–836.

[167] Ficker (1911), p. 835.

[168] *Ibid.*, p. 811.

[169] That warming begins earlier at high levels than at low levels, Ficker observed, is substantiated by the fact that "the pressure falls earlier, at the earth's surface, than the warming sets in," (1911), p. 817.

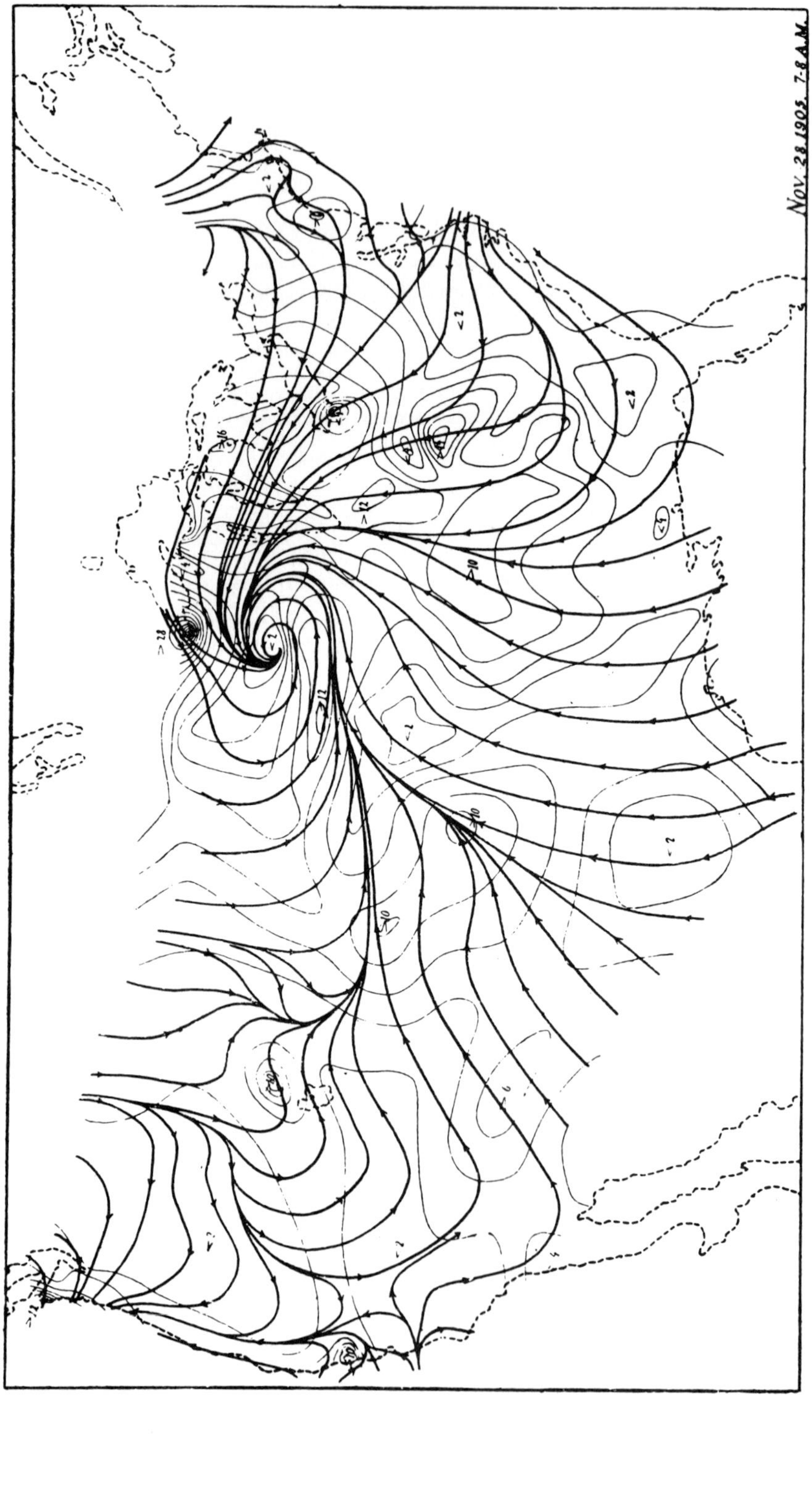

FIGURE 47. Lines of flow and curves of intensity of the air motion for November 28, 1905, over the United States by V. Bjerknes; from V. Bjerknes, "Synoptical representation of atmospheric motions," *Quart. Journ. Roy. Met. Soc.*, **36** (1910). Heavy arrow-headed lines are lines of flow; thin lines are curves of intensity (now called isotaches, given in meters per second). Note two distinct "lines of convergence" and a "point of convergence" within a storm centered in extreme western Wisconsin.

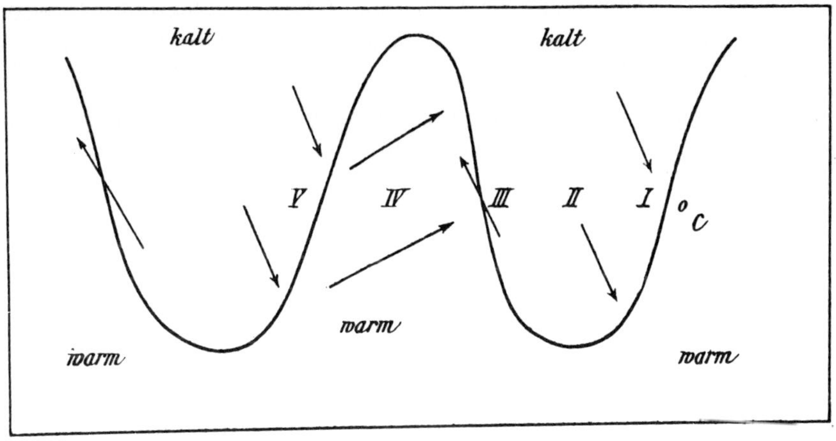

FIGURE 48. Scheme of warm and cold waves passing over North Asia by Ficker; from Ficker, "Das Fortschreiten der Erwärmungen in Russland und Nordasien," *Sitzber. Ak. Wien*, **120** (1911). The boundary between warm and cold air is represented by the isotherm. The wind system in the cold region is anticyclonic, in the tongue-shaped region cyclonic. Roman numerals indicate sequence of events during passage of cold wave and warm wave at an individual observation station. Wind changes and temperature variations during states III and IV correspond to those experienced during passage of barometric depression. I, V: outbreak of cold air with northwest wind, pushing under and lifting warm air in IV; pressure increase. II: lowest temperatures, high pressure, calms or weak and variable winds. III: rear of cold wave and front of warm wave; pressure decreasing. IV: very warm, moist southwest winds, ascending over colder air in III, pressure decrease.

of separation between the cold northern and warm southern current is inclined; the cold current pushes under the warm current like a wedge."[170]

The empirical and theoretical studies on surfaces of discontinuity carried out during the first two decades of the Twentieth Century, in conjunction with Margules' theoretical investigations on the source of energy in storms, clearly demonstrated that a store of potential energy could be accumulated in the atmosphere. As Brunt, however, remarked, there remained another problem:

> The fundamental difficulty involved in the adoption of Margules' work as an explanation of the genesis of motions in the atmosphere lies rather in explaining how the energy liberated in the way he discusses is able to organise itself into the horizontal circulations which we observe in the atmosphere.[171]

Margules himself briefly touched upon this problem with regard to the formation of storms in his last paper on the subject of meteorology. He hastily summarized these thoughts in an appendix in small print to the main body of his 1906 paper "Zur Sturmtheorie."[172] Apparently he wished to record his ideas on the work ahead that

---

[170] Hanzlik, "Die räumliche Verteilung der meteorologischen Elemente in den Zyklonen," *Denks. Ak. Wien*, **88** (1913), read 1911, p. 116.

[171] D. Brunt, *Physical and Dynamical Meteorology* (Cambridge, University Press, 1934), p. 285.

[172] Margules (1906b), p. 481. In the introduction to this paper Margules remarked: "Circumstances, into which I cannot enter here, give me cause, to write down hastily this report and appendix, and to bid farewell to meteorology."

he clearly foresaw, knowing that he would not embark on it himself. "Horizontal temperature gradients and masses with a great store of potential energy are everywhere," he noted, but the

> storm is relatively rare. The masses, associated with moderate velocities, remain in a near-stationary state, which maintains itself either through thermal processes, with vertical components of circulation, or purely dynamically. The conditions for the stability of this state are known. Disturbances of a certain, small amount do not lead to stormy motion, they can propagate like waves, without showing growth; they would soon be extinguished through friction. Are there larger disturbances of the dynamic equilibrium, which grow on their own, feeding from the potential energy, perhaps also from the store of kinetic energy?[173]

He suggested a simple model for the analytical treatment of this problem:

> First I would choose antiparallel straight currents of incompressible fluids for the undisturbed state in a rotating system with level topographies (Niveauflächen), or a current adjacent to a stationary mass.[174]

Of course, he mused, "which disturbance one needs to introduce, cannot be guessed at the outset. This can be the test of one's patience according to the axiom by Ostwald: one thinks last of the simplest." He admitted, "a calculator with sufficient knowledge of observations, with imagination and much patience perhaps will reach the goal."[175]

---

[173] Margules (1906b), p. 496.

[174] *Ibid.*, p. 497.

[175] The words just quoted were his last remarks on the subject of meteorology. Some of the following factors may have contributed to Margules' departure from meteorology: Margules suffered greatly from the lack of recognition of his work. He was a lonely man, in private life as well as in his scientific work. Apparently it was not always easy to deal with the sensitive Margules. His attitude toward meteorology had remained rather cool and, consequently, he could not muster the persistence and strength to continue his work. He gradually withdrew completely into the study of chemistry, which he had carried out throughout his life and which he considered his real passion. In 1906, a disagreement with the director of the Zentralanstalt at that time (Perntner) led to his final break with meteorology.

Chapter

7 Toward the Wave or Polar Front Theory of Cyclones

7.1 INTRODUCTION

The wave or polar front theory of cyclones was a most significant and far-reaching contribution toward describing, on the basis of sound dynamic and energetic reasoning, the observed three-dimensional structure of the cyclone, its evolution in time, and its role in the general circulation of the atmosphere. Developed under the leadership of V. Bjerknes, it represents an outstanding example of synthesis in meteorological theory, introducing novel ideas and, at the same time, incorporating and substantiating many of the results of Nineteenth Century and early Twentieth Century cyclone theory discussed in previous chapters. The element of continuity in the development of cyclone theory, however, has received little attention, or has been dismissed as negligible. In the following, therefore, emphasis is placed on discussion of the links rather than the contrasts between the polar front theory of cyclones and earlier investigations of storms.[1]

7.2 J. BJERKNES' MODEL OF THE FRONTAL CYCLONE

In 1919, in an eight page article entitled "On the structure of moving cyclones," V. Bjerknes' son Jacob Bjerknes, then 21 years of age, developed the

[1] I have attempted in this book to treat the meteorological literature related to the thermal theory of cyclones in a comprehensive manner prior to the date of 1906 (the date of Margules' "Sturmtheorie" and Shaw and Lempfert's "Life history . . ."), covering publications in the United States, England, the Scandinavian countries and countries in central Europe. The discussion of papers published after 1906 has been very selective and is restricted, for the most part, to papers that deal explicitly with surfaces of discontinuity observed in cyclones.

famous empirical frontal cyclone model of the "ideal cyclone."[2] In 1921 and 1922 J. Bjerknes and his colleague Halvor Solberg, also in his twenties, extended the theory by showing that the idealized cyclone of the first frontal model represented but a stage in the life cycle of cyclones which were subsequently seen as waves developing along an extended polar front.[3] The wave or polar front theory of cyclones, also called the "Norwegian" cyclone model, was completed in its essential features by the end of 1918 but, according to V. Bjerknes, the publication of the results was retarded until 1919 due to the heavy work load of the young scientists during the first years at the Bergen Institute.[4]

To a large degree, the development of the theory constituted the outcome of V. Bjerknes' systematic efforts, carried out over a period of 20 years, to develop sound synoptic and theoretical methods of analyzing atmospheric states and motions. These investigations, which have been discussed to some extent in the previous chapter, were accomplished at a number of institutions with the help of a group of talented assistants: in Stockholm from 1900 to 1908, in Oslo from 1908 to 1913, in Leipzig from 1913 to 1917, and then in Bergen from 1917 and in Oslo from 1927.

The intensive study of the three-dimensional structure of the atmosphere during the Leipzig period laid the foundations for attacking the problem of weather forecasting on the basis of physical principles, as V. Bjerknes had envisioned, and it formed the starting point for the achievements reached in Bergen.[5] During the first

---

[2] J. Bjerknes, "On the structure of moving cyclones," *Geofysiske Publikasjoner*, **1**, No. 1 (1919), 8 pp.; reprinted in *J. A. B. Bjerknes, Selected Papers* (Western Periodicals Company, 1975).

[3] J. Bjerknes and H. Solberg, "Meteorological conditions for the formation of rain," *Geofysiske Publikasjoner*, **2**, No. 3 (1921), 60 pp., and "Life cycle of cyclones and the polar front theory of atmospheric circulation," *Ibid.*, **3**, No. 1 (1922), 18 pp. The English titles indicate the trend, beginning with World War I, among authors of small countries to publish in English rather than the traditional German or French.

[4] V. Bjerknes, "On the dynamics of the circular vortex with applications to the atmosphere and atmospheric vortex and wave motions," *Geofysiske Publikasjoner*, **2**, No. 4 (1922), p. 1. V. Bjerknes communicated a summary of these results in a lecture before the Royal Meteorological Society, 7 November, 1919, "On the structure of the atmosphere when rain is falling," *Quart. Journ. Roy. Met. Soc.*, **46** (1920), 119–138 and in a note, "The meteorology of the temperate zone and the general atmospheric circulation," *Nature*, **105** (1920), 522–524.

[5] When speaking in 1938, on the occasion of the 25th anniversary of the Leipzig Institute, V. Bjerknes stated: "Now I ask myself: What would have happened, had we been able to carry through our program? The great atmospheric surfaces of discontinuities and their cutlines with the earth surface hardly would have escaped our attention. The entire 'polar front meteorology' or 'air mass meteorology' would then have developed in Leipzig, as far as I can judge it. But fate had determined it otherwise." Comparing the contributions of the Leipzig School with those of the Bergen School, V. Bjerknes emphasized: "However insignificant the contribution of the Leipzig School to the final success in Bergen may appear, this contribution is not only great but was *absolutely necessary for the final success*." See, V. Bjerknes, "Leipzig-Bergen," *Zeitschrift für Geophysik*, **14** (1938), pp. 56 and 60. During the years in Leipzig it was Bjerknes' primary goal to carry out "synoptic dynamic investigations . . . in order to reduce every phenomenon in the atmosphere to the laws of physics." The first step in this endeavor was to analyze "aerological observations from the synoptic point of view," which resulted in the first specialized series of publications of the Leipzig Institute: *Synoptische Darstellungen atmosphärischer Zustände über Europa* (1913–1919). The next step to be taken was the theoretical approach, namely, "to calculate future states of the atmosphere by means of the hydrodynamic and thermodynamic equations." Theoretical publications were published mostly in a second series of publications: *Spezialarbeiten aus dem Geophysikalischen Institut Leipzig* [see V. Bjerknes, "Robert Wenger," *Beitr. Phys. f. Atm.*, **10** (1922), 4 pp].

year at the Geophysikalische Institut in Leipzig, in 1913, Bjerknes was assisted by his two collaborators and Carnegie assistants Th. Hesselberg and H. V. Sverdrup and the German meteorologist R. Wenger.[6] By the end of 1914 the institute had over ten students and the staff of assistants was expanded. J. Bjerknes and Solberg became Carnegie assistants of V. Bjerknes in 1916. After a very promising start, however, working conditions became difficult when war broke out in 1914. The German assistants and research students were soon called to active duty and Hesselberg and Sverdrup returned to Norway.[7] Nevertheless, V. Bjerknes and his Scandinavian assistants were able to continue their studies, on a reduced scale.[7a] When living conditions increasingly worsened in wartime Germany, however, V. Bjerknes in 1917 decided to accept an invitation to return to Norway and establish a Geophysical Institute in Bergen. The two assistants who accompanied him to Bergen were his son and Solberg. Other Scandinavian collaborators were soon attracted to V. Bjerknes and his new Institute; S. Rosseland arrived in 1918, T. Bergeron, E. Bjørkdal and C.-G. Rossby in 1919, and E. Palmén and Sv. Petterssen and others soon followed. The mathematical physicists and meteorologists of the Scandinavian School of meteorology went on to develop a complete three-dimensional model of the cyclone, including concepts of fronts and air masses. This development is a fascinating story in itself and beyond the scope of this book. The following will therefore be restricted to a discussion of the three papers of J. Bjerknes and Solberg mentioned above, which set the stage for further empirical and theoretical studies.

In J. Bjerknes' first illustration of the moving cyclone (Figure 49), the central

---

[6] In 1905, when he was invited to give a lecture at the Carnegie Institution in Washington, Bjerknes outlined his plan of how to attack the problem of weather forecasting. "If at any time a lecture by me has been a success, it happened this time," Bjerknes commented afterward according to Bergeron ["V. Bjerknes," *Geofysiske Publikasjoner*, **24** (1962), p. 14]. As a result the Carnegie Institution granted him yearly funds until 1941 to employ assistants in his research work. When Bjerknes began to organize the Leipzig Institute with its ambitious program, he selected as collaborator Robert Wenger who had conducted extensive meteorological and aerological investigations at Teneriffa and leaned strongly toward theoretical meteorology. The first volume of the *Synoptische Darstellungen* was mostly the work of Wenger. His later studies dealt with instrumental and methodical errors of aerological observations. Wenger carried the main burden of the administrative and organizational work at the institute and succeeded Bjerknes as director when Bjerknes returned to Norway. In 1922 Wenger died prematurely at the age of 36 and the fruitful cooperation, which V. Bjerknes had envisioned between the Leipzig and the Bergen institutes, came to a halt. See H. Hergesell and V. Bjerknes, "Robert Wenger," *Beitr. Phys. f. Atm.*, **10** (1922), 8 pp.

[7] The most promising one, H. Petzold, was one of the five who fell in the war. As Bjerknes' first doctoral student at Leipzig Petzold had been assigned the investigation of the physical nature of lines of convergence. He selected an example of an advancing temperature discontinuity associated with a shift in wind direction. "He intended to investigate this phenomenon after the example of works by Köppen or Durand-Gréville," but on a three-dimensional scale made possible through improved aerological observations. "He was just commencing these investigations when he was called to military duty. . . . He fell in 1916 at Verdun." [See V. Bjerknes *et al.*, *Physikalische Hydrodynamik* (Berlin, Springer, 1933), Bibliographie mit historischen Erläuterungen, 786–787, and Bjerknes, *Zeitschrift für Geophysik*, *op. cit.*, (1938), p. 56, where he states: "Perhaps Petzold's investigation would have paved the way for the polar front meteorology."] J. Bjerknes was assigned to continue Petzold's work. He published his results on the propagation of lines of convergence in 1917, in his first scientific paper (*op. cit.*).

[7a] It would be interesting to know to what extent leading meteorologists of other countries were able to continue their research during the war. Such a discussion, however, is beyond the scope of this book.

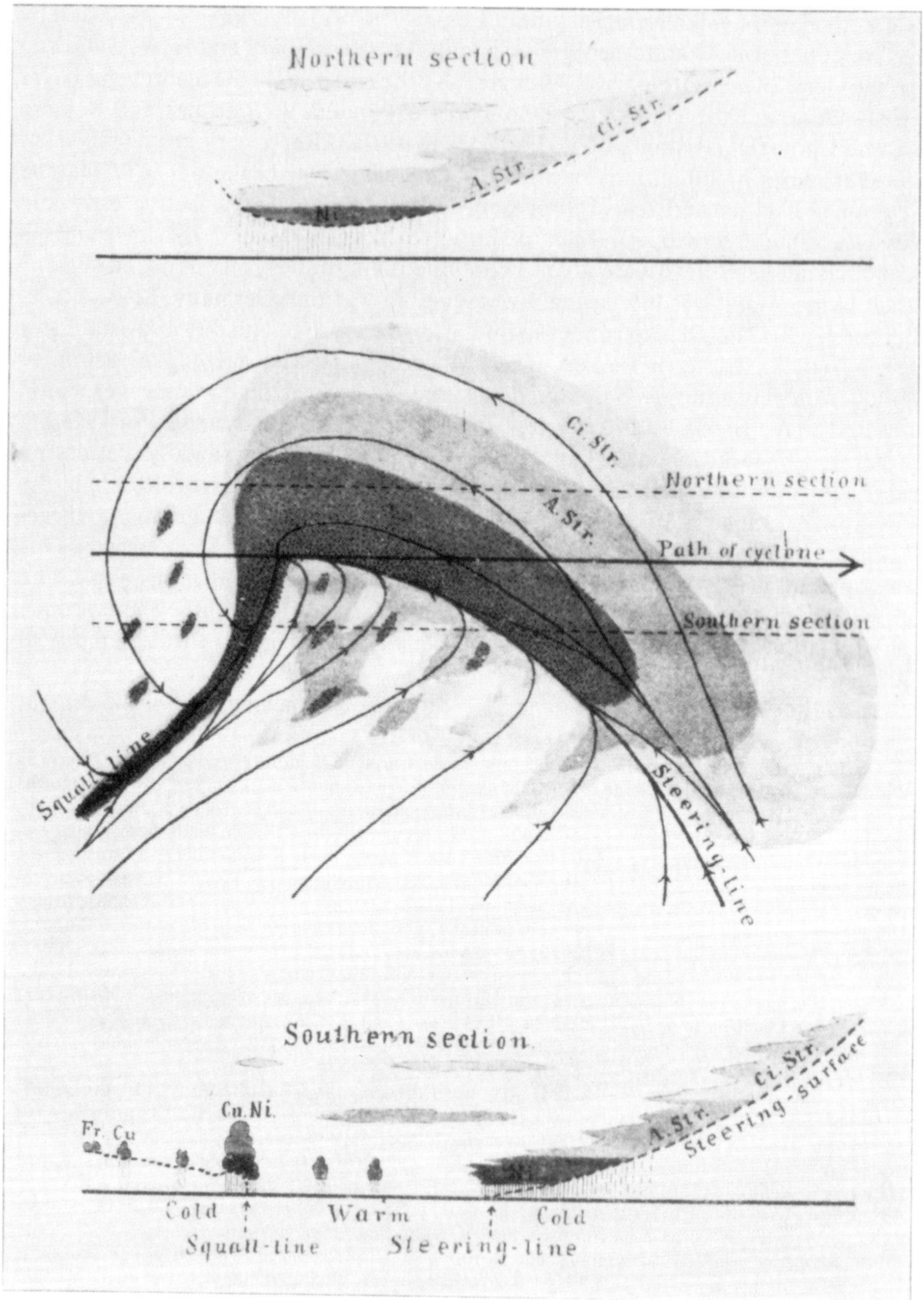

FIGURE 49. J. Bjerknes' model of the frontal cyclone; from "The structure of moving cyclones," *Geofysiske Publikasjoner,* **1** (1919). Horizontal view shows streamlines and two lines of convergence, bordering the "warm sector" of the cyclone (compare with Figure 47). Darkest shading depicts lowest clouds and precipitation, lighter shadings indicate middle and high clouds. The northern and southern cross sections parallel to the cyclone path indicate meteorological phenomena.

diagram represents a well-developed "idealized" cyclone and the lower and upper diagrams are vertical cross sections taken north and south of the path of the center.[8] The principal features of this model are "two lines of convergence . . . distinguished by characteristic thermal properties."[9] The first of these lines, J. Bjerknes noted, enters the cyclone from the front and appeared to indicate the direction of propagation of the cyclone:

> The tangent to the line at its terminus in the cyclonic centre seems to be identical with that of the path. As the line thus gives the momentaneous direction of propagation of the cyclone, it may, for practical purposes, be called the *steering line*.[10]

The line of convergence in the rear of the cyclone, Bjerknes stated, "is identical with the well known *squall line*."[11] The steering line and squall line are joined in the center of the cyclone, at the most northerly tip of the tongue of warm air bordered by the two lines. Warm and cold air flowing into the cyclone are separated by distinct boundary surfaces, "cutting the ground along the steering and squall line."[12]

In Figure 49, the lower cross section shows how the warm moist air flows up over the cold air, forming a system of clouds, and how rain falls through the cold air. In the rear the cold air flows underneath the warm air. The rising motion in the warm air is more violent and irregular at the squall line than at the steering line and the area of precipitation is less extensive. Bjerknes then explained the great breadth of the zones of clouds and precipitation in front of the steering line. He showed that the steering surface, along which the warm air ascends, has a very small angle of inclination with the ground so that higher clouds would reach 500 km or more ahead of the steering line. He proposed that one could calculate the angle of inclination with good approximation by applying Margules' "well known" formula for the equilibrium inclination of surfaces of discontinuity as a function of the differences of temperature and wind velocity on both sides. Estimating these differences on

---

[8] The investigations for this paper, published in 1919, had been completed a year earlier in 1918. V. Bjerknes gave an early report on the model, its practical use and first successful applications in forecasting weather for southern Norway, on 28 August 1918 in an address delivered at the Meeting of Scandinavian Geophysicists at Gothenburg. Bjerknes also presented a diagram containing the two lines of convergence named steering line and squall line. In agreement with J. Bjerknes' model of 1919, V. Bjerknes' diagram showed a broad zone of precipitation extending up to 200 km in advance of the steering line and a narrow band of precipitation along the squall line. However, in contrast to the later model of his son, these two zones of precipitation are connected by a large area of precipitation covering the northern portion of the warm sector. V. Bjerknes' address was subsequently published in parts at various places, including the *Mon. Wea. Rev.*, **47** (1918), 90–95 and *Met. Zeits.*, **36** (1919), 68–75.

[9] J. Bjerknes (1919), p. 1.

[10] *Ibid.*, p. 1.

[11] *Ibid.*, pp. 1–2.

[12] *Ibid.*, p. 3. The work at the Geophysical Institute in Bergen began on 1 July 1918. Shape and position of the squall line were first analyzed on 18 and 24 July. Steering and squall line, together with the associated patterns of cloudiness and precipitation were first analyzed on successive charts and joined at the center of the cyclone for 14–15 August. The vertical structure of a warm front was first analyzed in a cyclone approaching Scandinavia during 10–11 September 1919. The process of occlusion was identified by Bergeron for the weather situation of 18 November 1919. Solberg began to draw a polar front through members of a cyclone family by joining the cold front of one cyclone with the front of the next cyclone on the synoptic charts of 23–27 September 1919. For this information see original papers of Bjerknes and Solberg, and T. Bergeron in Godske *et al.*, *Dynamic Meteorology and Weather Forecasting* (Boston, Am. Met. Soc., 1957), p. 624, and Khrgian, *op. cit.*, pp. 214–216.

equilibrium inclination of surfaces of discontinuity as a function of the differences of temperature and wind velocity on both sides. Estimating these differences on synoptic charts, Bjerknes found as an average inclination for the steering surface the value of 1:100.[13]

Considering the "mechanics of the moving cyclones" in the final section of his short paper, J. Bjerknes stated that "the moving cyclone consists in the lower strata . . . of two opposite currents. . . . The cold current is screwed underneath the warm one, and the warm current screwed up above the cold one."[14] He also attempted to define the nature of the disturbance of equilibrium along a surface of discontinuity which would lead to storm formation. "The combined motion" of warm and cold currents, he suggested,

> propagates along the steering surface, not unlike a wave motion, the kinetic energy being rendered by the potential energy of the system of light and heavy air lying adjacent to each other horizontally. The cyclonic motion affects the transformation into a state with reduced potential energy, involving a reduced angle of inclination, or even a complete disturbance of the surface of discontinuity.[15]

Finally, Bjerknes considered the role of cyclones with respect to the general circulation of the atmosphere. "Generally speaking," he concluded "cyclones . . . may be said to be links in the interchange of air between the polar regions and the equatorial zone."[16]

Subsequent investigations by J. Bjerknes and Solberg made it evident that the term steering line was ambiguous and gave "rise to objections and even mistakes, as the 'steering line' has only nearest to the centre that direction tangential to the track of the cyclone to which the name should allude."[17] Shifting emphasis to the fact that the two lines of convergence were "thermal boundary lines," the steering line was renamed "warm front" and the squall line "cold front."[18] In addition, the analysis of streamlines, used in J. Bjerknes' cyclone model of 1919, was replaced by the analysis of isobars which is more easily performed on a routine basis. In their papers of 1921 and 1922 Bjerknes and Solberg also showed that the "idealized" cyclone described by Bjerknes in his paper of 1919 "is only a special case of the more general one, . . . changing regularly during the life of a cyclone."[19] Subsequently they clearly distinguished the life history of cyclones and cyclone families. As the cyclone develops, the cold air in the rear pushes forward, displacing the warm air upward and narrowing the tongue of warm air at the ground. "This process," they noted,

---

[13] Bjerknes noted on p. 5: "In the case which we are considering, the surface of discontinuity is a moving one, and thus the condition of equilibrium is not fullfilled. But in the case of slow moving systems, we are entitled to consider the deviations from the equilibrium small and reckon approximately with the equilibrium values."

[14] *Ibid.*, pp. 6–7.

[15] *Ibid.*, p. 7.

[16] *Ibid.*

[17] Bjerknes and Solberg (1921), p. 25.

[18] The terms warm front and cold front were introduced in 1920.

[19] Bjerknes and Solberg (1922), p. 4.

> transforms part of the potential energy stored in the initial system into kinetic energy. . . . This appears distinctly on the maps as an increase in wind force, and usually as a deepening of the depression.[20]

Eventually the cold front overtakes the warm front. Finally the cyclone consists entirely of cold air and becomes a nearly symmetrical vortex:

> It has no store of potential energy which can be directly transformed into kinetic energy, and the existing motion can only be maintained by the inertia of the moving air masses.[21]

In the Norwegian terminology this process, identified by Bergeron, was called the occlusion process.

After this brief discussion of the scientific content of the early papers of the Bergen meteorologists, we will now proceed to relate their work to the historical development of cyclone theory during the decades preceding it. J. Bjerknes himself, in the last two paragraphs of his 1919 paper, briefly evaluated earlier theories in the light of the frontal cyclone model. In his attempt to establish links to the past he carefully singled out the contribution of Margules. In fact, Margules' results are the only theoretical results utilized in Bjerknes' otherwise empirical paper. The new cyclone model, Bjerknes wrote, quoting Margules directly,

> may in great extent be considered as a verification of views developed theoretically by Margules: 'The phenomena in motion in great storm areas that we call cyclones are less intelligible than those of the boe-en (squalls). But these also, at least in medium and higher latitudes, consist of warm and cold masses of air lying adjacent to each other horizontally, cold air often spreading out over the earth in the lower strata behind the passing storm. It is therefore not unlikely that these storms are fed by the potential energy of an initial stage.'[22]

Furthermore, Bjerknes raised several significant points concerning the relation between the thermal theory of storms and the frontal cyclone model:

> . . . these results verify certain traits in various older theories of cyclones, while they disprove other traits in them. We are reminded both of Dove's old theory of the conflict between polar and equatorial currents as well as of the modern counter current theory. Ferrel's convectional theory is confirmed in its essential part inasmuch as the ascending air in the cyclone is warm, only that this warm air does not form a central core, but comes from the side, at the ground covering a warm sector. The general argument against the theory of Ferrel, that statistical investigations have proved a circular area around the centre of the cyclone to be cold rather than warm, does not disprove the principal point, that the ascending air is warm, but only the accidental assumption of the symmetrical structure of the cyclone.[23]

In this historical summary J. Bjerknes first referred to Dove who had identified polar and equatorial currents in the atmosphere and who believed that the replacement of one current by the other would give rise to storm. Bjerknes then

---

[20] *Ibid.*, p. 6.
[21] *Ibid.*, p. 7.
[22] J. Bjerknes (1919), 7–8.
[23] *Ibid.*, p. 8.

noted the similarities of the Norwegian model and Bigelow's model of flow patterns in midlatitude storms, although he mentioned only Bigelow's counter current model but not his name. In the remainder of the passage quoted above, J. Bjerknes underlined the fact that the convective or thermal theory was confirmed in its essential aspect, namely, that the ascending air in the moving cyclone is warm. Thus he saw the Norwegian cyclone model not in contradiction but in agreement with the thermal theory concerning its most essential feature. J. Bjerknes called Ferrel's assumption of thermal symmetry for the cyclone accidental; as has been described, Ferrel indeed had made this assumption more or less for reasons of mathematical convenience and analogy rather than on the basis of empirical evidence.

It comes somewhat as a surprise in this connection that J. Bjerknes referred to Dove's important linear two-current model of the 1840's and Ferrel's early convective model of the 1860's, but did not cite investigations of cyclones that were conducted between the 1860's and the time of Bigelow's studies around the turn of the century. Nor did he mention investigations of surfaces of discontinuity after 1900 by English and Austrian scientists, except for Margules' formula on the inclination of such surfaces. In the following we will draw upon results of cyclone research discussed in previous chapters to show that the relation between the thermal theory and the frontal cyclone model was even closer than J. Bjerknes indicated.

We have seen in preceding chapters that, according to the early convective theory as presented by Ferrel, the latent heat release in the central column of rising air was seen as the major source of local heating and the major source of energy in storms. This view was supported empirically by the first synoptic studies in Europe and the United States and by early theoretical studies on the energy budget of storms by Peslin and Reye around 1870. However, simultaneously with these studies, thorough synoptic investigations by Mohn began to point toward important modifications of this early convective theory. In 1870 Mohn concluded that two different types of air continuously converge in cyclones. He constructed a cyclone model in which vertical circulation and horizontal temperature distribution are no longer symmetrical with respect to the pressure distribution, but in which temperature, vertical motion, cloud formation and precipitation reach their maximum values ahead of the surface position of the cyclone center. Mohn's conclusions were supported by the observations of surface conditions and the movement of cirrus clouds in cyclones as studied by Ley during the 1870's. In the early 1880's Köppen attempted to analyze the three-dimensional structure of storms on the basis of limited Nineteenth Century upper air observations and by employing an elementary "indirect" aerology. He showed that the asymmetric temperature distribution in cyclones results in a "backward" inclination of the cyclone axis and that ascending motion takes place in the warm, front portion of the storm and descending motion in the rear. The two air currents involved in the cyclonic circulation, he proposed, remain distinct. Around the turn of the century these results on the role of thermal asymmetry in cyclones were further substantiated by V. Bjerknes and his student Sandström when they applied the circulation theorem in a quantitative test of the thermal theory on a large scale. Their work appeared to confirm the earlier suggestion of Mohn that a cyclone was propagated by the displacement of the center of vortex generating forces, namely the ascent of warm moist air in the front part of the storm.

Once it had become clear that two distinct air masses of different geographical origin and thermal properties played an essential role in the cyclonic circulation, the attention of meteorologists was also directed to the special problem of the boundaries between these air masses. Empirical studies concentrated on the investigation of the boundary between warm and cold air in the rear of the storm, i.e., the squall line, rather than on the less easily recognized boundary in the front portion of the cyclone. As J. Bjerknes pointed out in 1919, the squall line was well known to Nineteenth Century meteorologists. It was generally thought that along the squall line warm air was displaced upward by cold air advancing in the rear of the storm. Early Twentieth Century studies, for example Lempfert's and Corless' analysis of "line squalls" in 1910, confirmed these views. The processes taking place along the discontinuity surface that later became known as the warm front began to attract attention only around the turn of the century. Prior to this time, most meteorologists had believed that ascent of warm air took place throughout the volume of warm air due to convergence in lower layers.[24] This assumption appeared to explain the large extent of the area of clouds and precipitation in the front of the storm.[25] From 1898 onward Margules and Clayton made first attempts to investigate empirically the three-dimensional structure of the boundary between warm and cold air in the front portion of the storm, perceiving it as a surface of discontinuity. Margules, in particular, stressed that transport of air upward takes place largely along the surfaces of discontinuity, separating air masses of unequal temperature.

The trajectory analysis of surface air currents in storms carried out by Shaw and Lempfert in 1906 clearly demonstrated the discontinuity of meteorological elements along two lines of convergence. They showed conclusively that warm air was rising over the top of the cold air and that the cold air was flowing underneath the warm air, displacing it upward. Shaw's analysis of surface air currents was fully confirmed in the Norwegian cyclone model; in fact, V. Bjerknes himself stated in 1919 that in the cyclone model of 1911, reproduced in Figure 41, Shaw had provided

> a theory which is essentially identical with that derived from the charts before us, and which has been developed now by my son J. Bjerknes.[26]

Concurrently with the work of Shaw, V. Bjerknes conducted detailed investigations of lines of flow. A series of streamline charts published in 1910 indicated that two distinct lines of convergence were present in a cyclone. At that time, however,

---

[24] In contrast, J. Bjerknes proposed in the frontal model that "greater transport of air upwards takes place only along the two lines of convergence, steering line and squall line, where the warm and cold masses meet each other" (1919, p. 4).

[25] The occurrence of upper level clouds far in advance of the storm center was generally explained as due to cyclonic outflow of the ascending warm moist air in these layers, without utilizing the concept that here warm air was rising over cold air.

[26] V. Bjerknes, "The structure of the atmosphere . . . ," (1920), p. 129. J. Bjerknes and Solberg made a similar statement in their joint paper of 1921 (p. 25).

V. Bjerknes and his collaborators did not interpret these lines as temperature discontinuities. Further, in his studies on the advance of "warm and cold waves" in 1910 and 1911, Ficker described explicitly the temperature changes, wind shifts, vertical motions and the cloud cover and precipitation patterns associated with them.

At the end of his historical remarks J. Bjerknes also commented on "Hann's 'driven eddy' theory," noting that the general view of Hann, "that cyclones are merely partial phases of the general circulation, has been fully confirmed."[27] As has been indicated in previous chapters, the view of the mutual interdependence between cyclones and anticyclones and the general circulation became increasingly prominent during the last decades of the Nineteenth Century and in fact was closely related to the development of the thermal theory. The observation of thermal advection in storms pointed toward the concept of interdependence between cyclones and the general circulation. This concept is implied or stated explicitly in a number of Nineteenth Century papers since Mohn's publications of the 1870's. However, preoccupation with cyclone research and limited observations precluded any further exploration of this idea at that time.

In their articles of 1921 and 1922 J. Bjerknes and Solberg described the formation and further development of frontal cyclones, i.e., their life cycle, on the basis of the process of occlusion. In their paper of 1922 they also noted older observational evidence for the life cycle of cyclones; again, they did not mention names or give details:

> A very large percentage of European cyclones are occluded ones, being dying remainders of previously strong Atlantic depressions. The predominance of occluded cyclones in Europe has led to the statistical result that cyclones usually have a cold core. A special investigation of the relatively infrequent young deepening cyclones will certainly afford evidence of their asymmetric thermal structure.[28]

This brief statement requires some additional clarification and comment. It will be recalled that the controversy on the vertical temperature structure of cyclones, which began during the 1880's between American and European meteorologists, had resulted in two contrasting conclusions: A number of meteorologists, including Hann and Bezold, viewed as generally applicable the statistical result that, on the average, cyclones in Europe are cold in upper layers; they consequently argued against the thermal theory. In turn, they began to explore dynamic causes for storm formation. Other investigators attempted to reconcile the observed differences in the temperature structure of European and American storms by introducing the concept of stages in the life history of cyclones. Accordingly, the mature cold cyclones investigated by Hann were identified by Ekholm (1906) as the final stage in cyclone development, associated with an indirect thermal circulation; at the same time, growing traveling cyclones, regarded as thermally asymmetric and associated

---

[27] J. Bjerknes (1919), p. 8.

[28] Bjerknes and Solberg (1922), 7. They appear to refer here to Dines' statistical results which were quite sensational at the time and, in Dines' view, dealt the "death blow" to the convective theory (Section 6.5).

with an asymmetric vertical circulation, were seen as evidence of a direct thermal circulation. Ekholm's suggestion that the United States experienced predominantly growing cyclones while the cylones arriving at the European continent in most cases had reached a mature stage of development was widely accepted by the turn of the century.

Finally, the concept of the steering line applied by J. Bjerknes in his first paper on the cyclone model calls for a few historical comments. The search for atmospheric conditions that exert an influence upon the direction of propagation of storms, i.e., that have a steering effect, had been important throughout the period discussed in this book. J. Bjerknes' empirical steering rule elucidated a large number of earlier observations and statements on this subject. Thus, according to the early convective theory, cyclones moved in the direction of highest precipitation. This view was present in part in the concept of the steering line, which was associated with a broad band of precipitation. In 1870 Mohn related the path taken by a storm to the horizontal temperature distribution; he proposed that higher temperatures remain toward the south of the path of the storm center. Ley's statistical investigations during the 1870's had shown that traveling cyclones tend to leave higher temperatures and pressure to the right of their path, and in 1882 Köppen expressed the view that cyclones will move in the direction of the current with "the greatest total energy," i.e., a steering current. In 1922 J. Bjerknes and Solberg themselves proposed that the path of propagation was parallel to the isobars in the warm sector.[29]

Reviewing once more the names of scientists quoted by J. Bjerknes in his first paper, the question arises again why he referred to Dove's linear two-current theory, Ferrel's cyclone model and the work of Margules and Hann, but did not mention, for example, the work of his countryman Mohn, or Ekholm, Köppen, Shaw, Ficker and others. V. Bjerknes had long-standing contacts with Mohn and Ekholm and it must be assumed that the Bergen scientists were familiar with their work. In addition, V. Bjerknes remarked later that during his years as director of the Geophysikalische Institut in Leipzig from 1913 to 1917 the research of older and contemporary scientists was systematically reviewed in special colloquia. In these colloquia the scientists at Leipzig attempted

> to obtain an overview of the older works and the great meteorological problems, and to keep up to date in the new literature.[30]

It is therefore almost certain that the work of many of the scientists dealt with in this book was covered in the Leipzig colloquia.

It appears in retrospect that the omission of relevant references in the early publications of the Bergen School was somewhat arbitrary. For example, while J. Bjerknes singled out Margules' contributions above all others, V. Bjerknes did not even mention Margules' name in his detailed historical sketch of the development of

---

[29] *Ibid.*, p. 9.
[30] V. Bjerknes *et al.*, *Physikalische Hydrodynamik*, *op. cit.*, p. 783.

the polar front theory.[31] Similarly, J. Bjerknes did not refer to Shaw, while V. Bjerknes fully acknowledged Shaw's work in a report on the Norwegian cyclone model in 1919. To underline the impression of arbitrariness in referencing, it may suffice to point out that J. Bjerknes also did not cite the work of his father although he clearly utilized the principles of analyzing atmospheric states and motions developed by his father and without whose inspiration and guidance he would scarcely have commenced his work. The Bergen scientists apparently did not see it necessary or important to refer to relevant work they had read. They were evidently preoccupied with the presentation of their own viewpoint of the three-dimensional structure of the cyclone, its life history and its role in the general circulation of the atmosphere.

7.2 CONCLUDING REMARKS

The polar front theory of cyclones, presented by the Bergen School of meteorologists after World War I, frequently has been described as representing a sharp break with older theories. This view is supported by the fact that the Bergen scientists were working in physical isolation, cut off from outside scientific communication during the last years of the war. The impression of the complete novelty of their results is enhanced because they introduced an entirely new terminology and because of the altered graphical representation of meteorological conditions on synoptic charts. The fact that in their early publications they only sparingly quoted earlier achievements further tends to obscure the links to the past in their work.[32]

---

[31] *Ibid.*, pp. 777–790. In this account V. Bjerknes treats the historical development of the polar front theory within the framework of the larger historical problem of the diagnosis and prognosis of atmospheric states and motions by use of the laws of hydrodynamics and thermodynamics. Discussing the content of the Leipzig colloquia, Bjerknes remarked: "As was generally done at that time, we considered the theories of Dove as outmoded . . . The name of Blasius remained unknown to us. At that time, the "polar fronts," as we would call them now, drawn by v. Ficker . . . attracted our attention. In view of the large number of daily weather maps which all appeared to point towards continuity, we were able to view these signs of discontinuity [Ficker's results] as interesting exceptional phenomena only, and we made no attempt to follow up this important lead. On the other hand, the review of Helmholtz' meteorological work of 1888 in the colloquia—it was reviewed several times—had important consequences. . . ." Helmholtz' investigations on atmospheric waves led V. Bjerknes to postulate "that the atmosperic disturbances, as all disturbances, begin necessarily as small perturbations and as such can be analyzed through linear equations . . . However, the main task of the institute was the perfection of the synoptic representation of atmospheric states. . . . We had reached the point in this generously planned endeavor that everything appeared to advance smoothly and we were just about to broaden and deepen the work in order to attack seriously the main problems when the war curtailed any expansion of the work . . ." (pp. 783–786). In 1930 Bergeron made an attempt to fully reference early works related to the polar front theory of cyclones in his widely read "Ueber die dreidimensional verknüpfende Wetteranalyse," *Geofysiske Publikasjoner*, **5** (1930), 111 pp. That the Bergen scientists were familiar with works of prominent meteorologists dealt with in this book, is stated by V. Bjerknes in "Die Meteorologie als exakte Wissenschaft," Inaugural Address, 8 January 1913, University of Leipzig (Braunschweig, Vieweg, 1913), 16 pp., and "Leipzig-Bergen," (1938), *op. cit.*

[32] During the early 1920's, the majority of meteorologists, particularly weather forecasters, regarded the polar front theory as an abrupt break with the past. Ficker occupied a rather isolated position when he stated in 1923 that the polar front theory was not to be considered revolutionary but in accordance with "the historical development of meteorology during the last decades" [Polarfont, Aufbau, Entstehung und Lebensgeschichte der Zyklonen," *Met. Zeits.*, **40** (1923), p. 70]. See also the

In contrast to the view outlined above the polar front theory of cyclones is here seen as an outstanding synthesis reconciling new insights and findings with important earlier results in meteorological theory. I have shown in the preceding chapters that there is a significant continuity in the development of theories of cyclones from the time of the introduction of the synoptic chart to the announcement of the polar front theory of cyclones, and that this continuity is reflected in the work of many prominent meteorologists during that time. I have emphasized this continuity with regard to thermal aspects of storm formation and the source of kinetic energy in storms.

The recognition of the main forms of energy and physical processes operating in the atmosphere was essential to the problem of understanding the working mechanism of cyclones and their role within the general circulation of the atmosphere. An initial step in this direction was seen in the recognition by Espy that in addition to the mechanical forms of energy the latent heat of condensation plays an important part in the formation of storms. The thermal theory of cyclones took shape with the application of the principles of thermodynamics and the introduction of the synoptic chart in the 1860's and 1870's. Once the concept of conservation of energy had been clarified, investigators attempted on the basis of the theory of adiabatic temperature changes in dry and moist air to evaluate the quantity of heat available for conversion into kinetic energy in storms. Investigations of this kind led to the hypothesis that the latent heat released in ascending currents of warm and moist air in storms must be recognized as the major source of energy for the formation and maintenance of storms. Synoptic and statistical evidence at first appeared to support this simple convective theory but also began to hint at important modifications.

Key elements in the further development of the thermal theory over the next decades were observations of the upper atmosphere, in particular the observations of cloud motions, temperature observations from mountain tops, and temperature soundings by means of kites and balloons, and the physical interpretation of these observations. These studies made it clear that cyclones must be regarded as open systems, and that, as part of the general circulation, cyclones participate in meridional and vertical heat exchange in midlatitudes. Acceptance of this view became more urgent once it was realized that any kinetic-energy-producing solenoidal circulation between cyclones and anticyclones would reduce the potential energy available for conversion, and that this process could not sufficiently be offset by the release of latent heat in the ascending branch of warm moist air.

---

following more recent interpretations of the development of the polar front theory: T. Bergeron, "Methods in scientific weather analysis and forecasting. An outline in the history of ideas and hints of a program," in *Atmosphere and Sea in Motion*, B. Bolin Ed. (New York, Rockefeller Inst. Press, 1959); E. Palmén and C. W. Newton, *Atmospheric Circulation Systems* (New York, Academic Press, 1969), see Chapter V, "The polar-front theory and the beginnings of synoptic aerology," 118–127; and F. Ludlam, *The Cyclone Problem*, Inaugural Lecture, 8 November 1966, London University, Imperial College of Science and Technology, 19–49. The historical roots of the polar front theory discussed in this book are to some extent acknowledged in these three accounts, but the authors tend to emphasize the novelty of the new theory rather than the elements of continuity in its development.

Besides vertical convection the horizontal advection of air was recognized to be important as a source of localized heating in storms, and this led to systematic investigations of the effects of the confluence of air masses of different origin and properties in storms, in particular the resulting thermal asymmetry and the asymmetric vertical circulation. Further investigation strengthened the view that the potential energy associated with horizontal temperature contrasts is essential for the formation and maintenance of storms. Finally, attacking the problem of energy balance requirements quantitatively, Margules showed that the available potential energy, as determined by the horizontal temperature contrasts within a cyclone was sufficient, upon conversion, to explain the kinetic energy observed in storms. The distinction between traveling warm cyclones associated with a kinetic-energy-producing solenoidal circulation and stationary cold cyclones associated with a kinetic-energy-consuming solenoidal circulation reflected the recognition that the kinetic energy budget of storms must vary considerably during their lifetime. This distinction also intensified interest in the study of the life history of cyclones as opposed to earlier investigations that were concerned primarily with the conditions averaged over all stages of a cyclone. Thus, when viewed in perspective, in its essential features the thermal theory was absorbed into the Norwegian model of the frontal cyclone, which in turn has remained a cornerstone of synoptic meteorology until the present.

In the course of the Nineteenth Century investigations discussed in this book, the field of meteorology emerged as the science of the physics of the atmosphere. My purpose has been to trace the development of an idea that played an essential part in this process and to consider the diversity of intellectual and nonintellectual circumstances relating to its development. Proceeding in this way has made it possible to discuss the spirit and scope of meteorological thought of the period, which, in turn, provided a framework within which questions were asked and established the criteria for the acceptibility of the answers proposed. As a result, I have dealt with the work of members of the meteorological community at large rather than focussing solely on the contributions of the outstanding scientists of the period. I have attempted to determine what the practitioners of meteorological science themselves thought—what it feels like to believe in their theories—rather than to distort their thoughts by relating them too closely to the way we think. Proceeding in this manner, some of the dead ends and side alleys of research have been explored that reveal the mind at work often better than the results that proved to be correct. Although this book has been mainly concerned with the tracing of an idea, I have also tried to provide glimpses of the development of an applied science, the beginning of an international profession, and the diverse personalities of the participants.

SELECTED BIBLIOGRAPHY

W. v. Bezold, "Zur Thermodynamik der Atmosphäre," Erste und Zweite Mitteilung, *Sitzber. Ak. Berlin* (1888), 485–522, 1189–1206; reprinted in Bezold, *Gesammelte Abhandlungen aus den Gebieten der Meteorologie und des Erdmagnetismus* (Braunschweig, Vieweg und Sohn, 1906).

F. Bigelow, "Studies on the statics and kinematics of the atmosphere in the United States," II. Method of observing and discussing the motions of the atmosphere, *Mon. Wea. Rev.*, **30** (1901), 80–87; and III. The observed circulation of the atmosphere in the high and low areas, *ibid.*, 117–125.

F. Bigelow, "The mechanism of countercurrents of different temperatures in cyclones and anticyclones," *Mon. Wea. Rev.*, **31** (1903), 72–84.

J. Bjerknes, "On the structure of moving cyclones," *Geofysiske Publikasjoner*, **1** (1919), 1–8.

J. Bjerknes and H. Solberg, "Meteorological conditions for the formation of rain," *Geofysiske Publikasjoner*, **2,** No. 3 (1921).

V. Bjerknes, "Ueber einen hydrodynamischen Fundamentalsatz und seine Anwendung besonders auf die Mechanik der Atmosphäre und des Weltmeeres," *Kongl. Svenska Vet.-Akad. Handl.*, **31** (1898), 33 pp.

V. Bjerknes, "Circulation relativ zur Erde," *Met. Zeits.*, **19** (1902), 97–108.

V. Bjerknes, "Synoptical representation of atmospheric motions," *Quart. Journ. Roy. Met. Soc.*, **36** (1910), 267–286.

A. Buchan, "Examination of the storms of wind which occurred in Europe during October, November and December 1963," *Trans. Roy. Soc., Edinb.*, **24** (1865), 191–205.

A. Buchan, *A Handybook of Meteorology* (Edinburgh, W. Blackwood and Sons, 1st ed. 1867, 2nd ed. 1868).

H. H. Clayton, "Various researches on the temperature in cyclones and anticyclones in temperate latitudes," *Beitr. Phys. f. Atm.*, **1** (1905), 93–107.

H. Dines, "The vertical temperature distribution in the atmosphere over England, and some remarks on the general and local circulation," *Phil. Trans.*, Ser. A, **211** (1911), 253–278.

H. Dines, "Further contributions to the investigation of the upper air," Meteorological Office, *Geophysical Memoir*, No. 2 (1912).

W. H. Dove, "Ueber das Gesetz der Stürme," *Ann. Phys. Chem.*, **52** (1841); *Das Gesetz der Stürme* (Berlin, Reimer, 1861), 2nd ed.

W. H. Dove, *Meteorologische Untersuchungen* (Berlin, Sanders, 1837).

W. H. Dove, *Über Eiszeit, Föhn und Scirocco* (Berlin, Reimer, 1867).

N. Ekholm, "Étude des conditions météorologiques a l'aide des cartes synoptiques représentants la desité de l'air," *Bih. Kongl. Svenska Vet.-Akad. Handl.*, **16** (1891), Afd., 1, No. 5.

N. Ekholm, "Anwendung des Carnot'schen Satzes auf die Kreisläufe in der Atmosphäre," *Met. Zeits.*, **8** (1891), 366–372.

N. Ekholm, "Die Luftdruckschwankungen und deren Beziehung zu der Temperatur der oberen Luftschichten," *Met. Zeits.*, Hannband (1906), 228–242.

J. P. Espy, *The Philosophy of Storms* (Boston, Little and Brown, 1841).

W. Ferrel, "An essay on the winds and the currents of the ocean," *Nashville Journal of Medicine and Surgery*, **11** (1856), Nos. 4 and 5; reprinted in "Popular Essays of the movements of the atmosphere by Professor William Ferrel," *Professional Papers of the Signal Service*, No. 12 (Washington, Office of the Chief Signal Officer, 1882), 1–19.

W. Ferrel, "The motions of fluids and solids relative to the earth's surface," *The Mathematical Monthly*, **1** (1859) and **2** (1860); reprinted with notes by F. Waldo in *Professional Papers of the Signal Service*, No. 8 (Washington, Office of the Chief Signal Officer, 1882).

W. Ferrel, "Meteorological researches for the use of the coast pilot," Part II: On cyclones, tornadoes and waterspouts, *U.S. Coast and Geodetic Survey, 1878*, App. 10 (Washington, 1881).

H. Ficker, "Die Ausbreitung kalter Luft in Russland und Nordasien," *Sitzber. Ak. Wien*, Abt. IIa, **119** (1910), 1769–1837; and "Das Fortschreiten der Erwärmungen in Russland und Nordasien," ibid., **120** (1911), 745–836.

R. Fitzroy, *Weather Book* (London, Longman & Green, 1863).

C. Guldberg and H. Mohn, *Études sur les Mouvements de l'Atmosphère*, Part I and II (Christiania, A. W. Brøgger 1876 and 1880), translated by Cl. Abbe in "The mechanics of the earth's atmosphere," 3rd. collection, *Smith. Misc. Coll.*, **51** (1910), 122–248.

C. Guldberg and H. Mohn, "Die Bewegung der Luft in aufsteigenden Wirbeln," *Wien, Met. Zeits.*, **12** (1877), 257–268, 273–276.

J. v. Hann, "Zur Frage über den Ursprung des Föhn," *Wien, Met. Zeits.*, **1** (1866), 257–263.

J. v. Hann, "Die Gesetze der Temperatur-Änderung in aufsteigenden Luftströmungen und einige der wichtigsten Folgerungen aus denselben," *Wien, Met. Zeits.*, **9** (1874), 321–329, 337–346.

J. v. Hann, "Ueber das Luftdruckmaximum vom 23 Jänner bis 3 Februar 1876, nebst Bemerkungen über die Luftdruck-Maxima im Allgemeinen," *Wien, Met. Zeits.*, **11** (1876), 129–135.

J. v. Hann, "Studien über die Luftdruck-und Temperaturverhältnisse auf dem Sonnblickgipfel, nebst Bemerkungen über die Bedeutung derselben für die Theorie der Cyklonen und Anticyklonen," *Sitzber., Ak. Wien*, **100** (1891), 367–452.

S. Hanzlik, "Die räumliche Verteilung der meteorologischen Elemente in den Zyklonen," *Denks. Ak. Wien*, **88** (1913), 67–128.

H. v. Helmholtz, "Wirbelstürme und Gewitter," *Deutsche Rundschau*, **6** (1876), 363–380.

H. v. Helmholtz, "Ueber atmosphärische Bewegungen," *Sitzber, Ak. Berlin* (1888), 647–663; translated by Cl. Abbe in "The mechanics of the earth's atmosphere," 2nd collection, *Smith. Misc. Coll.*, **34** (1893), 78–93.

H. H. Hildebrandsson, *Essai sur les Courants Supérieurs de l'Atmosphère dans leurs Relation aux Lignes Isobarométriques* (Upsala, Berling, Imprimeur de l'Université, 1875).

H. H. Hildebrandsson, "Sur la distribution de éléments météorologiques autour des minima et des maxima barométriques," *Soc. R. des Sciènces* (Nova Acta), 1883.

W. Köppen, "Ueber die mechanischen Ursachen der Ortsveränderung atmosphärischer Wirbel," *Wien, Met. Zeits.*, **15** (1880), 41–53.

W. Köppen, "Ueber den Einfluss der Temperaturverteilung auf die oberen Luftströmungen und die Fortpflanzung der barometrischen Minima," *Ann. Hydr.*, **10** (1882), 657–666.

W. Köppen, "Ueber den Zufluss und Abfluss der Luft in Cyklonen und Anticyklonen, *Met. Zeits.*, **15** (1898), 161–168.

R. G. K. Lempfert and R. Corless, "Line-squalls and associated phenomena," *Quart. Journ. Roy. Met. Soc.*, **36** (1910), 135–170.

Cl. Ley, *The Laws of the Winds Prevailing in Western Europe*, Part I, (London, E. Stanford, 1872).

Cl. Ley, "Relation between upper and under currents of the atmosphere around areas of barometric depression," *Quart. Journ. Roy. Met. Soc.*, **3** (1877), 437–445.

E. Loomis, "On two storms which were experienced throughout the United States in the month of February, 1842," *Trans. Am. Phil. Soc.*, **9** (1846), 161–184.

M. Margules, "Ueber den Arbeitswert einer Luftdruckverteilung und über die Erhaltung der Druckunterschiede, *Denks. Ak. Wien*, **73** (1901), 329–345; translated by Cl. Abbe in "The mechanics of the earth's atmosphere," 3rd collection, *Smith. Misc. Coll.*, **51** (1910).

M. Margules, "Die Energie der Stürme," *Jahrbücher der K.-K. Zentralanstalt für Meteorologie und Erdmagnetismus*, **1903** (Wien, 1905), 1–26; translated by Cl. Abbe in "The mechanics of the earth's atmosphere," 3rd collection, *Smith. Misc. Coll.*, **51** (1910).

M. Margules, "Ueber Temperaturschichtung in stationär bewegter und ruhender Luft," *Met. Zeits.*, **23,** Hannband (1906a), 243–254.

M. Margules, "Zur Sturmtheorie," *Met. Zeits.*, **23** (1906b), 481–497.

H. Mohn, *Det Norske Meteorologiske Instituts Storm-Atlas* (Christiania, B. M. Bentzen, 1870).

H. Mohn, *Om Vind og Vejr* (Christiania, Mallings Bogtrykkeri, 1872), *Grundzüge der Meteorologie* (Berlin, Reimer, 1875), 2nd ed.

M. Möller, "Beziehungen zwischen dem Ober- und Unterwind einer Depression und den aus diesen resultierenden Wolkenformen," *Ann. Hydr.*, **10** (1882), 212–226.

H. Peslin, "Sur les mouvements généraux de l'atmosphère," *Bull. Hebd. l'Ass. Sci. France*, **3** (1868), 299–319.

W. C. Redfield, "Remarks on the prevailing storms of the Atlantic coast of the North American States," *Am. Journ. Sci.*, **20** (1831), 17–51.

Th. Reye, *Die Wirbelstürme, Tornados und Wettersäulen* (Hannover, C. Rümpler, 1872).

Th. Reye, "Ueber vertikale Luftströme in der Atmosphäre," *Zeits. für Mathematik und Physik*, **9** (1864), 250–276.

J. W. Sandström, "Ueber die Anwendung von Professor V. Bjerknes' Theorie der Wirbelbewegungen in Gasen und Flüssigkeiten auf meteorologische Beobachtungen in den höheren Luftschichten," *Kongl. Svenska Vet. Akad. Handlinger,* **33** (1900).

J. W. Sandström, "Ueber die Beziehung zwischen Luftbewegung und Druck in der Atmosphäre unter stationären Verhältnissen," *Oversigt, Kongl. Vet.-Akad. Förhandl.*, **57** (1902), 87–103.

N. Shaw and R. G. K. Lempfert, "The life history of surface air currents," *M. O. Memoir*, 174 (1906); reprinted in *Selected Meteorological Papers of Sir Napier Shaw* (London, MacDonald and Co., 1955), 15–131.

N. Shaw, "The meteorological aspects of the storm of February 26–27," *Quart. Journ. Roy. Met. Soc.*, **29** (1903), 233–258.
A. Sprung, *Lehrbuch der Meteorologie* (Hamburg, Hoffmann & Campe, 1885).
W. Thomson, "On the convective equilibrium of temperature in the atmosphere," *Memoirs of the Manchester Literary and Philosophical Society*, **2** (1865), 125–131. (Read 1862).
A. Wagner, "Die Temperaturverhältnisse in der freien Atmosphäre," *Beitr. Phys. f. Atm.*, **3** (1910), 57–167.

Appendix

Biographical Sketches of Leading Meteorologists and Scientists of the Period from 1830 to 1920

The scientists listed in this Appendix made important contributions to Nineteenth and early Twentieth Century meteorology and, in particular, to the development of the thermal theory of cyclones.[1] Their work forms the focus of this study.

The brief sketches are intended to provide in a condensed form information about important steps in the professional careers of the scientists listed, and some indication of their major contributions to science. Information on aspects of the personal lives of these scientists has been included only sparingly. In many cases I found the source material very meager, especially with regard to personal information; this is reflected in the brevity of a great number of the entries.

The bibliographical references at the end of each sketch consist primarily of obituaries and contemporary memoirs. Modern biographies and memoirs have been listed whenever available.

JOHANN FRIEDRICH WILHELM VON BEZOLD (1837–1907) was born in München, Germany, the son of a high government official. He studied physics in München and Göttingen (under W. Weber and B. Riemann). After receiving his doctorate in 1860 he was appointed assistant to the physicist von Jolly in München. In 1861 he became privatdocent, and he was named extraordinary professor of physics

[1] J. Bjerknes and H. Solberg, who in 1920 stood just at the beginning of their careers, have not been included in this list. Accounts of J. Bjerknes' professional career may be found in *J. A. B. Bjerknes, Selected Papers* (Western Periodicals Company, 1975), pp. 11–18, and in *Bull. Am. Met. Soc.*, **56** (1975), 1089–1090. J. Bjerknes wrote a memorial article on Solberg in *Bull. Am. Met. Soc.*, **55** (1974), 1371–1372.

in 1866. In 1868 he was appointed ordinary professor of mathematics and applied physics. In 1878 he became director of the meteorological institute in München and began organizing a meteorological station network in Bavaria. He was instrumental in the reorganization of the Preussische Meteorologische Institut in Berlin and was appointed its director in 1885. At the same time he received the first professorship in meteorology in Germany. He was president of the Deutsche Physikalische Gesellschaft, the Deutsche Meteorologische Gesellschaft and the Verein der Berliner Luftschiffahrt.

Bezold's publications during the early years in München include papers in electricity, color vision and atmospheric optics. As director of the meteorological institute in München, he published daily weather charts and forecasts and conducted extensive investigations of thunderstorms. At Berlin he carried out his far-reaching studies of the thermodynamics and dynamics of the atmosphere, collected in his *Gesammelte Abhandlungen*, 1906. He also began studies of the heat budget of the atmosphere and the earth's surface. He promoted the three-dimensional exploration of the atmosphere and developed theoretical methods and guidelines for the evaluation of balloon ascents. Late in his career he turned toward the study of terrestrial magnetism. He traced the historical development of physics and meteorology in a number of popular lectures and articles.

For biography, see G. Hellmann, *Wilhelm von Bezold* (Braunschweig, Vieweg, 1907), 33 pp.; contains list of publications. See also Süring in *Met. Zeits.*, **54** (1937), 201–202.

VILHELM FIRMAN BJERKNES (1862–1951) was born in Christiania (now Oslo), Norway, the son of C. A. Bjerknes, professor of mathematics. In 1880 he entered the university. After his graduation in 1889 and a year of study in Paris he became the assistant of H. Hertz in Bonn (1889–1891), doing research on electromagnetic waves. In 1892 he received his doctorate with a dissertation on electrodynamics. In 1893 he was appointed lecturer at the school of engineering in Stockholm and in 1895 he became professor of mechanics and mathematical physics at the university. Here he turned his attention to problems of geophysical hydrodynamics. In 1905 he was invited to lecture in the United States; as a result he received a grant from the Carnegie Institution (continued until 1941) which enabled him to employ his own research assistants wherever he stayed (including V. W. Ekman, H. U. Sverdrup, Th. Hesselberg, H. Solberg, T. Bergeron and his son J. Bjerknes). Bjerknes returned to Christiania in 1907. In 1912 he accepted a call to Leipzig as professor of geophysics and director of a new geophysical institute. In 1918 he returned with his assistants to Norway where he founded a geophysical institute in Bergen and created the Bergen School of meteorologists. Together with Hesselberg he reorganized the Norwegian weather service. He was professor in mechanics and mathematical physics in Oslo from 1926 until his retirement in 1932.

The continuation of his father's researches on hydrodynamic forces constituted an important part of Bjerknes' work. These investigations resulted in a two-volume work on *Vorlesungen über hydrodynamische Fernkräfte nach C. A.*

Bjerknes's Theorie (1900–1902). His work in classical hydrodynamics led him to develop his famous circulation theorem (1898). He immediately began to apply the theorem to the dynamics of the atmosphere and the ocean. He went on to propose an ambitious program for the prediction of the weather, based on the application of the laws of hydrodynamics to given initial conditions. His outstanding contribution to science for the next decades was the further development of theoretical meteorology. Important steps were the publication of the first two volumes of *Dynamic Meteorology and Hydrography* (1910/11, volume one written with Sandström, one of his most important collaborators) and *Physikalische Hydrodynamik* (1933), as well as his successful campaign for the introduction of the cgs system of units in aerological research. He provided the inspiration and organization for his young collaborators who eventually established the frontal structure of cyclones and the existence of the polar front. Bjerknes himself apparently never drafted a weather chart, but had an active and life-long interest in the manifestation and representation of hydrodynamic phenomena in nature. His perhaps most fundamental paper, "On the dynamics of the circular vortex with application to the atmosphere and atmospheric vortex- and wave motions" contains a clear exposition of his basic ideas in geophysical research. In turn, Bjerknes' assistants and collaborators advanced his ideas as researchers, organizers and teachers in Scandinavia, throughout Europe and in the United States.

For biography, see Devik, Bergeron and Godske in "In memory of Vilhelm Bjerknes," *Geofysiske Publikasjoner*, **24** (1963), 6–37 (includes list of publications) and Sverdrup in *Tellus*, **3** (1951), 217–221; see also M. Pihl in *Dictionary of Scientific Biography*.[2]

FRANK HAGAR BIGELOW (1851–1924) was born in Concord, Massachusetts. After graduating from Harvard in 1873, Bigelow entered the Episcopal ministry. He curtailed this career because of a lung ailment. Seeking drier climates, he became assistant at the Cordoba Astronomical Observatory in Argentina (1873–1876 and 1881–1883) which was directed by his Harvard colleague B. A. Gould. In 1884 he was appointed professor of mathematics at Racine College. He obtained a scientific post at the American Nautical Almanac in 1889 and became professor of meteorology at the Weather Bureau in 1891. In the same year he also became minister at St. John's in Washington. He resigned from these positions in 1910 and returned to Argentina where he joined the meteorological service. After his retirement in 1921 he traveled with his wife in Europe. He died of pneumonia in Vienna.

Bigelow's publications dealt with meteorology and terrestrial magnetism. He made important contributions to the theory of the general circulation of the

[2] The *Dictionary of Scientific Biography*, C. C. Gillispie, Ed. (New York, Scribner's, 1970–), is a comprehensive reference work in the history of science, covering all countries and times, and written by specialists from all over the world. A set of 14 volumes has been completed, with a supplement and index volume still to come. Each biographical article contains a bibliography consisting of works and secondary literature. Even though meteorologists are included only sparingly, the *Dictionary* stands out as a valuable research tool in the history of the earth sciences.

atmosphere and the theory of cyclones and anticyclones, treating both thermodynamic and dynamic aspects (a series of papers from 1902 to 1906). In these investigations, he focussed attention on the role of air currents of different thermal properties and geographical origin ("counter current" theory). He published two voluminous reports on the international cloud observations of 1896/97 and barometry in the United States and made detailed investigations of the flow patterns in upper levels. His publications of the early 1900's contain extensive critiques of the theories of atmospheric circulation systems held by earlier writers, especially Ferrel. Gradually he became convinced that a complete reformation of meteorological theory and a new practical organization of the field were necessary, and he devoted the last years of his life entirely to this goal. From 1910 onward he worked at the reformulation of the adiabatic equations and he published several books concerning a "Reformed Meteorology."

For biography, see A. J. Henry in *Mon. Wea. Rev.*, **52** (1924), 165–166.

ALEXANDER BUCHAN (1829–1907) was born in Kinnesswood, Kinrosshire, Scotland. His father, a weaver, died a day after his birth. Buchan attended the Free Church Normal College for teachers in Edinburgh (1848) and received an education in liberal arts at the university. In 1860 he left the university to become secretary of the Scottish Meteorological Society; he held this position throughout his career. From 1877 he was a member of the Meteorological Council (appointed by the Royal Society), which administered and directed the operations of the Meteorological Office. Buchan was instrumental in the foundation of the Ben Nevis high altitude observatory in 1883 (closed in 1905) and an observatory at its base in Fort Williams. He was the first recipient of the Symons Medal.

Buchan's publications were in meteorology, oceanography, biometeorology and botany. From 1861, he was editor of the *Journal of the Scottish Meteorological Society* and became its chief contributor (64 articles). He introduced significant improvements in the construction of synoptic charts and produced the first charts of storm tracks across the Atlantic. His *Handybook of Meteorology* (1867) was a widely used textbook. Buchan is best known for his work in climatology. In 1868/69 he constructed the first global charts of mean sea level barometric pressure and global wind charts (January, July and year). He prepared the meteorological report and contributed substantially to the oceanographic report of the Challenger Expedition of 1876. In his major work, *Report on Atmospheric Circulation* (1889), Buchan presented global charts of monthly mean temperature, pressure and wind direction for the entire year. In this work he was assisted by his niece Jessie Hill. Outside his professional work, he was active in the Free Church and had a strong interest in poetry. Robert Louis Stevenson was among his close friends.

For biography, see H. R. Mill in *Scottish Geographical Magazine*, **23** (1907), 427–431; W. N. Shaw in *Proc. Roy. Soc.* (A), **90** (1914), i–v; and "Contributions towards a memorial notice of A. Buchan," *Journ. Scott. Met. Soc.*, **14** (1907).

HENRY HELM CLAYTON (1861–1946) was born in Murfreesboro, Tennessee. Clayton was educated by private tutors, apparently because of his delicate health. He began studying storms in 1878; in 1882 he helped organize the Tennessee Weather Service. In 1884/85 he was assistant at the Observatory of the University of Michigan. From 1886 to 1909 he was assistant and meteorologist at the Blue Hill Meteorological Observatory, founded by A. L. Rotch in 1885. In 1910 he accepted the position of chief of the forecasting service in Argentina. Returning to the United States in 1919, he started a private weather service. From 1943 to 1945 he conducted research on long-range weather forecasting for the U.S. Government.

Clayton's studies of clouds, beginning in 1886, provided valuable knowledge on atmospheric flow patterns over North America. Around 1900 he introduced a cloud classification that differentiated between clouds according to their origin and physical nature. In 1894 he introduced with Rotch the systematic use of kites at Blue Hill and conducted studies on the aerological structure of warm waves and cold waves. In 1905 he directed the de Bort-Rotch expedition to the tropical Atlantic and explored the tropical atmosphere with kites and balloons. He attempted long-range forecasting on the basis of six to seven days periodicities, which he considered certain, and in 1894 he began issuing daily forecasts for the coming week. He conducted extensive research on the relation between weather changes and solar cycles and variations (*World Weather*, 1923, and *Solar Relations to Weather*, 1943).

For biography, see Fergusson and Brooks in *Science*, **105** (1947), 247–248.

LUDVIG AUGUST COLDING (1815–1888) was born in Brøndbyøster Parish, Denmark, the son of a landowner and retired sea captain. His education was guided by the physicist H. C. Ørsted, a family friend. In 1836 Colding became a journeyman; in 1841 he entered the Polytechnicum in Copenhagen. He studied mechanics under Ørsted, who was his teacher and counsellor, and he was appointed city engineer of Copenhagen in 1849. He took part in establishing a meteorological institute and prepared early synoptic weather charts. In 1869 he became professor at the Polytechnicum.

Colding published papers in engineering, physics, meteorology and oceanography. In the 1860's he developed a mathematical model for a tropical cyclone, applying the equations of classical hydrodynamics. He is best known for his early formulation of the principle of conservation of energy and his experimental determination of the mechanical equivalent of heat in 1843 (about simultaneously with Joule and J. Meyer).

For biography, see F. Dahl, "Ludvig A. Colding and the conservation of energy," *Centaurus*, **8** (1963), 174–188.

WILLIAM MORRIS DAVIS (1850–1934) was born in Philadelphia, Pennsylvania. He graduated from Harvard in 1869. After completing an engineering degree in 1870, he spent three years as a meteorologist at the observatory at Cordoba, Argentina. In 1879 he was appointed instructor in geology at Harvard and in

1885 he became professor of physical geography. After his retirement in 1912 he was visiting professor at several universities. Davis worked for the founding of the Geological Society of America, the Association of Geographers of America and the American Meteorological Society.

Davis published widely in geology, geomorphology and meteorology (about 500 titles). After joining the Harvard faculty Davis organized a network of student and amateur weather observers in New England and made detailed studies of thunderstorms and the sea breeze. His *Elementary Meteorology* (1894) was used as a college textbook for over three decades. Davis is best known for his pioneering studies of landscape analysis, classification of landforms and erosion cycles.

For biography, see R. A. Daly in *Biographical Memoirs*, National Academy of Science, **23** (1945), 263–303, and S. Johnson in *Dictionary of Scientific Biography*; a list of his papers is found in *Bull. Am. Met. Soc.*, **15** (1934), 57–61.

LÉON PHILIPPE TEISSERENC DE BORT (1855–1913) was born in Paris, the son of a wealthy engineer. He joined the staff of the Bureau Central Météorologique de France in 1878 and he became chief of the department of general meteorology in 1880. He resigned in 1892 to devote his time fully to experimental research. In 1896 he founded the Observatory for the Study of Dynamic Meteorology at Trappes, near Paris, and spent almost his entire fortune in its development. By 1906, 1100 ascents into the atmosphere had been recorded, first with kites and after 1898 with sounding balloons. De Bort organized and outfitted a number of expeditions to Russia, Lapland and other northern regions for the exploration of aerological conditions, as well as to the tropical Atlantic (together with his friend Rotch). He received the Symons Medal in 1908. He was never married.

In 1884 de Bort prepared global cloud charts for each month, and, as a member of the International Cloud Committee, he published and financed the *International Cloud Atlas* of 1895 (with his friend Hildebrandsson). His investigations of the general circulation on the basis of observations contrasted with earlier, mostly theoretical studies. He introduced the concept of "centers of action" when investigating the relation between variations of the Azores and Siberian highs and the Icelandic low, and European weather. Early in 1902, de Bort established the existence of the "isothermal zone," which he named the stratosphere. In collaboration with Hildebrandsson he prepared two magnificent volumes, *Les Bases de la Météorologie Dynamique*, tracing the development of meteorology and providing reproductions of numerous historically important charts and illustrations, often in their original size and color. In his later years, de Bort devoted his leisure time mostly to painting in oil.

For biography, see Shaw in *Quart. Journ. Roy. Met. Soc.*, **39** (1913), 158–161.

WILLIAM HENRY DINES (1855–1927) was born in Oxshot, Surrey, England. After completing an apprenticeship as a railway engineer, he entered Christ's College at Cambridge. He graduated in 1881 and stayed on for a year as "mathematical coach"; he continued teaching mathematics in correspondence classes. Dines joined the Royal Meteorological Society in 1881 and was its president in 1901/02. He was director of Experiments of the Upper Air for the Meteorological Office from 1905 to 1922. Supported in part by family income and in part by small grants of the Royal Meteorological Society, the British Association for the Advancement of Science and later the Royal Society, Dines never was a government employee, nor did he hold any professional position. He received the Symons Medal in 1914. Dines' father was a meteorologist, and both his sons became meteorologists.

Dines turned to meteorology after the Tay Bridge disaster of 1879, when the bridge was destroyed by a gale while a train was crossing it. He became member of the wind force committee of the Royal Meteorological Society and subsequently designed the pressure tube anemometer (1901). In 1901 Dines began his investigations of the upper air with kite ascents (at his house in Oxshot) and later he supplemented these with aerological observations at sea near the western shores of Scotland, using a meteorograph which he had constructed. In 1907 he started regular sounding balloon launchings (with another "private" meteorologist, C. J. P. Cave). His results, summarized in *Characteristics of the Free Atmosphere* (1919), presented a continuous challenge to contemporary cyclone theory. After World War I he collaborated with L. F. Richardson on studies of solar and terrestrial radiation. In 1920 he designed an ether differential radiometer, the Dines-radiometer, and designed and improved a number of other meteorological instruments.

For biography, see Shaw in *Proc. Roy. Soc.*, **119** (1928), xxiii–xxxi, reprinted in *Collected Papers of W. H. Dines* (London, Roy. Met. Soc., 1931).

HEINRICH WILHELM DOVE (1803–1879) was born in Liegnitz, Prussia (now Poland), as a member of a prosperous merchant family. His parents directed him toward an academic career because of concern for his delicate health. In 1821 he entered the University of Breslau where he met H. W. Brandes. Brandes instructed Dove in astronomical observations and introduced him to meteorology. From 1824 Dove studied in Berlin, receiving his doctorate in 1826 with a thesis "On the variations of the barometer." In 1828 he first met Alexander von Humboldt with whom he maintained regular contacts. After Humboldt's death in 1859 Dove participated in establishing the Humboldt Foundation for the support of scientists. Dove was privatdocent at Königsberg from 1826 to 1829. In 1830 he was appointed extraordinary professor of physics at Berlin and in 1844 ordinary professor. He supplemented his income with teaching at high schools and at a military academy. In 1849 he became director of the Preussische Meteorologische Institut, remaining in this position until his retirement in 1879. He was elected rector of the university in 1858. He received the Copley Medal of the Royal Society in 1853.

Dove was a voluminous writer, publishing more than 330 papers in physics and meteorology. He was a popular lecturer in experimental physics and edited (with Königsberger) the 8-volume work *Repertorium der Physik*. Dove's principal interests were in meteorology and climatology, and he profoundly influenced the development of these areas. Dove's scheme of the global wind system was based on the concept of polar and equatorial currents. In 1827 he first formulated the famous "Drehungsgesetz", defining the turning of the wind during the passage of a storm. His climatological studies covered a wide range of subjects; in 1848 he constructed isothermal charts for each month and studied secular variations of climate and the relation between climate and vegetation.

For biography, see H. Neumann, *Heinrich Wilhelm Dove, eine Naturforscher Biographie* (Liegnitz, H. Krumbhaar, 1925), 88 pp., and H. E. Landsberg in "Roots of modern climatology," *Journ. Washington Academy of Sciences*, **54** (1964), 138–139.

NILS GUSTAF EKHOLM (1848–1923) was born in Smedjebacken, Sweden, the son of a pharmacist. He entered the University of Upsala in 1869 and studied physics, mathematics and meteorology (under R. Rubenson and Hildebrandsson). He became a doctoral candidate in 1876. From 1876 to 1890 he was assistant at the meteorological institute in Upsala. Simultaneously, he taught at a technical school and the agricultural institute of Upsala. During the International Polar Year in 1882–83 he directed the Swedish polar expedition to Spitsbergen. He also organized the S. A. Andrées balloon expedition to the North Pole in 1896. In 1890 he was appointed assistant at the meteorological institute in Stockholm. After receiving his doctorate in 1898, he became docent in meteorology. In 1913 he succeeded Rubenson as director of the meteorological institute and became professor of meteorology. He held these positions until his retirement in 1918. After 1898 he also worked as a mathematician for a life insurance company.

Ekholm combined a thorough scientific training with the ability for practical application. He helped initiate a new epoch in cloud observations during the Spitsbergen expedition, when determining the altitude and velocity of clouds by means of baseline measurements with two theodolites. His work in hygrometry led him to develop a new psychrometric formula. He introduced improvements in the statistical treatment of climatological data and investigated the periodic variations of meteorological elements. His collaboration with S. Arrhenius (who was also a friend of V. Bjerknes) resulted in studies of the influence of cosmic phenomena on the weather. He also investigated climatic variations. While at the meteorological institute in Stockholm, Ekholm worked at the problem of weather forecasting. He began work at synoptic analogies and proposed a "dictionary of weather charts" which, he hoped, would simplify the preparation of forecasts. Later he turned to the method of isallobars which he developed for the prediction of future pressure distributions. He investigated the role of warm and cold currents of air for the development and propagation of cyclones.

For biography, see A. Ångström in *Svenskt Biografiskt Lexikon* (Stockholm, 1949).

JAMES POLLARD ESPY (1785–1860) was born in Westmoreland County, Pennsylvania. After graduating in 1808 from Transylvania University in Lexington, Kentucky, he taught school and studied law. In 1817 he moved to Philadelphia, teaching classical languages and mathematics. After joining the faculty of the Franklin Institute he developed a strong interest in meteorology. As chairman of the joint committee of meteorology formed by the Franklin Institute and the American Philosophical Society he organized a network of meteorological observers in Pennsylvania which eventually merged into J. Henry's meteorological network of the Smithsonian Institution. In 1840 he was invited to present his meteorological theories to the British Association for the Advancement of Science and the Academy of Science in France. In 1842 he was appointed professor of meteorology at the War Department and kept this government position until his retirement in 1857.

Espy's convective theory of storms grew out of his novel explanation of the formation of clouds and precipitation which was based on experimentation and invoked the concept of saturated adiabatic expansion of rising air. Advocating a centripetal inflow of air in storms, Espy clashed with Redfield on the issue of wind patterns in storms. In 1841 he summarized his ideas in his widely read *Philosophy of Storms*. His method of analyzing weather charts was soon outdated, and thus his four *Reports on Meteorology* (1843–1857), which contained not only his weather charts but also his views on a wide range of meteorological subjects, were little used. On his many popular lecture tours in cities, towns and villages he not only expounded his scientific ideas but also talked on moral and religious subjects.

For biography, see A. D. Bache in the Smithsonian Institution's *Annual Report* for 1859, 108–111; D. M. Ludlum in *Weatherwise*, **22** (1969), 224–229 and 245; and N. Reingold in *Dictionary of Scientific Biography*.

WILLIAM FERREL (1817–1891) was born in Bedford County, Pennsylvania. He received a limited education in a one-room school house, but taught himself science. From 1839 to 1841 he attended Marshall College, Pennsylvania. He graduated in 1844 at Bethany College, West Virginia, and taught school in Missouri and Kentucky. In 1854 he moved to Nashville, Tennessee. Through the efforts of B. A. Gould he obtained a scientific post at the American Nautical Almanac in 1858, and in 1867 B. Peirce brought him to the U.S. Coast Survey in Washington. In 1882 Ferrel joined the U.S. Army's Signal Service. After his retirement in 1886 he moved to Kansas City where some of his relatives were living. Ferrel became a member of the National Academy of Science in 1868. He was never married.

Ferrel's first scientific investigations dealt with tidal theory, whose treatment by Laplace he had found unsatisfactory. Ferrel provided the first quantitative treatment of tidal friction in 1856. While at the Coast Survey, Ferrel began improving the techniques of tidal prediction and in 1880 designed a mechanical tide predictor. His outstanding contribution to science was the development of geophysical hydrodynamics. He provided a comprehensive treatment of the deflective force of the earth's rotation and applied this concept in his mathematical theory of the general circulation of the atmosphere and the oceans (1859/60). He extended and developed his ideas over the next three decades and summarized them in his *Recent Advances in Meteorology* of 1887. He developed and modified Espy's convective theory of storms and contributed much to the popularity of this theory. Ferrel gained general recognition for his work late in his career.

For biography, see memorial articles by Newcomb, Abbe, Davis and Waldo in *Am. Met. Journ.*, **8** (1891), 337–369; *Biographical Memoirs*, National Academy of Science, **3** (1895), 267–286 which contains Ferrel's autobiography and list of papers; also see H. L. Burstyn in *Dictionary of Scientific Biography*.

HEINRICH VON FICKER (1881–1957) was born in München, the son of a historian and lawyer from Innsbruck, Austria. In 1902 he entered the University of Innsbruck to study geology. Influenced by W. Trabert he soon turned to meteorology. He was an enthusiastic mountain climber and sportsman and made 100 "ascents" for his dissertation on the "Innsbrucker Föhn" (1906). Subsequently, he became assistant at the Zentralanstalt für Meteorologie in Vienna. In 1909 he returned to Innsbruck as privatdocent. From 1911 to 1913 he was professor of geophysics at Graz and conducted a series of scientific balloon ascents. In 1913 he directed an expedition in the Pamir region. During World War I Ficker was a prisoner of war in Russia (1915–1918), working part of this time at the meteorological institute of the University of Kasau. In 1923 he succeeded G. Hellmann as professor of meteorology at Berlin and became director of the Preussische Meteorologische Institut. In 1934 he organized the German "Reichswetterdienst." He returned to Austria in 1937, and he was director of the Austrian weather service and professor at the University of Vienna until his retirement in 1953.

Ficker published widely in synoptic meteorology and climatology. In his papers on cold and warm waves in Russia and Asia (1910/11) he described most of the important features of the Norwegian cyclone model, but did not construct a general cyclone model. In a series of papers (1920–1923) he explored the interactions of troposphere and stratosphere in the development of cyclones. He stated that only low level cyclones and anticyclones could be explained by outbreaks of cold and warm air, while depressions extending into the stratosphere resulted from a combination of pressure changes in the lower troposphere (caused by thermal advection) and pressure changes in the upper troposphere and lower stratosphere (due to advective processes in the stratosphere). He regarded processes in the stratosphere as a steering mechanism. Ficker produced numerous studies of the trade wind circulation and thunderstorms and made important contributions to the climatology of Asia.

For biography, see H. Ertel in *Naturwissenschaften*, **29** (1941), 697–700, and Schneider-Carius in *Zeitschrift für Meteorologie*, **12** (1958), 98–111.

ROBERT FITZROY (1805–1865) was born in Ampton Hall, Suffolk, England, the son of an aristocratic family. He entered the Royal Naval College at Portsmouth in 1819, achieving the rank of lieutenant in 1824. In 1828 he was placed in charge of the *Beagle*. The *Beagle* voyages were part of the ambitious program of the British chief hydrographer Sir F. Beaufort for the charting of most of the earth's coast lines. For his second surveying voyage to South America Fitzroy selected the young Charles Darwin as naturalist. In 1831 they embarked on what was to be one of the most famous expeditions in history. While the two men enjoyed a close relationship during that journey, Fitzroy later took a public stand against Darwin's *Origin of Species* on account of his religious beliefs. Fitzroy was appointed captain in 1835. In 1841 he was elected Member of Parliament. He was governor of New Zealand from 1843 to 1845, a disastrous experience and the end of his political career. He retired from active service in 1850, but continued to rise in rank (vice admiral in 1863). He received the Gold Medal of the Royal Geographical Society and he was elected Fellow of the Royal Society in 1851. When the conference of maritime nations in Brussels (1853) recommended that the maritime nations organize the collection and dissemination of meteorological data, the Royal Society Committee named Fitzroy director of the newly founded British Meteorological Office (1855). Fitzroy became quickly and totally absorbed in his meteorological work, making available cheap barometers, setting up a telegraph station network and a system of storm warning cones in the ports, constructing weather charts and pioneering in the issue of daily weather forecasts. He summarized his meteorological views in a popular treatise, the *Weather Book* (1863). His forecasting service was successful with the public but was severely criticized by scientists. In the midst of the resulting controversy Fitzroy took his life.

For biography, see H. E. L. Mellersh, *Fitzroy of the Beagle* (London, 1968), 307 pp.; G. Basalla in *Dictionary of Scientific Biography*; and Sir George Simpson, "Fitzroy and weather forecasts," *Meteorological Magazine*, **84** (1955), 165–173.

JULIUS FERDINAND VON HANN (1839–1921) was born in Mühlkreis, near Linz, Austria. After his father's early death (1852) his mother opened a pension for pupils of the gymnasium in Kremsmünster. Hann attended the gymnasium from 1853. He entered the University of Vienna in 1860. After passing his teacher examination in 1863, he taught at high schools in Vienna and Linz. Hann began his meteorological studies while still at Kremsmünster. In 1865 he became co-editor of the *Österreichische Zeitschrift für Meteorologie* (merged with *Meteorologische Zeitschrift* in 1886). In 1867 Hann joined the staff of the Zentralanstalt für Meteorologie in Vienna. He obtained his doctorate in 1868 and in 1874 he was appointed professor of physical geography at the university. He became director of the Zentralanstalt in 1877. In 1897 he resigned to have more time for research and became professor of meteorology in Graz. He returned to Vienna in 1900, holding a professorship in cosmic physics. He retained the editorship of the *Meteorologische Zeitschrift* until 1920. He received the Symons Medal in 1920.

Hann was a voluminous writer with more than 1000 contributions covering a wide range of subjects in meteorology and climatology. He decisively influenced Nineteenth Century meteorology and climatology through his critical assessments of existing theories, his coordination of empirical results, and the collection and processing of climatological data on a global scale. He pioneered in the establishment of mountain observatories, and the results of his upper air research presented a constant challenge for existing theories of cyclones and anticyclones.

Hann advanced a dynamic hypothesis of cyclone formation as an alternative to the thermal theory of cyclones. He never showed much interest in weather forecasting. Throughout his career he studied diurnal variations of meteorological elements. In 1882 he demonstrated the dominant and universal character of the twelve-hour solar pressure variation. He developed various tabulation and statistical techniques for the treatment of climatological data. His *Handbuch der Klimatologie* (1883) and *Lehrbuch der Meteorologie* (1901) became standard texts in the field. Hann maintained a vast correspondence and seldom traveled far from home. He attracted scientists of great ability to Vienna and may be regarded as the originator of the Austrian School of meteorologists. He established professorships in meteorology at all Austrian universities at a time when most European countries had no chair in this field.

For biography, see F. M. Exner in *Met. Zeits.*, **38** (1921), 321–327; Ficker in *Das Wetter*, **38** (1921), 161–168; and G. Kutzbach in *Dictionary of Scientific Biography*.

Hermann von Helmholtz (1821–1894) was born in Potsdam, Germany. His father, a teacher, did not have enough money to send him to the university. Instead, Helmholtz committed himself to eight years service as an army surgeon and in return received an education at the Kaiserlich Medizinisch-Chirurgische Friedrich Wilhelm Institut in Berlin (1838–1842). He also took courses at the university, started a dissertation in physiology and studied mathematics privately. He received his M.D. degree in 1842 and was appointed surgeon to the regiment in Potsdam. In 1847 he read to the Physikalische Gesellschaft his memoir "On the conservation of forces," a mathematical treatment of the principle of conservation of energy. In 1848 he was appointed professor of physiology at Königsberg, where he wrote papers on physiological optics and acoustics and invented the ophtalmoscope (1851). During the 1850's he visited universities in England and met his life-long friend W. Thomson. In 1855 he was transferred to Bonn, where he wrote an important paper on the hydrodynamics of vortex motion (1858). In 1858 he accepted a chair in Heidelberg. His wife died in 1859 and he was remarried in 1861. In Heidelberg he conducted investigations on sensory physiology and on the motion of violin strings; he also became deeply concerned with epistemological issues. In 1871 Helmholtz accepted a call to Berlin with the condition that a new physics institute was to be constructed for him. In 1897 he became president of the newly founded Physikalisch-Technische Reichsanstalt. By that time he had become the most famous and prestigious German scientist and the government's chief advisor on scientific affairs. At Berlin, Helmholtz began publishing critical articles on theories of electrodynamic action. This work motivated Helmholtz' student H. Hertz to his later research. N. Shaw was also among Helmholtz' students. After 1876 Helmholtz published on the galvanic cell and the thermodynamics of chemical processes. Finally he turned his attention to theoretical mechanics, in particular the principle of least action. In meteorology, Helmholtz investigated discontinuous motions in a fluid (1868). Later he established the condition of dynamic equilibrium along surfaces of discontinuity. In 1888/89 he constructed a theoretical model of the general circulation (assuming that there are no eddy motions in the atmosphere), in which surfaces of discontinuity were an important factor.

For biography, see L. Königsberger, *Hermann von Helmholtz*, 2 volumes (Braunschweig, 1903), and R. S. Turner in *Dictionary of Scientific Biography*.

HUGO HILDEBRAND HILDEBRANDSSON (1838–1920) was born in Stockholm, Sweden. He was educated at the University of Upsala and he stayed at this institution throughout his career. After receiving his doctorate in 1866, he became assistant to A. J. Angström and was lecturer in physics and later in meteorology. He was attracted to meteorology through R. Rubenson, chairman of the meteorology section, who engaged his students in hourly recording of meteorological observations. Subsequently, Hildebrandsson was sent to visit the meteorological institutions in Europe. When Rubenson was named director of the Swedish weather service in 1878, Hildebrandsson was appointed professor at the university and director of the meteorological observatory. He held these positions until his retirement in 1907. He was elected a member of the International Meteorological Committee in 1891 and was its secretary from 1903 to 1907. He received the Symons Medal in 1920.

Hildebrandsson considered the coordination of observations as the basis of meteorological theory. In 1869 he organized observations of nocturnal frosts, ice conditions, etc., for the purpose of forecasting. In 1873 he organized 21 stations for the observation of cirrus clouds over Europe. His graphical and statistical evaluation of these data yielded important results on flow patterns in cyclones and anticyclones and the global wind circulation. In 1887 he published (with R. Abercromby) a new cloud classification, consisting of ten basic forms, which was adopted by the International Meteorological Committee in 1891. Together with Köppen and Neumayer, he published the first cloud atlas. The *International Cloud Atlas* (1896) was based on his system; it was financed by de Bort, his lifelong friend. With de Bort he investigated variations and interactions of "centers of action." Their fruitful collaboration culminated in the publication of two volumes, *Les Bases de la Météorologie Dynamique*, presenting the history and the current state of meteorological knowledge.

For biography, see N. Shaw in *Quart. Journ. Roy. Met. Soc.*, **48** (1922), 425–428, and W. Köppen in *Met. Zeits.*, **42** (1925), 355–357.

NIELS H. C. HOFFMEYER (1836–1884) was born in Denmark. The son of a military officer, he started out on a military career. During long periods of recuperation from a rheumatic condition he developed an interest in meteorology. After leaving the military he became director of a steel factory and civil servant at the war ministry, but he continued to work in meteorology. In 1872 he succeeded in establishing a small meteorological institute in Denmark, which quickly expanded under his leadership. He established meteorological stations in the Danish colonies of Greenland, Iceland and Faroe. Observations from these stations made it possible to study systematically the meteorological processes over the North Atlantic, in particular the Icelandic low. In 1874 he began publishing the so-called Hoffmeyer synoptic charts which were intended for research purposes and were highly valued by European meteorologists. Unfortunately, there was not sufficient general interest in these charts, and due to financial difficulties Hoffmeyer had to terminate publication in 1879. Aside from his work in synoptic meteorology, he studied the influence of the distribution of water and land on temperature and barometric pressure.

For biography, see W. Köppen in *Met. Zeits.*, **1** (1884), 87–88.

WLADIMIR PETER KÖPPEN (1846–1940) was born in St. Petersburg (Leningrad), the son of a historian and mathematician. His German grandfather had come to Russia as personal doctor of the czar. Köppen spent much of his youth at the family estate in the Crimea, where he developed an early interest in climate. In 1864 he went to St. Petersburg where he took courses in zoology and botany and studied meteorology privately through the use of L. F. Kämtz' library. Later he went to Heidelberg and Leipzig. His dissertation (1807) was entitled "Heat and the growth of plants." In 1871 he became assistant at the meteorological observatory in St. Petersburg, directed by H. Wild. At the first meteorological congress in Vienna (1873) he made important contacts with leading European meteorologists. In 1875 he was named director of the department of storm warnings and forecasting at the newly founded Deutsche Seewarte, Hamburg. In 1879 he was appointed director of its department for research meteorology and remained in this position until his retirement in 1919. He was director of the kite station Grossborstel near Hamburg after 1903. He was editor of the *Annalen der Hydrographie* and co-editor of the *Meteorologische Zeitschrift*, and was instrumental in the founding of the Deutsche Meteorologische Gesellschaft.

Köppen produced some 500 publications over a span of 70 years, mostly in meteorology and climatology. Through his papers, textbooks and personal contacts he had great influence on European meteorologists. During the 1870's and 1880's he published extensively on the theory of cyclone formation and propagation, cyclone tracks (continued by W. von Bebber) and squall lines. He studied the connection between cloud forms and weather. With Möller, he developed a method of graphical addition for the construction of the first upper air weather charts. His climatological work culminated in his classification of climates of 1918 which he continued to perfect until 1931 (*Grundriss der Klimatologie*). His classification was quantitative, and took into account temperature, precipitation and the corresponding development of organic life and agriculture. When Köppen's son-in-law and close friend A. Wegener became professor of meteorology in Graz in 1924, Köppen moved with him. Together with Wegener, Köppen wrote *Die Klimate der geologischen Vorzeit*, making the continental drift theory the basis of his paleoclimatological work. Throughout his career he investigated the periodicities of weather and climate. More than eighty years old, he started editing the multivolume *Handbuch der Klimatologie* (1939). Köppen wrote extensively on cultural and social problems, and he worked for a calendar reform and the diffusion of the world language esperanto.

For biography, see the memoir by his daughter Else Wegener-Köppen, *Wladimir Köppen, ein Gelehrtenleben für die Meteorologie*, Grosse Naturforscher, **8** (Stuttgart, Wiss. Verlagsbuchhandlung, 1955), 199 pp.; F. Loewe in *Quart. Journ. Roy. Met. Soc.*, **67** (1941), 389–391; and R. Süring in *Met. Zeits.*, **57** (1940), 281–284.

WILLIAM CLEMENT LEY (1840–1896) was born in Bristol, England. He was tutored by his father, a former schoolmaster who had become vicar. He began studying clouds and their behavior when he was a child. In 1857 Ley entered Magdalen College at Oxford and graduated with an M.A. in 1864. He was ordained in 1863 and appointed curate at King's Chapel at Breinson in Herefordshire. In 1874 he was transferred to Ashby Parva in Leicestershire. He resigned in 1892 due to illness. He was elected fellow of the Royal Society in 1873, and in 1879 he became inspector for the Meteorological Council of stations in England. He was married and had eight children.

Ley's main contribution to meteorology was the statistical analysis of meteorological parameters in cyclones and their interrelations. He pioneered in the study of the motion of cirrus clouds and the relation between flow patterns observed in upper levels and the surface pressure distribution in cyclones. His sometimes startling results, such as the "backward" inclination of the cyclone "axis", stimulated the investigation of atmospheric circulation systems in three dimensions. He summarized his results in his book *Laws of the Winds Prevailing in Western Europe* (1872). He also produced a new classification of clouds (1894) which, however, found little acceptance. His *Aids to the Study and Forecast of the Weather* (1880) was widely used in England.

For biography, see the obituary in *Quart. Journ. Roy. Met. Soc.*, **23** (1897), 103–105.

RUDOLF GUSTAV KARL LEMPFERT (1875–1957) was born in Manchester, England. He entered Emmanuel College in Cambridge, taking a "first" in both parts of the natural science tripos (1896 and 1898). Subsequently, he became assistant to Shaw at the Cavendish Laboratory, and, in 1900, school master at Rughby. When Shaw was named director of the Meteorological Office in 1902, he appointed Lempfert to be his personal scientific assistant. The two men maintained a close and lifelong friendship. Lempfert was appointed superintendent of instruments in 1905, of statistics in 1906 and of forecasting in 1910. His administrative duties greatly increased with the expansion of the Meteorological Office during World War I. After the war Lempfert became assistant director of the Meteorological Office, and he held this post until his retirement in 1938. He was president of the Royal Meteorological Society in 1930/31.

Probably most important among Lempfert's numerous publications was "The life history of surface air currents" (1906), written in collaboration with Shaw. Lempfert drew all the charts in the memoir, traced the air trajectories and wrote the discussions of individual cases (parts II and III), while Shaw supervised the work and wrote part I. Two important papers on squall lines followed in 1906 and 1910 (with Corless). In 1955 he edited Shaw's papers and he played a major role in the establishment of the Sir Napier Shaw Memorial Library at the Cavendish. Coming from a musical family, Lempfert himself was an accomplished violinist. In 1916 he married a well known musician.

For biography, see J. S. Dines in *Quart. Journ. Roy. Met. Soc.*, **84** (1958), p. 87.

Elias Loomis (1811–1889) was born in Willington, Connecticut, the son of a country pastor. He graduated from Yale College in 1830, and attended a theological seminary in 1831/32. In 1833 he became tutor under Olmsted in the natural sciences; together with Olmsted he rediscovered Halley's comet on its return in 1835. After studying for a year in Paris he became professor of mathematics and natural philosophy at Western Reserve College, Ohio, and established an observatory. From 1844 to 1860 he was professor of natural philosophy at the University of the City of New York. In 1860 he was called to Yale, where he held a professorship in natural philosophy and astronomy for the rest of his life.

Loomis published in astronomy, physics and meteorology. He also wrote numerous, widely used textbooks in these fields. His most important contributions were in meteorology. His early synoptic weather charts (1846) signaled the beginning of modern synoptic meteorology. In 1871 Loomis embarked on a long series of synoptic-statistical investigations of cyclones and anticyclones. Loomis was strongly interested in geomagnetism. From 1833–1844 he charted the earth's magnetic field for the United States and in 1860 he prepared the first chart of the frequency distribution of auroras. His astronomical investigations dealt with the observation of meteors. He also determined the latitude and longitude for various locations. After the early death of his wife Loomis led a rather isolated life. He compiled an extensive genealogy of the Loomis family.

For biography, see H. A. Newton in *Biographical Memoirs*, National Academy of Sciences, **3** (1895), 213–252; G. A. Daniels in *American Science in the Age of Jackson* (New York, Columbia University Press, 1968); and G. Kutzbach in *Dictionary of Scientific Biography*.

Max Margules (1856–1920) was born in Brody in the western Ukraine. He studied mathematics and physics at Vienna until 1877 and at Berlin from 1879 to 1881. In 1882 he resigned from his post as privatdocent at the University of Vienna. He joined the staff of the Zentralanstalt für Meteorologie, where he had worked for a short period from 1877 to 1879. He retired early, at the age of fifty (1906). He remained unmarried and without close friends; he literally starved to death during the austere post war period in Vienna, refusing any contributions beyond his meager pension.

While at the Zentralanstalt, Margules continued with his physical-chemical investigations, and his early publications dealt with electrodynamics, physical chemistry of gases and hydrodynamics. From 1890 to 1893 his papers dealt with oscillation periods of the earth's atmosphere, the solar semidiurnal barometric pressure oscillation and oscillations of a periodically heated atmosphere. Partly due to the influence of Hann, who stressed the joint role of theory and observation in meteorology, Margules organized during the 1890's a small station network for the purpose of studying the progression of warm and cold waves and sudden variations in pressure and wind during the passage of storms. In the course of these investigations he sharpened the concept of air masses. From 1901 to 1906 Margules produced a series of papers which provided the first thorough theoretical analyses of atmospheric energy processes. In 1903 he recognized a new source for the production of kinetic energy, the potential energy which is liberated during isentropic redistribution of air masses of different temperature in unstable equilibrium. His results formed the basis for the achievements of the Vienna School of meteorologists, including F. M. Exner, W. Trabert and Ficker. In 1906 Margules developed a formula for the slope of surfaces of discontinuity, using methods developed by Helmholtz. He also attempted to determine the magnitude of the frictional dissipation of kinetic energy. One of his last meteorological investigations, which dealt with the development of temperature inversions by descending motion and divergence, contributed to the understanding of anticyclones. Like Hann and Bezold, Margules considered weather forecasting as premature; he has been quoted as saying that forecasting is "immoral and damaging to the character of a meteorologist."

For biography, see Exner in *Met. Zeits.*, **37** (1920), 322–324; Ficker in *Das Wetter*, **37** (1920), 161–165; and G. Kutzbach in *Dictionary of Scientific Biography*.

HENRIK MOHN (1835–1916) was born in Bergen, Norway. He entered Bergen's cathedral school, intending to study theology. Gradually his interest turned to physics, astronomy and meteorology. He studied philosophy and mineralogy at the University of Christiania, where he also attended lectures of C. A. Bjerknes in mathematics. He graduated in 1858. He continued to study astronomy at the observatory in Christiania with P. Waage and C. Guldberg, and was appointed observer in 1861. He was instrumental in the founding of the Norwegian Meteorological Institute in 1866. He was appointed director of the institute and at the same time professor of meteorology at the university. He held these posts until his retirement in 1913. He was a member of the International Meteorological Committee from 1873.

Mohn's numerous publications cover all aspects of meteorology. His *Storm-Atlas* (1870) marked the beginning of his far-reaching synoptic and theoretical investigations of cyclones. His major work "Étude sur les mouvements de l'atmosphère" (1876 and 1880), written in collaboration with Guldberg, influenced the development of dynamic meteorology in Europe for the remainder of the century. He studied the meteorology and oceanography of the North Atlantic and directed the Norwegian North Atlantic expedition 1876–1878. He helped organize and process the results of other polar expeditions (Nansen 1893–1896, Fram expedition 1898–1902) and Amundsen's antarctic expedition. He produced extensive investigations on the climate of Norway (*Klima-Atlas for Norge*, 1917), and he studied thunderstorms in collaboration with Hildebrandsson. His widely used textbook on the principles of meteorology (1872) passed through many editions and was translated into most European languages except English.

For biography, see V. Bjerknes, *Professor H. Mohn* (Kristiania, Grøndahl & Sons, 1917), pp. 9; Th. Hesselberg in *Norsk Biografisk Leksikon*, **9**, 290–295; and Hann in *Met. Zeits.*, **34** (1917), 82–84.

MAX MÖLLER (1854–1936) was born in Hamburg, Germany. He studied civil engineering and became master builder for the harbor in Hamburg. He also had a strong interest in meteorology; from about 1880 onward he maintained close contacts with Köppen and other meteorologists at the Deutsche Seewarte in Hamburg. In 1889 he was appointed professor of hydraulics and meteorology at the Polytechnicum in Karlsruhe and he became professor of hydraulics at the Polytechnicum in Braunschweig in 1890. He held this position until his retirement in 1935.

Möller was widely recognized in his field, and he published a two-volume textbook in hydraulics. For decades he worked on the theory of waves. He published a number of important papers in meteorology, including articles on the theory of cyclones and anticyclones and the general circulation of the atmosphere. He repeatedly evaluated Ferrel's theory of the general circulation, and eventually he became interested in long-range weather forecasting.

For biography, see comments by Leichtweiss, "Max Möller 80 Jahre alt," *Zeitschrift für Binnenschiffahrt* (Berlin), **66** (1934), p. 16.

GEORG VON NEUMAYER (1826–1909) was born near Neustadt, Germany. He interrupted his studies at the Polytechnicum and at the University of München to become a sailor. In 1850 he went on his first voyage. Upon his return he taught navigation in Hamburg and Trieste. After a trip to Australia (1852–1854) he began collecting funds for the foundation of a meteorological observatory in Melbourne, partly to expand nautical meteorology, and partly to establish a base for the geophysical exploration of Antarctica. Neumayer won the assistance of the King of Bavaria and returned to Melbourne to found the observatory in 1856. In 1864 he returned to Germany with plans for a central institution for hydrography and maritime meteorology, the future Deutsche Seewarte. When the Seewarte was established in Hamburg in 1875, Neumayer left his influential post as chief hydrographer to the navy to become its director (until his retirement in 1903); he called Köppen from Russia to become chief scientist at the Seewarte.

Neumayer's scientific investigations dealt mostly with terrestrial magnetism. His contribution to meteorology was not so much that of a scholar but that of an organizer and administrator.

For biography, see W. Köppen in *Met. Zeits.*, **26** (1909), 403–407.

WILLIAM C. REDFIELD (1789–1852) was born in Middletown, Connecticut, the son of a seafarer. After completing an apprenticeship as saddle and harness-maker in 1810 and some traveling in Ohio, he made saddles and kept store in Connecticut for a decade. Widowed twice, he moved to New York in 1824. In 1822 he began a career as a marine engineer and "transportation promotor", beginning with a steam boat on the Connecticut river and expanding to the Hudson river in 1824. Later he served as superintendent of the Steam Navigation Company; he also promoted railroad transportation. He played a major role in the transformation of the Association of American Geologists and Naturalists into the American Association for the Advancement of Science and was its first president in 1848. Yale University awarded Redfield an honorary degree in 1839.

Redfield was self taught in science. He established himself as a leading American scientist through his work in meteorology and paleontology during the 1830's. Examining the orientation of fallen trees after the passage of a hurricane across New England in 1821, he published his results on the counterclockwise circulation in storms in a paper of 1831. Stimulated by his son's work during the 1830's, Redfield developed an interest in paleontology and became the first American specialist in fossil fish.

For biography, see D. Olmsted in *Am. Journ. Sci.*, **24** (1857), 355–373; W. J. Humphreys in *Dictionary of American Biography*; G. A. Daniels, *American Science in the Age of Jackson* (New York, Columbia University Press, 1968); and H. Burstyn in *Dictionary of Scientific Biography*.

KARL THEODOR REYE (1838–1919) was born in Cuxhaven, Germany. During his childhood close to the stormy North Sea he developed a lasting interest in meteorology. In 1856 he entered the Polytechnicum in Hannover. He continued his studies in engineering and mathematics at the Polytechnicum in Zürich (1859–1860) and obtained his doctorate in mathematics at Göttingen (1861). Subsequently, he was privatdocent in Zürich and taught geometry. In 1870 he accepted a call as professor of geometry to the newly founded Polytechnicum in Aachen. He was professor of mathematics at the University of Strassbourg from 1872 until his retirement in 1908. In 1919 he was expelled from Strassbourg which had become French after World War I. He died shortly after moving to Würzburg.

Reye's early publications include papers on problems of geometry, mathematical physics, mechanics and meteorology. His meteorological publications on the thermodynamics of the atmosphere and his widely known book on storms (1872) appeared over a period of twelve years after 1864. At Strassbourg he became increasingly absorbed in mathematics and made important contributions to the geometry of position.

For biography, see *Vierteljahresschrift der Naturforschenden Gesellschaft in Zürich*, **64** (1919), 849–850, and Süring in *Met. Zeits.*, **36** (1919), 271–272.

JOHAN WILHELM SANDSTRÖM (1874–1947) was born in Sweden. After leaving school he began to work in a factory. When he was sent to Stockholm on a scholarship of his factory, he was noticed by I. Bendixson, professor of mathematics and a friend of V. Bjerknes and Ekholm. Bendixson directed Sandström's education in mathematics, and upon Bendixson's and Ekholm's recommendation Sandström became a student of V. Bjerknes in 1898. Sandström later became one of Bjerknes' closest collaborators. From 1919 to 1939 he was director of the meteorological division of the Meteorological and Hydrological Institute in Stockholm.

In a paper of 1902 Sandström applied V. Bjerknes' circulation theorem and also employed the thermal wind concept. Together with Helland-Hansen he computed tables for the application of the circulation theorem to the oceans. He was joint author with V. Bjerknes of the first volume of *Dynamic Meteorology and Hydrology* of 1910. In 1910 he proposed a new representation of the frictional force and in 1916 Sandström extended Bjerknes' circulation theorem to include a thermodynamic cycle. Later in life Sandström turned his attention to the study of the Gulf Stream and its influence on climate.

For biography, see E. Gold in *Nature*, **159** (1947), 395–396.

WILLIAM NAPIER SHAW (1854–1945) was born in Birmingham, England. He attended King Edward's School in Birmingham and studied mathematics and natural sciences at Emmanual College, Cambridge. He was a student of C. Maxwell, and also studied a semester under Helmholtz in Berlin. In 1879 he became demonstrator at the Cavendish Laboratory; in 1887 he was appointed lecturer in experimental physics and in 1898 assistant director of the laboratory. Shaw began his meteorological work in 1879 with investigations in hygrometric methods and instruments. In 1897 he was appointed member of the Meteorological Council. He forsook his university career at Cambridge, when accepting the post of secretary of the Council in 1900. He was director of the Meteorological Office from 1905 until his retirement in 1920. In 1907 he became reader in meteorology at the University of London. From 1920 to 1924 he was the first professor of meteorology at Imperial College. He was president of the International Meteorological Committee (1906–1923), and received the Symons Medal in 1910 and the Royal Medal in 1923. Shaw was knighted in 1915.

Shaw made outstanding contributions to meteorology as an organizer, researcher and teacher. He transformed the Meteorological Office by introducing trained scientific staff and shifting emphasis to studies of the physics of the atmosphere. Characteristic of his approach was the introduction of the bi-weekly evening discussions of foreign papers at the Meteorological Office. He reorganized and centralized the British weather service and various observation systems, and he worked enthusiastically for the cause of international meteorology. In his pioneering study, "The life history of surface air currents" (written in collaboration with his friend Lempfert, 1906), he developed the analysis of air trajectories; his results pointed the way toward air mass analysis and the concept of fronts. He introduced the principle of isentropic analysis and devised a thermodynamic diagram (the tephigram). He carried out numerous investigations of the conditions of the upper atmosphere. After his retirement he produced a four-volume work, *Manual of Meteorology* (1926–1931), which is a unique account of the historical roots and mathematical basis of meteorology. His great interest in the historical development of meteorology is reflected in many of his articles and lectures. Shaw devoted much effort to educating the public on meteorology and related subjects, and he served on a number of advisory committees.

For biography, see memorial article in *Obituary Notices of Fellows of the Royal Society of London*, **5** (1945), 202–230, with selected bibliography; see also R. Corless and E. Gold in *Quart. Journ. Roy. Met. Soc.*, **71** (1954), 187–194. A complete list of his works is in *Selected Meteorological Papers of Sir Napier Shaw* (London, 1955).

ADOLF FRIEDRICH WICHARD SPRUNG (1848–1909) was born near Perleberg, Brandenburg, Germany. He entered the University of Leipzig to study pharmacy. In 1872 he changed to physics and chemistry. After receiving his doctorate in 1876, he intensified his meteorological investigations and moved to Hamburg to work at the Deutsche Seewarte. In 1880 he was appointed assistant. In 1886 he was called to Berlin as scientific superintendent at the meteorological institute which was then reorganized under Bezold. In 1892 Sprung became superintendent of the meteorological-magnetic observatory at Potsdam, holding this position for the rest of his life.

While in Hamburg, Sprung collaborated closely with Köppen with whom he maintained a close personal friendship. Sprung became quickly and thoroughly familiar with the results of synoptic meteorology through his routine work, involving daily and monthly weather reports. At the same time, he made important contributions to theoretical meteorology. In 1881 he introduced the concept of the circle of inertia. Upon the request of Neumayer, director of the Seewarte, Sprung wrote the first German textbook on theoretical meteorology, *Lehrbuch der Meteorologie* (1885), in which he strived to relate theoretical results to the findings of synoptic meteorology. The book was widely used into the Twentieth Century. At Berlin Sprung turned to the construction of meteorological instruments. He designed a balance barograph with a sliding weight or "rider". Later he applied the principle of the balance beam in the construction of a number of meteorological recording instruments. In connection with the international cloud year he introduced an automatic cloud camera for photogrammatic observations of clouds and their heights.

For biography, see Köppen in *Met. Zeits.*, **26** (1909), 215–216.

SIR WILLIAM THOMSON, Baron Kelvin of Largs (1824–1907), was born in Belfast, Ireland, son of a professor of engineering. In 1832 the family moved to Glasgow where his father became professor of mathematics. Thomson and his brother were educated at home. At the age of eleven Thomson entered the University of Glasgow. During a trip to Paris in 1839 he became acquainted with the work of Fourier and Laplace. In 1841 he entered Cambridge and he graduated in 1845. During a second trip to Paris in 1845, when he worked at the laboratory of Regnault, he read Clapeyron's paper on the work of Carnot. In 1847 he met J. P. Joule who became his close collaborator. In 1846 he became professor of natural philosophy at the University of Glasgow, and he remained in this position for the rest of his life. He was knighted in 1866 and raised to peerage in 1892. In 1890 he became president of the Royal Society.

Together with Helmholtz, his life-long friend, Thomson shaped Nineteenth

Century physics. His more than 300 papers bear on nearly every branch of physical science. During his lifetime his fame derived mostly from his application of physics, i.e., the invention of telegraphic and scientific instruments. He produced outstanding results in electricity. Perhaps his most important contributions were in thermodynamics. Thomson proposed the absolute scale of temperature in 1848, and in 1851 he presented a paper on the dynamic theory of heat which contributed much to the universal acceptance of the principle of conservation of energy and also contained the first statement of the second law of thermodynamics. In 1862, Thomson showed from the earth's rate of cooling that the habitable earth could be no more than 200 million years old, reducing this number to 20 to 40 million years in 1899. These values were opposed by geologists who estimated the earth much older. In 1867 Thomson suggested that the atoms of matter were vortex rings in the ether. From the early 1850's Thomson worked on submarine telegraphy. Taking into account that seawater acted as a conductor, he recommended a number of improvements and changes in the construction of the transatlantic cable. His advice that only a small signal current be used was adopted when the second transatlantic cable was laid in 1866. The mirror galvanometer (1858) and the automatic syphon recorder (1867) were an outcome of this research. He also produced a number of naval instruments (including the tide gauge and predictor and the harmonic analyzer) and introduced experimental work as an integral part of the training of scientists.

For biography, see J. Buchwald in *Dictionary of Scientific Biography*.

NAME INDEX

n refers to a footnote (or footnotes) on the page referenced.

SUBJECT INDEX

n refers to a footnote (or footnotes) on the page referenced.

PICTURE CREDITS

Fig. 3: From Dove, *Meteorologische Untersuchungen,* 1837

Figs. 4, 7, 8, 9: From *Transactions of the American Philosophical Society*

Figs. 5, 6: From Espy, *Philosophy of Storms,* 1841

Fig. 10: From *Report to the Chief of the Weather Bureau,* Government Printing Office, 1900

Fig. 12: From *Daily Bulletin of Weather-Reports,* Government Printing Office, 1873

Figs. 13, 19: From *Poggendorff's Annalen der Physik und Chemie*

Figs. 14, 20: From Fitzroy, *Weather Book,* 1863

Fig. 15: From Hellmann, *Neudrucke von Schriften und Karten über Meteorologie und Erdmagnetismus,* 1897

Fig. 16: From *Transactions of the Royal Society, Edinburgh*

Fig. 17: From Mohn, *Grundzüge der Meteorologie,* 1875

Fig. 18: From Mohn, *Det Norske Meteorologiske Instituts Storm-Atlas,* 1870

Fig. 21: From *Deutsche Rundschau*

Fig. 22: From Guldberg and Mohn, *Études sur les Mouvements de l'Atmosphère,* 1876

Fig. 23: From *U. S. Coast and Geodetic Survey*, 1878

Figs. 24, 45, 46, 47: From *Quarterly Journal of the Royal Meteorological Society*

Fig. 25: From Ley, *Laws of the Winds in Western Europe,* 1872

Fig. 26: From *Société Royale des Sciences d'Upsal*

Fig. 27: From Bezold, *Gesammelte Abhandlungen,* 1906

Figs. 28, 30: From *Annalen der Hydrographie und maritimen Meteorologie*

Figs. 29, 31: From *Meteorologische Zeitschrift*

Figs. 32, 33, 35, 36, 37: From *Kongl. Svenska Vetenskaps-Akademiens Handlingar*

Fig. 34: From *Beiträge zur Physik der freien Atmosphäre*

Figs. 38, 39: From *Monthly Weather Review*

Figs. 40, 44: From Shaw and Lempfert, *Life History of Surface Air Currents,* M. O. Memoir, 1906

Fig. 41: From Shaw, *Forecasting Weather,* 1911

Fig. 42: From *Jahrbücher der K.-K. Zentralanstalt für Meteorologie und Erdmagnetismus*

Fig. 43: From Hildebrandsson and de Bort, *Les Bases de la Météorologie Dynamique,* 1906

Fig. 48: From *Sitzungsberichte der Wiener Akademie der Wissenschaften*

Fig. 49: From *Geofysiske Publikasjoner*

All other illustrations prepared by author